DECISION PROCESSES

DECISION PROCESSES

Edited by

R. M. THRALL · C. H. COOMBS

R. L. DAVIS

JOHN WILEY & SONS, INC., NEW YORK

LONDON

PRINTED IN THE UNITED STATES OF AMERICA

PREFACE

The past few years have seen a rapid development in the mathematical formulation and testing of behavioral science theory. The problem has been attacked from many different standpoints by persons widely scattered both geographically and in field of specialization. In an effort to coordinate some of this activity the University of Michigan made a proposal to the Ford Foundation to hold an eight week seminar on The Design of Experiments in Decision Processes which would have as participants a small group of mathematicians, statisticians, psychologists, economists, and philosophers. The proposal was approved and the seminar was held in the summer of 1952 in Santa Monica, California. This location was chosen because of the common interest of the RAND Corporation in the problems of the seminar, and the seminar benefited considerably from participation of RAND employees and consultants as well as from the services of the RAND business office.

In addition to the participants who were supported by the Ford Grant and those loaned by RAND, several regular participants were supported by the Office of Naval Research (through contracts with the University of Michigan, the University of Minnesota, and Princeton University) and still others by the Cowles Commission. There were also frequent visitors from the University of California at Los Angeles and from others in the Los Angeles area.

The results of the seminar included a great deal of stimulation of empirical research and of further theory construction. It was decided to publish a volume on the proceedings of the seminar allowing about a year for the completion of some of the research growing out of it. The editors have also included some additional papers which are closely related to the purposes of the seminar.

The authors of the volume do not expect that it will be a definitive work, but rather regard it as a vehicle for raising a number of basic questions and perhaps also providing some guideposts towards answers to some of these questions. Accordingly, an informal and relatively speedy method of printing seemed suitable. Since the method of printing did not permit proof reading by the authors, and also in the interests of speed, the authors gave permission to the editors to do all of the proof reading and to make such minor technical changes (e.g. in footnotes, references, styles of formulas) as might render the total presentation more uniform and understandable. Much that might have been standardized has been left intact in the interest of presenting each author pretty well in his own manner. Nevertheless, there have also been many minor changes; consequently any error encountered in the final text may well be of the editors' making. In any event, all such errors in detail are to be charged to the editors.

A list of regular participants and the titles of the papers given at the formal sessions of the seminar are given as Appendices A and B.

The title "Decision Processes" does not imply that the papers are limited to the branch of statistics bearing that name. The individual papers range in character from pure mathematics to experiments in group dynamics, but all are directed at the application of mathematics to behavioral sciences in general and at decision processes in particular. The range and interrelationship of these papers are discussed in the introductory chapter. It is the hope of the editors that mathematicians and behavioral scientists will find some of the papers of interest to them and that a few will find them all of interest.

The editors' task would have been impossible without the help of many referees who included seminar participants, authors, and also the following persons: Raoul Bott, A. H. Copeland, Sr., I. S. Copi, D. A. Darling, Ward Edwards, J. R. P. French, Lawrence Klein, D. G. Marquis, John McCarthy, T. M. Newcomb, G. Y. Rainich and A. W. Tucker. The editors also wish to express their appreciation to Wiley and Sons and to the compositors Edwards Brothers for their fine cooperation in the making of this book.

R. M. Thrall, C. H. Coombs, R. L. Davis

CONTENTS

CHAPTER I

INTRODUCTION TO "DECISION PROCESSES"

by

Robert L. Davis*

UNIVERSITY OF MICHIGAN

For over two thousand years the chief preoccupation with decision problems concerned whether or not a given action or decision would be good, right, or otherwise well calculated to achieve some desired effect. Philosophers often presented these problems in terms of a dilemma. The decision-maker faced a known situation and if there were more than two alternative courses of action available to him, these usually were at best a class of actions which differed essentially in but one component (thus permitting him to define and hew to a "mean").

Perhaps even more of a restriction than that on alternative courses of action is the implicit assumption in these early formulations that decisions were to be made on the basis of one known situation. To be sure, reasonable thinkers must always have allowed in some loose qualitative way for information whose accuracy was only probable; but the device of making separate analyses for each of the relevant potential "states of nature" would have been bootless before the invention of the calculus of probability. It is the concept of mathematical expectation that lends this device its appeal and power.

Also awaiting analysis was the question of how to say precisely what "the desired effect" was to mean; in fact there are

---

*The editors delegated to this author the task of writing a chapter designed to serve as introduction and to some extent as amalgam for the book and the kinds of ideas it deals with. While he is responsible for selection and organization of the material to accomplish this, as well as for the writing, many of the ideas here are the outgrowth of numerous editorial conferences of the past year. In particular, the word "we" used in discussing matters of opinion refers to all three editors.

1

some who say it is still waiting. But at least today we have
formally well developed theories of preference and utility; most
men work within this framework and those who question it seem
usually to do so concerning the interpretation to be given for the
abstract system.

These are the main ingredients of the change that has taken
place over the past two millenia since rational philosophy first
attacked decision problems. They were not all put together at
once. Whether a systematic probability calculus began with
Fermat and Pascal, as hitherto generally supposed, or actually
with Cardano, the fact is that the science of statistics has chiefly
grown up within the present century. Again, Daniel Bernoulli
used a utility concept more than 200 years ago to analyze the St.
Petersburg paradox; but whether we look to him or to the line
of 19th Century economists including Bentham, Gossen, Jevons,
Edgeworth and culminating in Pareto, we do not find a rigorous
formulation of utility theory until the past quarter-century.
Finally, it was only after the late war that the work of von
Neumann in game theory and of Wald in statistical decision
theory came to the attention of any wide class of mathematicians,
philosophers and scientists, and led to a basic reorientation concerning decision problems.

Thus what we may call the modern look in decision theory is
somewhat less than ten years old. It is just in the past two years,
in fact, that we have begun getting books - ranging from technical
monographs through textbooks and popularizations - explicitly
dealing with decision processes. Now such of these books as we
have read are entirely different from this volume in at least two
respects: (1) they present what is in some sense a "finished"
part of the theory, and (2) they are written from a unified point
of view. (In particular, many deal solely with the restricted
topic known as "statistical decision theory"; while this theory is
basic to the approach of several of our authors, much of the volume lies quite outside its purview). To account for these differences requires another brief historical digression.

It is probably clear that if anyone announces that he has a decision theory which either "explains" how people actually make
decisions (in the way any scientific theory "explains" its subject
matter) or prescribes how people should make decisions, this
will be of great interest not only to other professed decision
theorists, but in general to economists, sociologists and psychologists, to philosophers, and to mathematicians. The interest of
the social scientists is clear: someone offers to tell them something about their own field. Whether the philosopher is interested

because of the proposed removal from his own realm of one more body of hitherto purely speculative material, or rather because of his interest in methodology and scientific principles, decision processes attract serious philosophical attention. Mathematicians taking to these matters often content themselves with pointing out that the source of much interesting new mathematics lies in early development of deductive theories designed for application to the real world.

Since the fall of 1950 a seminar on the application of mathematics to social science has met regularly at the University of Michigan under the sponsorship of the Departments of Economics, Mathematics, Philosophy, Psychology, and Sociology. Mathematical ideas have sometimes been explored for their possible application in social science, and theoretical systems of the social sciences have been studied for their possible formulation mathematically. It became apparent in the first two years of its operation that much of the material most interesting to the seminar dealt with decision processes. How this led to the summer project at Santa Monica in 1952 is detailed in the preface. The important thing here is the variety of the personnel at this summer conference, and of their interests. Some were concerned with more or less the whole problem, some with aspects of it which only the initiate could tell might be related to decision processes. It is this variety, together with the fact that none of these participants was interested in mere reformulation of standard parts of the theory (unless for the purpose of setting up a new attack), that accounts for the differences between this volume and other books seemingly devoted to the same subject.

Certain merits and shortcomings of our volume are almost inevitable consequences of these facts. It would be unrealistic to expect a coherent and unified attack on decision theory from such a group at the present stage. With authors of varied background and habits of exposition, we get a total output which must seem uneven in style, which in dealing with such different problems also does so at markedly different depths of penetration, and in which the individual authors are not noticeably in agreement on some of the fundamental questions in the whole theory (such as the nature of "utility" and "subjective probability", for instance). On the other hand, this variety is necessary to a presentation of any reasonable sample of the current activity in decision problems. Thus, although we cannot even claim to present here all of the kinds of approach to decision processes which have been developed to date (and no doubt the simplest and most effective ones still await development), we can say that to the best of our knowledge this book is representative of the latest work in our subject in all the disciplines concerned.

We could start a catalogue of the diversified viewpoints represented here by recognizing the distinction between those whose interests were primarily formal and theoretical and those with a more experimental orientation. It would be incorrect to say that more than one or two of our authors are <u>primarily</u> experimentalists, but several others among the social scientists at least matched their interest in theory with a record of experimental training and experience. The mathematicians and philosophers, on the other hand, had by profession been previously concerned with purely formal theories. The position of the economists in this regard may seem anomalous: classically, they have worked with purely formal theory, founded on introspection, although the subject they studied was an empirical one of great practical importance in human affairs.

One result of these differences was the division between those most interested in working out the logical consequences of a theory or a set of axioms, and those most interested in finding out how people acted. There is a related and somewhat subtler distinction which, as often as it is recognized and properly described, nevertheless keeps obscuring communication and understanding between various scientists. That is the distinction between the theory which is in some sense principally descriptive or predictive and that which is solely normative. The classical economic approach to the problems of decision, for instance, was phrased in terms of the activity of the "rational man". These notions were formalized in what is now called statistical decision theory, and a great many of our participants in the Santa Monica conference were primarily interested in the kinds of problems encountered here. But many others - chiefly, perhaps, the psychologists and sociologists - considered it a basic flaw that this theory had no apparent relation to observed behavior.

The words "normative" and "rational man" seem unfortunate. It may be that the first economists to think in these terms actually intended to set forth what a man <u>should</u> do if he were rational; the intention of modern formulators of normative theory is usually much more modest. Each constructs an abstract system about which he says in effect: "If a person's behavior is such that under the proper interpretation it can be said to satisfy the requirements of this system, then his behavior is what is called 'rational' in my theory." For instance, the theory of zero-sum two-person games can be taken as normative theory in the sense that it gives instructions according to which a man will be able to maximize his expected payoff in such a game, assuming he can find the solution. But this does not say anyone should use this theory in playing an actual game: it may be that he can more easily secure this maximum expected payoff in some other way, or it may be that he is an iconoclast who sees no sufficient connection between mathematical expectation and the outcome of any play of the game to justify the procedure.

Game theory illustrates another source of confusion in interdisciplinary discussions. For von Neumann and Morgenstern evidently intended not only a normative interpretation for their theory, but also that it provide foundations for a new analysis of the empirical processes of economic exchange. Now discussion of any theory which like this is intended to have both normative and empirical applications must proceed in terms of careful discrimination as to what aspect of the theory is concerned. Thus criticism of empirical applications of the theory must be set apart from strictures on its normative implications. And of course both types of argument should be distinguished from any attack on the abstract theory. Perhaps because these distinctions are so obvious, they are not always formulated explicitly in expert discussion; even with experts this can lead to argument at cross-purposes.

The breakdown between empirical and formal approaches is helpful in our organization of only part of the book: the fourth part can be said to consist of experimentally oriented papers, although one is by a statistician and another by four mathematicians. The second part leans a little in this direction too.

The distinction between the normative and descriptive aspects of the theories they present affords even less help in classifying the papers, because so many - as in the example of game theory - are clearly intended to have some interpretation in each sense. Chapters III through VI and possible Chapter XII might be supposed to be most nearly concerned with the normative aspects of the topics they discuss.

Not feeling either of these distinctions to provide a sound basis for division of our book into parts, we nevertheless found a more or less natural division in terms of subject matter. Even this partitioning of the contents is in some degree artificial; we will now try to point to some of the interconnections and comparisons between various papers.

First, as to Chapter II. The genesis of this paper is described on its first page. These ideas had been fairly well shaken together by the time of the summer meeting of 1952. There they were presented early and may have served somewhat the same semi-introductory function they serve here. Even when you talk to a very erudite audience you often find it expedient to make a brief survey of the foundations of your subject - just to establish terminological agreement and start people thinking along your lines. This chapter gives a sort of quasi-formal status to three terminological practices which were perhaps fairly common among social scientists before, but which are somewhat different from ordinary scientific and mathematical usage. Thus the "mathematical model" - quickly shortened in use to "model" - here seems somewhat different from what the typical mathematician or logician would expect.

Any system may be a "model". It may, for instance, in some remarkable case, be only a model for itself. In general, the same system may provide a model for many other systems in being a realization of each either under "interpretation" or under "abstraction". Thus, for example, a mathematician might construct a system of colored fluids and pipes and valves as a model for a particular kind of equation in the abstract mathematical theory called hydrodynamics; but the same system of liquids and pipes - if fortunately conceived - might serve an engineer as model for the flow in a river network. In applications to social science "model" is usually used for the more abstract system, in contradistinction to common mathematical usage. Again, the word is so widely used that it has now become customary to use it even when there is no abstraction or interpretation at issue. This has the (rather uneconomical) effect of making it practically synonomous with "abstract system".

Thus "mathematical model" here means simply "formal deductive system"; a mathematical model together with a given interpretation of the model in the "real world" constitutes a "theory", while "real world" itself is a term intended to denote what social scientists mean when they talk about the real world, whether that is to be taken as itself another (and probably simpler, more immediately understandable) linguistic system, or simply as a set of specifications for making measurements, or as whatever your form of epistemology will buy.

This chapter's introductory treatment of measurement theory in terms of the theory of relations provides a basis for generalization, as well as a guide to precise statement of problems falling within the existing framework, that may serve for a great many kinds of discussion in the social sciences.

PART ONE

Two of the five chapters which form the first part of the book
deal explicitly with the standard statistical decision problem.
Two others discuss the application of statistical decision methods
to the problems of group choice, and the last of these chapters
is chiefly concerned with shades of distinction possibly arising
in the probability statements so essential in the statistical decision analysis.

Although Leo Goodman's paper "On Methods of Amalgamation"
is actually concerned with the group choice problem, it serves
as a good introduction also to the very similar problem of finding a statistical decision function. Like the papers of Milnor
and of Radner and Marschak following it, this paper starts with
the game viewpoint concerning decision problems. By "the
game viewpoint" we intend to describe the statement of such
problems in terms of matrices whose entries are the values of
utility functions: in the decision problem for individuals, the
entry u_{ij} can be taken to be the utility of the outcome consequent
upon selection of the ith alternative course of action in the event
the "true state of nature" is the jth of the possible states. As
Goodman points out this is formally similar to one simple
formulation of the problem of group choice. He shows how a
number of special means of obtaining social choice functions
can be subsumed under one method of amalgamation, and goes
on to discuss the relations between this method and several
others.

Chapters IV and V are alike in many respects. In "Games
Against Nature", John Milnor looks at three lately proposed
criteria for decision-making together with a modernized version
of the standard Laplace criterion. As in so many cases in statistics and other young disciplines, such criteria have usually
been advanced in company with proofs that they possess one or
several intuitively desirable properties not possessed by competing criteria, and the argument left at that. But Milnor shows
that by now we have too much of a good thing: in fact it is impossible for any criterion to possess all of the properties which
have been advanced as intuitively desirable. This discussion
brings the fundamental differences among the four criteria into
sharp focus. Milnor then proposes another and less restrictive
set of "desirable properties" which he proves can be simultaneously satisfied, though he cannot construct such a criterion which
is computationally practicable.

Radner and Marschak, in their "Note on Some Proposed Decision Criteria", discuss certain undesirable properties of two of the four methods Milnor considered (actually they use a slight generalization of the Hurwicz criterion). In the game they construct for this purpose the Hurwicz criterion runs counter to common sense in dictating that a strategy be chosen on the basis of but one observation where it is obviously reasonable to make a great many. They illustrate the "dependence on irrelevant alternatives" of Savage's minimax-regret criterion by considering the solutions it prescribes in two cases: one where the player may use any strategy, and the other where he is required to use what they call a "maximum likelihood rule". Though he will actually use a maximum likelihood rule in the first case also - even when not required to - the minimax-regret strategies call for different numbers of observations in these two cases.

In "Social Choice and Strength of Preference", Coombs returns us to the problem of group choice. Here he applies his measurement theory and technique for "ordered metric scales" to derive a social utility function which explicitly weights individuals' strength of preference. Assuming a common unit of measure for utility, and with certain other restrictions, he shows how to get such a social utility without having to measure individual utilities numerically. The resulting utility may be described as giving the "least disliked" alternative as the social choice. He compares his procedure with several others common in psychological measurement and also illustrates it with an experiment.

Finally, Vail's paper on "Alternative Calculi of Subjective Probabilities" leaves formal structures aside to consider questions concerning the variables that figure in formulations of all these problems. Not all of these questions, as he points out, have anything to do with uncertainty; it is clearly desirable to dispense with those which do not before taking up, as he does in some detail, the various interpretations which might be given to the word "probability". (It is perhaps not entirely clear that the so-called "objective probability" is quite as simple as his treatment indicates.) In addition to mathematical probability and "objective" probability we may distinguish at least two kinds of psychological or subjective probability: the individual's guess as to what number best approximates his concept of objective probability for an event, and his "degree of belief". These need not be the same. Another valuable distinction concerns the nature of the event in question. Is it in every relevant aspect unique? Or is it a member of a finite - or of an infinite - class of somehow similar events? Vail classifies choice problems according to such distinctions and discusses empirical implications of this classification.

PART TWO

Perhaps some readers will be surprised to see that learning theory plays a sufficient role in our subject to merit a separate part of this book. First we should make it clear to non-psychological readers that within that discipline the topic ordinarily identified as "learning theory" has far broader scope than might be guessed from merely reading these three chapters. Much of what psychologists mean by learning theory is concerned with analysis, or at least classification, of what are regarded as determinants of human behavior in learning situations; our three chapters give this feature of the subject only incidental mention. But a certain class of learning experiments happens to be based on one of the simplest imaginable decision situations. And for handling this kind of data our authors have developed methods which are at once part of the modern treatment of decision processes and also offshoots of the traditional learning theory of psychology.

The Bush-Mosteller linear operator model in learning theory has by now been extensively developed and applied to many learning experiments. In Chapter VIII Bush and Mosteller have collaborated with the mathematician G. L. Thompson to give an extensive discussion of the formal structure of their model and some of its mathematical consequences. Psychologists will be aware from their own literature of the many applications this model has found, while others may feel this introduction to the subject more immediately illuminating for its purely formal character.

On the surface, their formulation of the problem confronting the individual in terms of alternatives, outcomes, and the alternative-outcome pairs called events is similar to that of statistical decision theory. A first difference occurs in that the probabilities associated with these events may depend on the alternative chosen. And from here on they move in a quite different direction. The fundamental distinction lies in the sequential nature of the learning experiment. Thus the individual's tendencies at trial n to choose the various alternatives are given by the components of a probability vector $p(n)$; the authors seek to describe the way this vector changes from trial to trial. They analyze these changes on the basis of three assumptions: (i) that the change from one trial to the next is given in operator form: $T_{jk}p(n) = p(n+1)$, where the stochastic operator T_{jk} depends solely on the event E_{jk} which occurred on trial n ("Markov hypothesis"); (ii) that each T_{jk} is linear, and (iii) that the T_{jk} satisfy their (rather restrictive) "Combination of Classes" requirement.

Independently of Bush and Mosteller, W. K. Estes had developed a stochastic theory of learning which in many respects resembled theirs. His Chapter IX deals with a part of his work which strikes close to the problems of decision theory; it happens that the mathematical formulation of this special case in his theory can also be obtained from the Bush-Mosteller model. (However, this paper represents only one particular application of the Estes theory which is in general more concerned with the determinants of the learning changes than the Bush-Mosteller.) Estes reports here one experiment, which in addition to illustrating this feature of his theory is also interesting for having led to a great deal of discussion at Santa Monica and to considerable further experiment since then. (Some of this discussion appears in Chapter XVIII; see also our remarks on that chapter.)

"On Game-Learning Theory and Some Decision-Making Experiments," by M. M. Flood, studies games in which a player learns to improve his strategy during the course of a sequence of plays. In such games the situation can be regarded as "static" if the opponent uses a constant mixed strategy throughout the sequence of plays; allowing him to vary his strategies creates a more general "dynamic" problem. Even though first examination of game-learning involves only the "static model", Flood finds it necessary to combine game theory with the Bush-Mosteller learning theory in his analysis. Within this context he discusses the results of Monte Carlo computations and some pilot experiments with human subjects.

PART THREE

Perhaps the most controversial theme in our whole subject was that of utility. Here again it is helpful to distinguish the different kinds of objections that can be raised. Some of these are that: (1) the utility scheme does not describe the actual behavior of individuals at all faithfully; (2) the assumption that people even act as if they were maximizing utility cannot be sustained by empirical observation; (3) utility cannot even provide a sound basis for normative theory because, for instance, individuals could not find any consistent empirical interpretation for utility statements, or (4) the logical formulation of abstract utility theory is inconsistent. (We believe the von Neumann-Morgenstern axioms constitute a counterexample to the last statement.)

Utility has always been a vexing issue. A considerable portion of the economic and philosophical disputation of the past century dealt with various aspects of this concept. To avoid confusion with these purely historical matters, we will mention several questions concerning the older concepts of utility which are not at issue in current debate. First, there is no connotation in the kind of utility discussed in this volume of any "utilitarian" or welfare character. On the other hand, neither do our authors insist on any particular hedonistic psychological interpretation for their utilities (parts of Bohnert's paper only seem to be exceptional here). Finally, philosophers have frequently contested the validity of utility statements on the grounds that what was intended was not an "extensive magnitude", or some such argument; they often implied that in order to be used it had to be measured and that in order to be measured it had to be measured on something at least as strong as a ratio scale (see Chapter II). The von Neumann-Morgenstern theory and its application in game theory provide a counterexample here too. It turns out that utility so defined is to be measured on the weaker interval scale, and in the papers by Hausner and Thrall we see that even this can be somewhat weakened without loss of the practical applications.

Discussions of utility characteristically begin with a preference ordering on a set of objects, prospects of events. Abstractly, the starting point is just a chain order defined on some set. Now in the face of uncertainty, preference alone is not sufficient to determine "rational" grounds for choosing one course of action over another; at the simplest level, for instance, most people would prefer $110 to $100, but would prefer an outright gift of $100 to a 50-50 chance of winning $110. Considerations of this kind lead in the von Neumann-Morgenstern approach to assuming initially that the given set of prospects is "closed under" probability combination, i.e., that it is substantially what Hauser and Thrall call a mixture space. Now a utility function is classically a certain kind of real-valued function so defined on the set of prospects as to preserve the preference order. Starting - for such practical reasons as suggested above - with a mixture space, it is straightforward to get the utility function: just extend the preference ordering to the whole mixture space in a way that fits with the probability combinations.

The path taken by Gerard Debreu in the first chapter of Part Three is more direct. For game theory and statistical purposes one wants the probability combinations, but they are unnecessary in many economic applications. Debreu asks when we can reasonably expect to be able to define a real-valued function on an arbitrary chain ordered set in such a way as to preserve the order. He then shows that if the given set is any separable connected topological space in which the topology fits with the given order in a certain natural way, then the (preference) ordering can be extended to a utility function. He further shows that the assumption of connectedness can be given up by additionally assuming perfect separability (second countability). The latter statement gives the theorem for any subset of Euclidean space in which the relative topology matches the given ordering in the prescribed way.

An objection to their utility axioms which von Neumann and Morgenstern mentioned lies in the "Archimedean" nature of the utility: which means, in this case, that if A, B and C are any elements of the mixture space ranked in that order under the preference relation, there is a probability p such that B is equivalent in preference to the combination consisting of "A with probability p or C with probability 1 - p". This overlooks the possibility of any summum bonum or summum malum, and Thrall gives examples in which it might be reasonable to reject this Archimedean property.

The multidimensional utility theory that answers these objections was developed in several steps, all taking place at the RAND Corporation. In the fall of 1951 Thrall and Norman Dalkey worked out this theory for the finite-dimensional case. Melvin Hausner and J. G. Wendel followed shortly with a generalization to infinite dimension which also presented the Thrall-Dalkey results in simpler, better unified form. Then in the 1952 project Thrall and Dalkey continued this development with a study of possible applications of this more general utility concept.

In "Multidimensional Utilities", Hausner attacks the abstract problem of constructing and characterizing utility in the non-Archimedean case by splitting the problem into two parts. First he considers mixture spaces, and shows that any one can be imbedded in a vector space; then he introduces order axioms to make the mixture space into a (non-Archimedean) utility space, which he shows can be imbedded in an "ordered vector space". Finally he characterizes these ordered vector spaces.

In the next chapter, Thrall undertakes a discussion of the utility axioms both from the mathematical point of view and from that of empirical interpretation. He constructs examples to show the abstract desirability of several of the axioms and possible objections to others. Finally he indicates that the non-Archimedean utilities can still be used to get the results of game theory; in particular, they permit computation of solutions.

In Chapter XIV Jacob Marschak carries out an extensive analysis of the activities of "teams" on the basis of utility theory, game theory and statistical decision procedures. This analysis, as he points out, is purely normative: how should a team act to maximize its gain? A "team" here is essentially a group for which there is a known group utility function which coincides with the common utility function of all the members. By weakening his requirements on solidarity of interest he defines first a "foundation" and then a "coalition". The activities of the team members include making observations, performing actions, sending messages and giving orders. He analyzes a number of cases to determine the best rules of action and communication (a "rule" states for each member of the team what response he should make to every possible situation). The relatively difficult manipulations required even for these simple cases show for one thing how desirable further development and simplification of the theory would be, while on the other hand they serve to emphasize how difficult would be any analysis at all without the machinery of this formalization.

In the last chapter of this part we have a dissenting note. Herbert Bohnert brings together some of the objections that are still offered to any suggested interpretation of the utility concept. While many of the former objections are banished in the modest assertions of von Neumann-Morgenstern utility theory, and while this theory is certainly unexceptionable from an abstract viewpoint, Bohnert questions - among other things - whether we can ever say what kind of a thing "E" is in the sentence "The utility of E for x at time t equals u utiles". ("Utile" is a popular word for a "unit" on the utility scale established by any given utility function; of course, utility is only invariant up to change of origin and scale-factor.) Certainly several of Bohnert's objections seem serious in considering any empirical interpretation of utility; especially so since there is a tendency in parlor discussions to answer difficult points by saying "That has to be included in the utility function". This tendency can lead to a utility function which must, eventually, be defined at any given time for all possible future states of the universe. Whether such objections have the same force in many fairly straight-forward applications discussed by our authors is another matter. In any event we are hardly in a position to dispense with the utility concept. Leaving aside its many special applications in economics, we have suggested above that it is a natural con-comitant of the analysis of any choice situation involving un-certainty. There utility was ushered in with the preference ordering of a given set of probability combinations. This situa-tion arises in any choice problem under uncertainty. In game theory and in the general statistical decision problem there is a set of outcomes on which we assume a preference ordering, and as before the element of uncertainty introduces utilities. For any presently conceivable attack on these problems requires the great simplification of summarizing preference in the face of risk with one quantity - an expected value. It is the utility con-cept that justifies this simplification. (With the assumptions of utility theory the two-person zero-sum game is ready for solu-tion - since we assume opposing utilities for the two players. In statistics we have a game against nature, but we cannot gen-erally assume utilities for this opponent or that nature is "hos-tile". Expected loss is thus not yet determined and this leads to the problems concerning decision criteria discussed in Chap-ters IV and V.)

Himself recognizing the value of the utility concept, Bohnert concludes his paper with a brief suggestion for a new kind of definition of utility; this rests on Carnap's concept of logical probability and makes use of the notions of modal logic. It avoids the feature he found most objectionable in other defini-tions - that the domain of the utility function was undefined or undefinable - because this domain is now a set of propositions in a language system (we are not certain, though, whether his replacement of Carnap's "sentence" by "proposition" is entirely harmless in this respect). But the language systems to which Carnap has succeeded in extending his notion of logical proba-bility are rather limited; and it is our impression that very few logicians - let alone statisticians or scientists - are yet con-vinced of the eventual practicability of Carnap's program. Since Bohnert's definition schema is not sufficiently detailed for us to be certain of its nature even within a Carnap language, it may seem more remote from application than those he criticizes.

PART FOUR

There is really no sharp line in our book between "experimental" papers and theoretical ones. Chapter IX and possibly Chapter X might be considered primarily experimental, on the one hand, while on the other it might be argued that Chapter XVII was primarily theoretical and belonged either in Part One or Part Three, or that Chapter XVIII should have followed the Estes paper in Part Two. Nevertheless, we found it most natural to place these last two with other more purely experimental papers.

Hoffman, Festinger and Lawrence chose for examination from the standpoint of general psychology one of the crucial problems in the theory of n-person games. The von Neumann-Morgenstern theory requires that players decide on <u>coalitions</u> strictly on the desire to maximize their returns. That is, in rational play of the three-person game, for instance, each player is willing to enter into either of the available two-man coalitions, and he decides between these solely on the basis of his expected gain from membership. Thus in the "simple majority game" some pair of the three players will form a coalition and win the stakes; but game theory cannot predict in this case which pair will do so - nor how they will divide the profits afterward.

These authors felt that the consequences of this analysis were contrary to everyday experience, particularly in the apparent instability of the coalitions in the simple majority game. To them it seemed likely that other factors besides monetary or "point" advantages would in this case be decisive in determining coalitions, and that the coalitions would in fact become predictable and relatively stable. In particular they conjectured that one of these factors would depend on the individual's concern over his relative status among the players, and that a second would be the importance he assigned to the task of succeeding in the game. They support these contentions with the description of a carefully designed and executed experiment.

It would be misleading, of course, to conclude from this that the game-theory analysis of the simple majority game is wrong; the games these authors describe are very different games, with players' utility systems quite different from the symmetric ones of the simple majority game. What might be maintained, however, is that the kind of utility consideration they here introduce is at once among those which are very hard to treat in game theory, and yet of a kind which may naturally be expected to obtain in most observations of actual behavior. They have given an example of a gamelike situation which may be better treated in the context of general psychology than in the theory of games.

"On Decision-Making Under Uncertainty", by Coombs and Beardslee, presents at first a very general theory which is at least in part designed both as an empirical descriptive framework and as a normative theory. After laying down their general definitions the authors give an intuitive analysis of a number of important features of their theory on the basis of certain restrictive assumptions. Here they enlist the reader's geometrical intuition by an imbedding in Euclidean 3-space. This permits easy visualization of the relations they discuss between various experiments, as well as of the designs for new experiments suggested by the theory. In these terms they compare, for instance, the assumptions underlying the well known Mosteller-Nogee and Preston-Barrata experiments. Thus the former gave a measure of utility on the assumption of a linear relation between psychological and objective probabilities, while the latter measured psychological probability assuming linearity between utility and money. Coombs and Beardslee further report a pilot experiment carried out in Santa Monica which indicated that with increasing "stake" the subject tended to prefer those offers involving greatest certainty, even though they were of reduced utility.

In his second contribution to our volume Flood examines the behavior of subjects in "prediction experiments" of the Estes type (Chapter IX). Flood sought an experiment to test the hypothesis that subject behavior was "mixed" or "pure" according as the subject believed the events being predicted followed a pattern or were randomly determined. Here, "pure" behavior is characterized by the subject's choice at some point in the sequence of trials of a single best strategy (to which he thereafter adheres), and "mixed" behavior occurs when the subject gives no evidence of any intention to settle on one pure strategy. A stationary stochastic process is one whose probability distributions do not change with time, and in general "non-stationarity" is merely the denial of this changelessness. In these experiments it happens to be reasonable to suppose that "non-stationarity" usually involves the subject's assuming that the events being predicted are determined according to some (eventually guessable) pattern. Flood reports in this paper the results of two pilot experiments which may lend support to his (emminently reasonable) hypothesis. (The editors feel that his discussion of the remarks of "various game theorists in the audience" may be misleading. It is our recollection that in his initial report Estes left an impression with the audience that his subjects had reason to believe the process was random, and we further recall that no one failed to preface remarks about "rationality" or "proper strategies" with a more or less explicit assumption about payoff utilities, such as "If they wanted to maximize their scores...".)

Our final paper furnishes evidence of the educational compass of our summer in Santa Monica. Here four pure mathematicians report on a series of experiments which they themselves devised, carried out and analyzed. To be sure, these experiments lay close to the authors' professional interests; they dealt with questions concerning the empirical interpretation of some fundamental concepts in the theory of n-person games.

The n-person game is analyzed by von Neumann and Morgenstern in the framework of coalitions and side-payments within these coalitions. (This analysis leaves the theory inapplicable from the very start to most many-person parlor games such as bridge and hearts.) Nothing is said about how coalitions are formed, except that the resulting coalition must be among those prescribed by "solutions". Whatever the process of their formation, it seems to admit of no realistic interpretation in typical economic situations, since for large n communication difficulties would prevent consideration of some (possibly optimal) coalitions.

The payoffs to the players are given as components of vectors. A "solution set" is a set of these vectors with certain (necessarily rather weak) properties expressed in terms of "dominance". The important thing is that there are in all known non-trivial cases far too many "solutions"; you cannot even tell from the solution set what coalitions should be formed. And if you knew this, you still could not tell how members of the winning coalition would split the swag among themselves. Briefly, there are seemingly always too many solutions (though it cannot be proved that there always is even one), and these solutions are very "un-solutionlike".

Such objections to the original approach of von Neumann and Morgenstern led to formulation of various new concepts in the n-person theory. Thus Nash's analysis of non-cooperative games and his definition of equilibrium points there do away with pre-game coalitions and side-payments. Again, the Shapley value is a function which permits a prospective player to assign a sort of potential value to each of the "roles" or "positions" in a game. And Milnor gave upper bounds for the amounts each player or set of players "ought" to be able to receive from a game.

Now whether these or similar concepts are actually realized in empirical plays of n-person (cooperative or non-cooperative) games is a question that must be answered before we can discuss the merits of game theory as a mathematical model for the economic theory of exchange. For the expected generalization from games of strategy to economic problems will proceed by means of the theory of general n-person games. This is one side to the desirability of experiment in n-person games. The other is that observing how people actually play games may well suggest new concepts deserving of formalization in the theory. These four authors discuss a number of experiments, principally in light of the question: How may such experiments be sharpened for either one of these two purposes?

Some readers might appreciate comment on the varying degrees of mathematical difficulty of our papers. The only papers, we feel, that require any real mathematical sophistication for understanding the proofs are those of Milnor (IV) and Hausner (XII). On the other hand, papers which contain sufficient mathematical detail to demand fairly close reading include: Radner and Marschak (V), Bush-Mosteller-Thompson (VIII), Flood (X), Debreu (XI) and Marschak (XIV). Finally, although the experiments and results of the four-authored paper on experimental n-person games are either well explained or self-explanatory, a fair knowledge of game theory may be prerequisite to a complete grasp of the purposes and possible significance of the experiments.

CHAPTER II

SOME VIEWS ON MATHEMATICAL MODELS AND MEASUREMENT THEORY*

by

C. H. Coombs, H. Raiffa, R. M. Thrall

UNIVERSITY OF MICHIGAN, COLUMBIA UNIVERSITY
AND UNIVERSITY OF MICHIGAN

We shall undertake first to review the role of mathematical models in a science and then briefly discuss the models used in classical measurement theory. This will be followed by a generalization of measurement models. Illustrations will be introduced when needed to clarify the concepts discussed.

I. THE ROLE OF MATHEMATICAL MODELS

We shall use the terms "physical objects," "real world," and "object system" synonymously to signify that which the empirical scientist seeks to study, including such objects as opinions or psychological reactions. The scope and content of a domain is selected by the scientist with the intent of discovering laws which govern it or making predictions about it, or controlling or at least influencing it.

There are potentially at least as many ways of dividing up the world into object systems as there are scientists to undertake the task. Just as there is this potential variety of object systems,

*This paper is an outgrowth of a number of sessions on measurement theory in an interdisciplinary seminar on the application of mathematics to the social sciences held during the academic year 1951-1952 by the authors. While the influences of the separate authors are sometimes distinguishable, the paper is a truly joint product. The authors are listed alphabetically. This research was carried out under ONR Contract Nonr 374 (00) NR 041-011 and a Ford Foundation Behavioral Studies grant. A version of this paper has appeared in Psychological Review 61 (1954), 132-144.

so also is there a potential variety of mathematical systems. Let us describe the nature of a mathematical system. (For a more detailed discussion of the nature of mathematical systems, see [8], [12], and [13].) A mathematical system consists of a set of assertions from which consequences are derived by mathematical (logical) argument. The assertions are referred to as the axioms or postulates of a mathematical system. They always contain one or more primitive terms which are undefined and have no meaning in the mathematical system. The axioms of the mathematical system will usually consist of statements about the existence of a set of elements, relations on the elements, properties of the relations, operations on the elements, and the properties of the operations. Particular mathematical systems differ in the particular postulates which form their bases. It is evident then that the variety of mathematical systems is limited only by the ability of man to construct them.

Our view of the role that mathematical models play in a science is illustrated in Figure 1. With some segment of the real world as his starting point, the scientist, by means of a process we shall call abstraction (A), maps his object system into one of the mathematical systems or models. By mathematical argument (M) certain mathematical conclusions are arrived at as necessary (logical) consequences of the postulates of the system. The mathematical conclusions are then converted into physical conclusions by a process we shall call interpretation (I).

Let us start with a specific real world situation $(RW)_1$ and by process A map it into a mathematical system $(MS)_1$. We can look at $(MS)_1$ as a model of $(RW)_1$. Looked at in reverse, we can start with consideration of $(MS)_1$ and then $(RW)_1$ can be viewed as a model of $(MS)_1$ and the process of going from $(MS)_1$

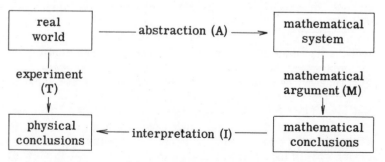

Fig. 1. The Symmetrical Roles of Experiment and Mathematics

to $(RW)_1$ we call "realization." Thus, "realization" is the converse of "abstraction." Now, given $(MS)_1$ we might be able to find a real world situation, $(RW)_2$, such that by assigning meanings to the undefined terms of the mathematical system the assertions about "sets of elements," "relations," and "operations" in $(MS)_1$ become identified with objects or concepts about $(RW)_2$. That is, $(RW)_2$ may be another model of $(MS)_1$ and the process of going from $(RW)_1$ to $(MS)_1$ to $(RW)_2$ often indicates subtle analogies between systems such as $(RW)_1$ and $(RW)_2$. To the mathematician who often starts with an abstract system the model is a concrete analogue of the abstract system. To the social scientist who starts with phenomena in the real world the model is the analogue in the abstract system.

In establishing a model for a given object system one of the most difficult tasks is to attempt a division of the phenomenon into two parts; namely that part which we abstract (A) into the basic assumptions or axioms of the abstract system and that part which we relegate to the physical conclusions, and which we reserve as a check against the interpretations from the abstract system. In a given object system there is no unique partition of the phenomena and which partition is made depends on the creative imagination of the model builder. Indeed, there are models in the physical and biological sciences for which there are no experimentally verified or verifiable correlates in the real world for the undefined terms, relations, and operations in the abstract model. A similar situation prevails on the abstract system side, namely, it is often possible in a given abstract system to interchange the roles of certain axioms and theorems. Thus, in a given system there is no unique method of splitting the mathematical propositions into axioms and theorems. In going from the abstract system to the object system we have the parallel processes of realization and interpretation. It is quite common to consider these synonymous; however, we prefer in this discussion to reserve the word "interpretation" for the process which maps the mathematical conclusions (rather than the axioms) into the object system.

Let us summarize briefly up to this point. Beginning with a segment of the real world, the scientist, by an entirely theoretical route, has arrived at certain conclusions about the real world. His first step is a process of abstraction from the real world, then a process of logical argument to an abstract conclusion, then a return to the real world by a process of interpretation yielding conclusions with physical meaning. But there is an alternative route to physical conclusions and this is by way of working with the object system itself. Thus, the scientist may begin with the real world segment in which he is interested and proceed directly to physical conclusions by a process of observation or experiment (T).

The path (T) (experimentation) from the real world to the physical conclusions needs further scrutiny. Usually in theory construction the scientist embarks on model building after he has many facts at his disposal. These facts he partitions into two parts—one part serves as a springboard for the abstraction process (A); the other part serves as a check on the model by making comparisons with these initial facts and the interpretations (I) stemming from the model. If a specific interpretation is not at variance with a fact in the initial reservoir, but at the same time not corroborated by our a priori notions of the object system, then the model perhaps has contributed to our knowledge of the object system. The scientist next tests this tentative conclusion by setting up a plan of experimental verification, if this is possible. Often direct verification may not be possible, and corroboration stems from examination of experimental evidence which supports claims of the model quite indirectly. That is, motivated by interpretations of the model, the scientist sets up an experimental design, obtains observations by experimentation, makes a statistical interpretation of these observations into physical conclusions, and compares the conclusions with those of the abstract route in order to appraise the model. As suggested by a referee (Frederick Mosteller) of this paper, it would be appropriate to generalize Figure 1 as shown in Figure 2. The route A_2EI_2 in Figure 2 is summarized

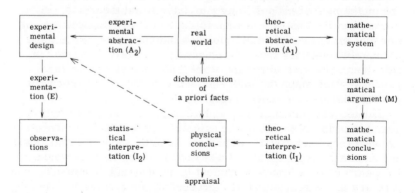

Fig. 2. A Generalization of Figure 1

by the route T in Figure 1. If the physical conclusions of the process A_1MI_1 are at variance with the a priori facts or with conclusions arrived at via A_2EI_2 (and if more confidence is placed in the experimental route than in the theoretical route) then the suitability of the model is suspect.

The task of a science looked at in this way may be seen to be the task of trying to arrive at the same conclusions about the real world by two different routes: one is by experiment and the other by logical argument; these correspond, respectively, to the left and right sides of Figures 1 and 2. There is no natural or necessary order in which these routes should be followed. The history of science is replete with instances in which physical experiments suggested axiom systems to the mathematicians and, thereby, contributed to the development of mathematics. On the other hand, mathematical systems developed under such stimulation, in turn, suggested experiments. And there have been many instances of mathematical systems developed without reference to any known reality which subsequently filled a need of theoretical scientists. The direction that mathematics has taken is in considerable part due to its interaction with the physical sciences and the problems arising therein.

It is illuminating here to observe the way in which the models of the mathematical theory of probability and statistics fit this picture. As in any abstract system the mathematical theory of probability is devoid of any real-world content; and as in any other mathematical system the axioms of probability specify interrelationships among undefined terms. It is common to let the notion of probability itself be undefined and to attempt to capture in the axiomatic structure properties of probability motivated by the interpretations we have in mind (e.g., gambling games, physical diffusions processes, etc.). Given an association of probabilities to prescribed elementary sets, the axioms of probability dictate how one must associate probabilities with other sets. How we make these preliminary associations, providing we have consistency, is not relevant to the purely abstract system. When we come to apply the probability model we are confronted with the problem of identifying real events with abstract sets in the mathematical system and the measurement problem of associating probabilities to these abstract sets. Experience has taught us that if we exploit the notion of the relative frequency of occurrence of real events when making our preliminary associations then the interpretations from the model have a similar frequency interpretation in the real world. To be sure, our rules of composition in the formal system were devised with this in mind. We associate probabilities in one way rather than in another way in the process (A) so that when we generate AMI, our interpretations are in "close" accord with results of experimentation, T, when T is possible. When T is not possible we have to rely to a great extent on analogy.

An extremely important problem of statistics can be viewed as follows: For a priori reasons we may have a well-defined family of possible probability associations. Each element of this family, when used in the abstraction process (A), generates by AMI a probability measure having a frequency interpretation over real events. In addition, we are given a set of possible actions to be taken. Preferences for these actions depend in some way on the relative "appropriateness" of different probability associations in the abstraction process, A. By conducting an experiment, T, and noting its outcome we gain some insight into the relative "appropriateness" of the different probability associations and thus base our action accordingly. Variations of this problem, which involves the entire AMI-T process, have been abstracted sufficiently so that models of mathematical statistics include counterparts of all these ingredients within the mathematical system itself.

In a given model we may be confronted with the problem of deciding whether the AMI argument gives results "close enough" to the experimental results from T. We often can view this problem involving a complete AMI-T process as the real world phenomenon to which we apply the A process sending it into a formal mathematical statistics system. The statistics system analyzes step M and our interpretation I takes the form of an acceptance or rejection statement concerning the original theory.

The process of measurement, corresponding to A in Figure 1, provides an excellent illustration of the role of mathematical models. There are many types of observations that can be called "measurement." Perhaps the most obvious are those made with yardsticks, thermometers, and other instruments, which result immediately in the assignment of a real number to the object being measured. In other cases, such as the number of correct items on a mental test or the size of a herd of cattle, the result of measurement is a natural number (positive integer). In still other cases, such as relative ability of two chess players, relative desirability of a pair of pictures, or relative hardness of two substances, the result is a dominance (or preference) relation. We might even stretch the concept of measurement to include such processes as naming each element of some class of objects, or the photographic representation of some event, or the categorization of mental illnesses or occupations.

The process of measurement may be described formally as follows. Let $P = \{p_1, p_2, \cdots\}$ denote a set of physical objects or events. By a measurement A on P we mean a function which assigns to each element p of P an element $b = A(p)$ in some mathematical system $B = \{b_1, \cdots\}$. That is, to each element of P, we associate an element of some abstract system B (the process A of Figure 1). The system B consists of a set of elements with some mathematical structure imposed on its elements. The nature of the set P and the actual mapping into the abstract space B comprises the operation of measurement. The mathematical structure of the system B belongs to the formal side of measurement theory. The structure of B is dictated by a set of rules or axioms which states relationships between the elements of B. However, no connotation can be given to these elements of B which is not explicitly stated in the axioms, i.e., their labels are extraneous with respect to considerations of the structure of B.

After making the mapping from P into B, then one may operate with the image elements in B (always abiding by the axioms, process M of Figure 1). Purely mathematical results obtained in B must then be interpreted back in the real world (the process I of Figure 1), to enable one to make predictions or to synthesize data concerning set P.

If the manifestations of P (as a result of the process T of Figure 1) are in conflict with the results of process I obtained from B, then one must search for a new cycle AMI. Suppose that we have a family of abstractions $\{A_\alpha\}$ from the given situation P, and suppose that M_α, I_α complete the cycle begun with A_α. Among all of the available cycles $A_\alpha M_\alpha I_\alpha$ we seek one, say $A_0 M_0 I_0$, which is "closest" to T according to some criterion. Some models have a criterion built in to judge closeness and others of a more deterministic nature require an exact fit.

The process T represents the experimental or operational part of model building, the process M represents the formal or logical aspect. The processes A and I are really the keys to the model and serve as bridges between experiment and formal reasoning.

It might be well here to draw clearly the distinction between a model and a theory. A model is not itself a theory; it is only an available or possible or potential theory until a segment of the real world has been mapped into it. Then the model becomes a theory about the real world. As a theory, it can be accepted or rejected on the basis of how well it works. As a model, it can only be right or wrong on logical grounds. A model must satisfy only internal criteria; a theory must satisfy external criteria as well.

An example of the distinction between models and theories lies in the domain of measurement. A measurement scale, such as an ordinal, interval, or ratio scale is a model and needs only to be internally consistent. As soon as behavior or data are "measured" by being mapped into one of these scales, then the model becomes a theory about that data and may be right or wrong. Scales of measurement are only a very small portion of the many formal systems in mathematics which might serve as image spaces or models, but will be discussed here as they constitute very simple and immediate examples of the role of mathematical models. First to be discussed will be the models of conventional measurement theory and then a generalization of these models will be presented.

II. MATHEMATICAL MODELS OF CLASSICAL MEASUREMENT THEORY

The first comprehensive classification of the mathematical models used in conventional measurement theory was made by Stevens [9]. He classified scales of measurement into nominal, ordinal, interval, and ratio scales, the latter two christened by him. A more complete discussion of these scales is contained in a later work by him [10], and also in Coombs [3], [5] and Weitzenhoffer [11]. Because of the literature available on these scales and because they constitute a restricted class of models they will be briefly summarized here only to provide a basis for generalization in the next section.

The mathematical model of measurement is said to be nominal if it merely contributes a mapping A_O of P into M_O without any further structure on M_O. A nominal scale M may be subjected to any 1-1 transformation without gain or loss in information.

An ordinal scale of measurement is implied if there is a natural ranking of the objects of measurement according to some attribute. More precisely, the ordinal scale is appropriate if the objects of measurement can be partitioned into classes in such a manner that: a) elements which belong to the same class can be considered equivalent relative to the attribute in question; b) a comparative judgment or an order relation can be made between each pair of distinct classes (for example, class x is more

than class y); c) there is an element of consistency in these
comparative judgments—namely, if class x is more ____ than
class y and class y is more ____ than class z, then class x is
more ____ than class z (that is, the comparative judgment or
order relation is transitive). For example, the familiar socio-
economic classes, upper-upper, lower-upper, upper-middle,
lower-middle, upper-lower, and lower-lower, imply the measurement of socio-economic status on an ordinal scale. The numbers 1, 2, 3, 4, 5, 6, or 1, 5, 10, 11, 12, 14, or the letters
A, B, C, D, E, F, could designate the six classes without gain
or loss of information.

The measurement is said to be an interval scale when the set
M consists of the real numbers and any linear transformation,
$y = ax + b$ ($a \neq 0$), on M is permissible. Measurement on an
interval scale is achieved with a constant unit of measurement
and an arbitrary zero. An example of an interval scale is the
measure of time. That is, "physical events" can be mapped into
the real numbers and all the operations of arithmetic are permissible on the differences between all pairs of these numbers.

If the set M consists of the real numbers subject only to the
transformation group $y = cx$ where c is any non-zero scalar,
the scale is called a ratio scale. Measurement on a ratio scale
is achieved with an absolute zero and a constant unit of measurement. The scalar c signifies that only the unit of measurement
is arbitrary. In a ratio scale all the operations of arithmetic are
permissible. The most familiar examples of ratio scales are
observed in physics in such measurements as length, weight, and
absolute temperature.

III. A GENERALIZATION OF MEASUREMENT MODELS

An axiomatic basis for certain scales of measurement will be
presented in this section. Other scales can be generated by
forming mixtures (or composites) of these. Indeed, some of the
scales listed in the diagram shown in Figure 3 can be regarded
as composites of others.

We will now list defining axioms for each of these systems
and briefly discuss their roles. It is not claimed that this list
is exhaustive; it is presented to illustrate certain possibilities
for significant generalizations of scales used in the classical
theory. The arrangement in the diagram is from top to bottom
in order of increasing strength of axioms; a connecting line indicates that the lower listed system is a special case of the
higher one.

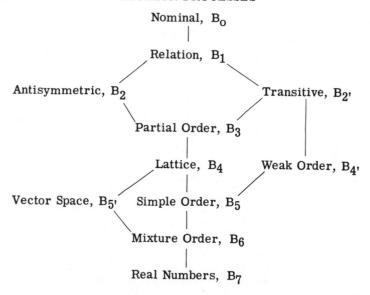

Fig. 3. Measurement Scales

B_0, The Nominal Scale. A nominal scale, B_0, may be considered a mathematical system consisting merely of a set of elements. We define the index of B_0 to be the number of elements in B_0. (The index may be finite or infinite.)

Examples of segments of the real world that are mapped into nominal scales are psychiatric classifications, job families, and disease types.

The nominal scale, B_0, is the most primitive step in any system of measurement. The set of elements is partitioned into classes such that there is a relation of "equality" or equivalence between pairs of elements from the same class. The nominal scale is fundamental since the process of discrimination is a necessary prerequisite for any more complex form of measurement.

B_1, The Relation Scale. Perhaps the smallest step that may be taken to strengthen this mathematical system is to introduce a relation between some pairs of elements. In technical language, a relation R on a set B_1 is a set of ordered pairs (b, b') of elements of B_1. We write bRb' to indicate that (b, b') is one of the pairs included in t   relation R, and call the set B_1 a relation scale. It is important to recognize that for R to constitute a very useful relation, not all possible pairs (b, b') from B_1 can be included in the relation R.

With some risk of misinterpretation or distortion, these concepts might be illustrated as follows. Consider a set of persons identified by a nominal scale, B_0. Let us now define the relation R on B_0 to be "loves." Thus R consists of the ordered pairs (a, b) for which, a loves b.

The particular relation used here as an illustration is one whose mathematical properties are mostly negative. We cannot conclude from a loves b and b loves c, that a loves c, or that b loves a, or that b does not love a. For example, if John loves Mary and if Mary loves Peter, it may well be that, far from loving him, John would like to see Peter transported to the South Pole. In the terminology to be introduced below, we would say that love is not symmetric, is not asymmetric, and is not transitive.

B_2, The Antisymmetric Relation Scale. A relation R on a set B is said to be antisymmetric if aRb and bRa together imply that a is identical with b. An example is the relation $\geq$ for real numbers. A statement such as, "Picture a is at least as good as picture b" illustrates an antisymmetric relation on a collection of pictures, provided that there are not in the collection two distinct pictures of equal merit, i.e., two pictures about which the judge is indifferent.

Closely connected to the concept of antisymmetry is that of asymmetry. A relation R on a set B is said to be asymmetric if aRb implies bR'a (where bR'a means that b is not in the relation R to a). The mathematical prototype of asymmetry is the relation $>$ for real numbers. Verbal forms for asymmetric relations include such statements as, "Picture a is better than picture b," or "Player a beats player b in a game."

Antisymmetry and asymmetry are seen to be at the root of statements of comparison. These two classes of relations can be regarded as the most primitive types of order relations. At the opposite pole from these concepts is that of symmetry. A relation R is said to be symmetric if aRb implies bRa. For example, the relations "is a sibling of," "is a cousin of," and "is the same color as" are all symmetric.

If S is an asymmetric relation on a set B, we can obtain from it an antisymmetric relation R by the definition: aRb means either aSb or a = b. Conversely, if R is antisymmetric and we define aSb to mean aRb and a $\neq$ b, then S is asymmetric. It is customary to use the symbols, $\leq$, $\geq$ for antisymmetric relations and to use $<$, $>$ for the associated asymmetric relations.

$\underline{B_{2'}}$, The Transitive Relation Scale. A relation R is said to be transitive if aRb and bRc imply aRc. In the physical world, preference judgments which are not transitive are frequently regarded as inconsistent or irrational. However, situations such as that of three chess players, each of whom can beat one of the other two, show that transitivity is not a requirement of nature.

The chess player relation is antisymmetric but not transitive. An example of a relation that is symmetric and transitive is given by a communication system where each link is bidirectional; here aRb is given the meaning "there exists a chain of links starting with a and ending with b." If the links are not required to be bidirectional, the relation is still transitive but is no longer symmetric. Note that in this example it is quite possible to have aRa, i.e., a chain beginning at a and ending at a. (This chain must have at least one element different from a.)

The relation "a is the rival of b" (say as suitors of a particular girl) is symmetric and is almost transitive. If aRb and bRc, we can conclude aRc unless a = c; but we can hardly regard a as being his own rival. This type of relation arises frequently in studies of social structures. We say a relation R is quasi-transitive if aRb, bRc, and a $\neq$ c imply aRc. The sibling relation is also quasi-transitive. Of course, if R is quasi-transitive we can define a new relation S to be the same as R except that also aRb, bRa imply aSa. In some instances S is just as good a model as R, but in others the extension from R to S destroys the usefulness of the model.

As an example consider the structure matrix $A = \|a_{ij}\|$ of some society. Thus we set $a_{ij} = 1$ if person i has direct influence on person j and set $a_{ij} = 0$ otherwise. One must decide in accordance with the purpose of the investigation whether or not to set the diagonal element a_{ii} equal to 0 or to 1. (The relation "i has direct influence on j" is not transitive even if we take each $a_{ii} = 1$, but this example nevertheless illustrates the kind of problem involved in the contrast between transitivity and quasi-transitivity.)

If the relation aRb meant a "is higher in socio-economic status than" b and this required that a had more income and more education than b, then the relation R would be asymmetric and transitive.

B_3, The Partly Ordered Scale. A relation $\geq$ which is re-flexive, antisymmetric, and transitive is called a partial order. If for some pair a, b, neither of the relations a $\geq$ b, b $\geq$ a holds, we say that a and b are incomparable relative to $\geq$. In the case of a preference relation, incomparability is not the same thing as indifference. We call a set a poset (partly ordered set), if there is a partial order relation defined on B.

If a $\geq$ b, we also write b $\leq$ a; if a $\geq$ b and a $\neq$ b, we write a $>$ b or b $<$ a.

A partial order may be illustrated as follows. Suppose that on a mental test no two individuals in a group pass exactly the same items. Now let a $\geq$ b symbolize the relation "a passed all the items b did." Then a $>$ b means that "a passed all the items b did and at least one more." This poset reflects multi-dimensionality of the attributes mediating the test performance and some interesting mathematical problems arise regarding the partial order as a "product" of simple orders. The result is a non-metric form of factor analysis with some of the same problems as factor analysis [3].

Next we consider the mental test example modified so as to allow the possibility that two individuals a and b pass exactly the same items. Then in the above notation we have a $\geq$ b and b $\geq$ a, but not b = a. Hence, $\geq$ no longer gives a partial order. However, if we define a I b to mean a $\geq$ b and b $\geq$ a, it is not hard to show that if we identify individuals with the same test performance then $\geq$ is a partial order relation. Or, alterna-tively, we could consider $\geq$ as a partial order relation on the set of possible test performances. It is customary to make such identifications and speak of a partial order as though it were ac-tually on the initial set rather than on the identified classes or on the test results.

Another example of a partial order is implicit in the treat-ment of the comparative efficiency of mental tests on a "cost-utility" basis [1]. "Cost" is the fraction of potentially success-ful people who are eliminated by a test; "utility" is the fraction of potential failures who are eliminated by the test. If for their respective cutting scores one test has a higher utility and a lower cost than another it is a superior test, but if it had a higher utility and a higher cost the two tests would be incomparable un-less the relative weight of excluding a potential success to includ-ing a potential failure were known.

A basic problem in the theory of testing hypotheses in statis-tical inference is to test a simple hypothesis, H_0 ("null hypothe-sis"), against a single alternative hypothesis, H_1, by means of experimental data. A test, T, associates to each experimental outcome the decision to accept H_0 or to accept H_1 (but not both!). Each test T is appraised by a pair of numbers, namely, the probability of accepting H_1 if H_0 is true, $P_T(H_1|H_0)$, and probability of accepting H_0 if H_1 is true, $P_T(H_0|H_1)$. Given two tests, T' and T'', then T' is said to be as good as T'' ($T' \geqq T''$) if and only if

$$P_{T'}(H_1|H_0) \leqq P_{T''}(H_1|H_0)$$
$$P_{T'}(H_0|H_1) \leqq P_{T''}(H_1|H_0)$$

The relation $\geqq$ on the set of all tests is an example of a partial order.

B4, Lattice. Let B be a poset relative to a relation $\geqq$. If a, b, c are elements of B and $c \geqq a$, $c \geqq b$, we say that c is an upper bound of a and b. If also $c \leqq x$ for every upper bound x of a and b, we say that c is the least upper bound of a and b and write $c = a \cup b$. In terms of the example of mental testing, c could be a person who passed exactly those items which were passed by at least one of a and b. Analogously, if $d \leqq a$, $d \leqq b$, we say that d is a lower bound of a and b, and if also $d \geqq y$ for all lower bounds y of a and b, we say that d is the greatest lower bound of a and b and write $d = a \cap b$. In our example d could be a person who passed exactly those items passed by both a and b.

A pair a,b need not have a least upper bound, nor a greatest lower bound. For example, if a passed items 1, 2, 3, 4; b passed 1, 2, 5, 6; c passed 1, 2, 3, 4, 5, 6, 7; c' passed 1, 2, 3, 4, 5, 6, 8; and there are no other persons, then both c and c' are upper bounds to a and b but there is no least upper bound. Also in this case there are no lower bounds for a and b and hence no greatest lower bound.

A poset is said to be a lattice if, for every pair a,b, both $a \cup b$ and $a \cap b$ exist. The lattice is an intermediate model between a partial order and a vector space.

George Miller (personal communication) has recently investigated the use of a lattice theoretic treatment of information in experimental psychology. To each item of information he associates (process A) an element of a lattice. If two items of information are associated respectively with elements x and y of the lattice then: 1) the item which consists of the information common to the original items is associated with the element $x \cap y$; 2) the item which consists of the information contained

in either of the original items is associated with the element
$x \cup y$. As used by Miller an item of information might consist
of a cue or a sequence of cues in an experimental situation. The
common procedure is to summarize the structure of the experiment by means of a lattice, given an experimental setup. However, the abstract lattice in turn can motivate new types of experimental situations and indicate analogies between experimental designs which otherwise would not be apparent.

B_4', Weak Order. A transitive order $\leqq$ is defined on B_4',
and has the property that for every pair a,b either $a \leqq b$ or
$b \leqq a$. If both $a \leqq b$ and $b \leqq a$, we say that a and b are indifferent. Indifference is an equivalence relation (i.e., is reflexive,
symmetric, and transitive).

A weak ordering would be illustrated by the military ranks of
second lieutenant, first lieutenant, captain, major, etc. Each of
these would constitute an equivalence class and for any two offi-
cers (a,b), either $a \geqq b$ or $b \geqq a$, or both.

B_5, Chain. A poset in which every pair is comparable is
called a chain (or simple order, or linear order, or complete
order). Alternatively, a chain is a weak order in which each
indifference class consists of a single element. Here every
pair of elements is ordered.

The previous example of a weak ordering of military rank
could be converted into a chain if date of rank, standing in class,
etc., were taken into account. Then, for every two distinct elements, a,b, either $a > b$ or $b > a$.

The ordinal scales of classical measurement theory are examples of chains.

B_5', Partly Ordered Vector Space. A special case of lattice
is provided by a real vector space (or a subset of a vector space).
A vector $x = (x_1, \cdots, x_n)$ is an ordered set of n real numbers
called the components of the vector. We define $x \leqq y$ to mean
that $x_i \leqq y_i$ for each component. (Here the second symbol $\leqq$
refers to the usual ordering of real numbers.) This definition
makes the vector space into a poset, and this poset is a lattice
which is called a partly ordered vector space.

A partly ordered vector space is illustrated by the comparability of individuals in mental abilities. Conceiving of intelligence
as made up of a number of primary mental abilities, each of these
constitutes a component or dimension. Then, it may be said of
two individuals x and y that y is at least as intelligent as x if
and only if y has as much or more of each component as x does.

The term "vector" is sometimes used in a more general situation. If $C_1, \cdots, C_n$ are chain orders we may consider vectors or n-tuples $c = (c_1, \cdots, c_n)$ where the i-th component c_i lies in the chain order C_i ($i = 1, \cdots, n$). The set C of all such vectors c is called the <u>Cartesian product</u> of $C_1, \cdots, C_n$ and is denoted by $C = C_1 \times \cdots \times C_n$. We can make C into a poset by a process analogous to that used above for real vector spaces. Note that a real vector space is the special case of a Cartesian product of n factors $C_1, \cdots, C_n$ each equal to the set of real numbers.

<u>B6, Simply Ordered Vector Space, or Utility Space.</u> A real vector space (or subset) in which $x < y$ is defined lexicographically, i.e., $x < y$ if $x_1 = y_1, \cdots, x_{i-1} = y_{i-1}, x_i < y_i$ is a special case of simple order.

A lexicographic ordering can be illustrated by a manner in which we might expect a fortune hunter to impose a chain order on a set of unmarried women. Presumably, financial assets would be the principal component and he might construct a weak ordering of the ladies into, say five classes, on this basis. Then he would turn to the second component, say beauty, and within each of the financial classes construct a simple ordering of the ladies on this component. Any two ladies (a,b) would then be simply ordered as follows:

1) If a were in a higher financial class than b, a would be preferred to b.
2) If a were in the same financial class as b, then preference would be determined by their relation on the beauty component.

<u>B7, Real Numbers.</u> The transition to scales using the real numbers has been given additional importance by the development of von Neumann-Morgenstern utilities. Even though one may wish to arrive here in order to have a simple index when a decision is to be made, it may frequently be desirable not to get here all at once, but to keep the components at a weaker level until it is necessary to map into the real numbers.

Measurement scales involving the real numbers, the interval scale and the ratio scale, have been discussed at length in the literature [3], [5], [9], [10], [11] and will not be pursued again here.

IV. FURTHER EXTENSIONS

The various mathematical systems discussed here as available for measurement have been illustrated with objects of the real world mapped into the elements of an abstract system. A further level of abstraction is provided by defining a "distance function" in the abstract system, in which ordered pairs of elements in the abstract system are mapped into elements of another abstract system about which a variety of assertions may be made. In the context of measurement, these pairs of elements may correspond to "differences" between pairs of objects in the real world. These differences may themselves then be mapped into an appropriate abstract system such as one of those discussed here.

A number of these types of scales have been discussed by one of the authors [4, Chapter 1]. An illustration is the ordered metric scale in which the objects themselves satisfy B_5, a simply ordered scale, and ordered pairs of objects, regarded as "distances" between them, satisfy B_3, a partly ordered scale. Such scales are now being utilized for the measurement of utility and psychological probability in experiments on decision making under uncertainty [6], [7].

V. SUMMARY

One role of mathematical models is to provide a logical route to go from characteristics of the real world to predictions about it. The alternative route is by observation or experiment on the real world itself. The view expressed here is that these two routes are coordinate.

The various scales used in measurement serve as an illustration of the application of mathematical models and are subject to the same constraints as other mathematical models. That is, if the axioms underlying the scale are not satisfied by that segment of the real world which is mapped into it, then the interpretations of the mathematical conclusions may have no reality or meaning. Thus, to insist that measurement always constitutes the mapping of physical objects into the real number system is to impose on the real world an abstract theory which may be invalid.

A partial ordering of various alternative mathematical systems available for measurement has been presented with illustrations in order to reveal the relative strengths of these scales to which the real world must conform to permit their application.

We make no claim to completeness in this list of models for measurement theory. Our purpose is to point out the richness of the set of possible models and to give some examples that show how the use of more general models can extend the domain of classical measurement theory.

None of the discussion here should be taken as an argument for the use of weaker scales in the place of stronger scales for their own sake. The measurement scale utilized constitutes a theory about the real world and the stronger the theory the better, so long as it is correct. The addition of axioms to a scale which are not satisfied by the real world is a step away from the path of progress.

BIBLIOGRAPHY

1. Berkson, J., "Cost-utility" as a measure of the efficiency of a test. Journal of the American Statistical Association, 42 (1947), 246-255.

2. Birkhoff, G., Lattice Theory, New York: American Mathematical Society, 1948.

3. Coombs, C. H., Mathematical models in psychological scaling, Journal of the American Statistical Association, 46 (1951), 480-489.

4. Coombs, C. H., A theory of psychological scaling, Engineering Research Bulletin (University of Michigan), 1952, No. 34.

5. Coombs, C. H., The theory and methods of social measurement, In L. Festinger and D. Katz (Eds.), Research Methods in the Behavioral Sciences, New York: Dryden Press, 1953.

6. Coombs, C. H., Social Choice and Strength of Preference, Ch. VI, Infra.

7. Coombs, C. H. and Beardslee, D. C., On decision making under uncertainty, Ch. XVII, Infra.

8. Kershner, R. B. and Wilcox, L. R., The Anatomy of Mathematics, New York: Ronald Press, 1950.

9. Stevens, S. S., On the theory of scales of measurement, Science, 103 (1946), 677-680.

10. Stevens, S. S., Mathematics, measurement, and psychophysics, In S. S. Stevens (Ed.), Handbook of Experimental Psychology, New York: John Wiley, 1950.

11. Weitzenhoffer, A. M., Mathematical structures and psychological measurements, Psychometrika, 16 (1951), 387–406.

12. Weyl, H., Philosophy of Mathematics and Natural Science, Princeton: Princeton University Press, 1949.

13. Wilder, R. L., Introduction to the Foundations of Mathematics, New York: John Wiley, 1952.

CHAPTER III

ON METHODS OF AMALGAMATION

by

Leo A. Goodman*

UNIVERSITY OF CHICAGO

1. INTRODUCTION AND SUMMARY

The problem which shall be the concern of this paper is closely related to the problem of social choice and individual values [1], the theory of statistical decisions [26], the theory of games against nature [21], the problem of normative behavior under uncertainty [20], and the problem of cooperative aggregation [12]. Let us first state the problem formally. We are given a finite matrix U

$$U = \begin{Vmatrix} u_{11} & u_{12} & u_{13} & u_{14} & \cdots & u_{1c} \\ u_{21} & u_{22} & u_{23} & u_{24} & \cdots & u_{2c} \\ u_{31} & u_{32} & u_{33} & u_{34} & \cdots & u_{3c} \\ u_{41} & u_{42} & u_{43} & u_{44} & \cdots & u_{4c} \\ \cdot & \cdot & \circ & \cdot & & \cdot \\ \cdot & \cdot & \cdot & \cdot & & \cdot \\ \cdot & \cdot & \cdot & \cdot & & \cdot \\ u_{r1} & u_{r2} & u_{r3} & u_{r4} & \cdots & \end{Vmatrix}$$

of utilities u_{ij} which measure the utility of row i for column j.

*Part of this research was carried out while the author was a member of the University of Michigan Summer Seminar on Design of Experiments on Decision Processes. A part of this work was prepared under an Office of Naval Research contract. Some of the results were presented at a joint meeting of the Econometric Society and the Institute of Mathematical Statistics at Michigan State College, East Lansing, Michigan, on September 2, 1952. The author is indebted to Harry Markowitz of the Rand Corporation for many helpful suggestions.

The problem is to devise rules (methods of amalgamation) for choosing the row with the "greatest utility."

In games against nature [21], the rows represent possible strategies among which the player must choose and the columns represent possible states of nature. The payoff to the player when he chooses strategy (row) i is given by the entry u_{ij} if nature is in state (column) j. Here the entry u_{ij} represents a von Neumann-Morgenstern utility. The problem is to determine criteria or devise rules which the player might use for choosing the strategy (row) which will give him the "greatest utility."

In the problem of social choice and individual values [1], the rows represent possible social choices among which the "best" choice is to be made and the columns represent the individuals' values. That is, the value which individual j ascribes to social choice i is given by entry u_{ij}. The entries may represent the utility of social choice i for individual j, but will usually only describe the rank order assigned to social choice i by individual j (e.g., $a_{ij} = 1$ if individual j ranks social choice i as his least preferred social choice, $a_{ij} = 2$ if individual j ranks social choice i as next to the least preferred social choice, . . .). The problem is then to amalgamate the values of the different individuals (columns) in order to make the social choice which is "most preferred" by the group of individuals.

In the theory of statistical decisions or the theory of normative behavior under uncertainty, the rows represent courses of action and the columns represent the possible states of the world (see, e.g. [23]). The expected income resulting from act i is u_{ij} if the world is in state j. The problem is to choose the "best" course of action.

In the problem of cooperative aggregation the rows may represent different alternatives and the columns represent different bases of comparison, e.g., price, efficiency, and looks in comparing automobiles. Then the problem is to amalgamate the different bases of comparison in order to arrive at a method for deciding which is the "best" alternative.

These problems have been studied by economicts, psychologists, sociologists, statisticians, mathematicians, and philosophers. Since the formal aspects of these problems are so closely related to each other, one would expect that some of the results which have been obtained by, say, the statisticians would be related to results obtained by those studying the problem of social choice and individual values (and vice versa). Furthermore, one would expect that some of the results by, say, the statisticians would have implications for the problem of social choice (and vice versa). Some of these relations and implications are studied in this paper. A general method of amalgamation is presented which includes as special cases (a) the Laplace criterion for the problem of statistical decision, (b) the method of majority rule when this rule leads to a social choice, (c) the "reasonable" social welfare function of A. H. Copeland, and (d) the Bayes solution to the statistical problem. This general method of amalgamation may also be used in order to develop still other criteria which are special cases.

2. SOME METHODS OF AMALGAMATION

Suppose that $\sum_{j=1}^{c} u_{ij}$ is considered as a measure of the utility of row i in the case where the utilities are real numbers. Then the best row would be the one for which the average of the entries is greatest. This method of amalgamation has been called the Laplace criterion. Articles 690, 719, 806, 990 of [24] discuss the history of this criterion. (I am indebted to Churchill Eisenhart and Dick Savage of the Bureau of Standards for their historical research on this problem which brought this reference to my attention.)

If relevant probabilities associated with the columns may be computed (i.e., if a number $p_j \geq 0$ may be assigned to column j for $j = 1, 2, \cdots, c$), then another method of amalgamation, called the Bayes solution [3], may be used. Then $\sum_{j=1}^{c} u_{ij} p_j$ may be considered as a measure of the average utility of row i and the best row would be the one for which the average utility is greatest. The Laplace criterion is obtained if p_j is the same for all j.

The method of majority rule for the problem of social choice is another criterion for amalgamation which may be described as follows. The entries in the matrix U are taken to be utilities, and with respect to any pair u, v of utilities it is assumed that one of the following three decisions can be made: (1) u is preferred to v, (2) v is preferred to u, (3) neither is preferred to the other. With each pair u, v we associate a number $\hat{s}(u,v)$ which equals +1, -1, 0 respectively according as (1), (2), or (3) holds. Then row i will win a majority of the votes in an election with row k, if $\hat{\phi}(i,k) = \sum_{j=1}^{c} \hat{s}(u_{ij}, u_{kj})$ is positive. Row i is considered best if it will win a majority of the votes in an election with every other row. That is, that row i is chosen for which $\hat{\phi}(i,k)$ is positive for all $k \neq i$. A row with this property may not exist and in that case no "best" row is obtained.

A. H. Copeland [11] has suggested another method of amalgamation which he calls a "reasonable" social welfare function. This method is a modification of the method of majority rule which permits the rows to be ordered. Copeland's social welfare function might be paraphrased in the following manner. Let sgn x be the signum function of x:

$$\text{sgn } x = \begin{cases} +1 \text{ for } x>0, \\ 0 \text{ for } x = 0, \\ -1 \text{ for } x<0. \end{cases}$$

We consider $\hat{\hat{\phi}}(i) = \sum_{k=1}^{r} \text{sgn } \hat{\phi}(i,k)$ as a measure of the utility of row i, and choose that row for which $\hat{\hat{\phi}}(i)$ is greatest.

A general method of amalgamation will now be presented which will help to make clear the relations between the preceding methods and which will suggest still other methods of amalgamation. This general method will have as special cases all of the preceding methods including the method of majority rule when that rule leads to the choice a "best" row: With each pair u, v we associate a real number $s(\overline{u,v})$ which is positive when u is preferred to v, negative when v is preferred to u, and zero when neither is preferred to the other. Let $t(x)$ be a non-decreasing function of x and let $p_j \geqq 0$ be any number assigned to column j. Then row i is better than row k by an amount $\phi(i,k)$ if $\phi(i,k) = \sum_{j=1}^{c} s(u_{ij}, u_{kj})p_j$ is positive. As a measure of the utility of row i, we take

$$\sum_{k=1}^{r} t[\phi(i,k)]$$

and choose that row with the greatest utility.

The choice of p_j depends on whether relevant probabilities (weights) may be assigned to the columns. In the theory of statistical decisions, these p_j will be the a priori probabilities associated with the various states (columns) of nature. In the problem of social choice, the p_j might be the weight assigned to the values of individual j or the influence which individual j has in arriving at a best social choice. The function $s(u,v)$ measures how much importance is to be given to the preference between the two utilities u and v. The function $t(x)$ measures how much importance is to be given to the amount x that row i is better than another row in determining the utility of row i. For example, in the case where the utilities are real numbers and $s(u,v) = sgn(u-v)$, then only the fact that one utility is greater than another utility has significance; and the amount by which it is greater is considered irrelevant. Also, if $t(x) = sgn\, x$ then only the fact that row i is better than row k has significance; and the amount by which it is better is considered irrelevant.

In the special case where $t(x) = x$, the utility of row i may be written as

$$\sum_{k=1}^{r} \phi(i,k) = \sum_{j=1}^{c} \left[\sum_{k=1}^{r} s(u_{ij}, u_{kj}) \right] p_j .$$

We might consider $\sum_{k=1}^{r} s(u_{ij}, u_{kj}) = \phi_j(i)$ as a measure of the utility of row i for column j. Hence, the utility of row i may be written as $\sum_{j=1}^{c} \phi_j(i) p_j$, a weighted sum of the utility of row i for the various columns.

For the Bayes solution, it is assumed that the utilities are real numbers, $s(u,v) = u - v$, and $t(x) = x$; and the Laplace criterion is obtained if further the p_j is a constant a. For the method of majority rule $p_j = a$ and $s(u,v)$ is restricted to the values +1, -1, 0. The Copeland solution is obtained if further $t(x) = sgn\, x$. That is, in the method of majority rule and in the Copeland solution, the strength of individual j's preference $s(u_{ij}, u_{kj})$ is considered irrelevant; only the fact of whether or not he prefers row i to row k is of significance.

Suppose we now consider the following modification of the Copeland solution where $t(x)$ is taken equal to x rather than $sgn\, x$. Then as a measure of the utility of row i, we have

$$\sum_{k=1}^{r} \phi(i,k) = \sum_{k=1}^{r} \sum_{j=1}^{c} s(u_{ij}, u_{kj}) = \sum_{j=1}^{c} \sum_{k=1}^{r} s(u_{ij}, u_{kj}) .$$

Now the rank order $\bar{a}_{ij}$ assigned to row i by person j is, in fact

$$\bar{a}_{ij} = \frac{1}{2}\left[\sum_{k=1}^{r} s(u_{ij}, u_{kj}) + r + 1\right].$$

Hence, the measure of the utility of row i is

$$2\sum_{j=1}^{c} \bar{a}_{ij} - c(r+1).$$

Therefore, this modification of the Copeland solution may be stated as follows: Replace the entries in the matrix by the rank order assigned by each column, and then apply the Laplace solution to the ranks. By modifying the values of the p_j in the Copeland solution, the rule that the Bayes solution should be applied to the ranks is obtained.

Still another method of amalgamation which is not included among those already described herein is the minimax (maximin) principle. This principle states that in the case where the utilities are real numbers we should choose that row where the smallest entry in the row will be as large as possible; that is, maximize the minimum entry. This principle is sometimes applied to a matrix (e.g. of losses) which may be obtained from the original matrix u of utilities. When probability mixtures of rows (mixed acts) are also considered, the best row (or the best probability mixture of rows) will be the solution of the matrix considered as the matrix of a two person zero sum game.

Modifications of the minimax principle have been suggested by Hurwicz [19] and by Savage [23]. (See also Chapter IV.)

3. SOME RELATIONS AND IMPLICATIONS

For the statistical problem, it has been pointed out (e.g. [23]) that knowledge of the values of the entries u_{ij} in the matrix U implies economic knowledge not often available to the working statistician. There are often problems of a computational nature which make it difficult to determine the values of the entries. For some problems, which the statistician might face, it may not be possible to determine the values of the entries u_{ij}, but he may be able to determine a rank order for the rows i for any given state of nature j. In this case, the statistician's problem is very similar to the problem of social choice where individual values are expressed as preferences or as rankings.

For some problems of social choice, the strength of individual preferences may also be obtained. In that case, the entries u_{ij} will describe the strength of the individual j's preference for social choice i. The problem of social choice is then very similar to games against nature and the statistician's problem.

It is interesting to note that a result obtained by Blackwell and Girschick [8] for the problem of statistical decisions is related to the work of Markowitz and Goodman [15,16] on the problem of social choice and individual values. Blackwell and Girschick [8] show that if there is (1) a complete order of all the possible rows (the u_{ij} range over a continuum), (2) Pareto optimality, and (3) independence of origin (indifference of nature) which requires that the complete ordering remain invariant under addition of a constant to the utilities for a given state of nature, then the ordering is representable by a linear function $\sum\limits_{j=1}^{c} u_{ij} p_j$ where u_{ij} is the utility of row i when nature is in state j and $p_j \geq 0$ is a set of weights which are interpretable as a priori probabilities. In [2], Arrow points out that conditions (1), (2), and (3) had been suggested by Markowitz and Goodman in [15] as possibly reasonable conditions to be imposed upon a social welfare function (ordering of social choices). In [15] and [16] the weights p_j are interpretable as the amount of influence which individual j has in making the social choice.

An interesting relation exists between the work of Clyde Coombs [10] and Duncan Black [5]. In [10] Coombs suggests three different methods for obtaining social utilities. We shall be concerned only with the first two methods. The first method gives "equal weight to each individual and weights each preference by its strength." He finds that the rank order assigned by the median individual will be the rank order of the social choices. Another way of saying this would be as follows: Consider the scale on which the stimuli (rows) fall. Now place each individual (column) on this scale at the point which he prefers the most. Then the median individual according to this ordering is the one who determines the social choice. Coombs considered a second method where each individual had equal weight and each preferential judgment (vote) was weighted equally. Coombs found empirically for the experiments he had performed that these methods gave quite similar results. The second method considered by Coombs is similar, though not identical with the method of majority rule. The following theorem due to Black [5] determines the best social choice when the method of majority rule is used: For single peaked preferences (the Coombs model in [10] satisfies this condition), the majority choice may be obtained by looking only at the first choice of the median individual when all of the individuals are considered arrayed according to the underlying scale. Hence this theorem shows that the first choice obtained by majority rule will be identical with the first choice obtained by Coombs' first method.

Coombs has shown that the entire rank order of the median individual will be the rank order obtained by the social utility based on strength of preference if the conditions of his model in [10] are satisfied. The theorem by Black [5] determines the first choice for the method of majority rule, but it does not discuss the entire rank order. (The second choice for the method of majority rule is that choice which wins a majority over all other choices except the first choice. The third choice for the method of majority rule is that choice which wins over all other choices except the first and second choices, et cetera.) It seems interesting to note that Black's theorem cannot be extended to the entire rank order. That is, it is not generally true that the rank order of the median individual will be the rank order obtained by the method of majority rule when the condition of single peakedness is satisfied. (See [5].) A numerical example may be given to illustrate this point. However, it is true that if the conditions of Coombs' model in [10] are satisfied, then the rank order of the median individual will be the rank order obtained by the method of majority rule; this is due to the fact that for Coombs' model the majority will prefer j to k if and only if the median individual prefers j to k. For suppose that i is to the left of k on the J scale (i.e., $Q_{hij} < Q_{hik}$), then if the median individual is nearer j than k, it follows that all the individuals to the left of the median individual will be nearer j, and hence the majority will prefer j. Also if the majority is nearer j than k, it follows that the median individual will be nearer j than k. It has been shown that the rank order obtained by majority rule is determined by the median individual in Coombs' model, as was the social utility based on strength of preferences. Hence, the method of majority rule and the social utility based on strength of preferences both lead to the same rank order in Coombs' model.

BIBLIOGRAPHY

1. Arrow, Kenneth J., Social Choice and Individual Values, Cowles Commission for Research in Economics Monograph No. 12. New York: John Wiley and Sons, Inc., 1951, pp. ix, 99.

2. Arrow, Kenneth J., The Meaning of Social Welfare: A Comment on Some Recent Proposals, Stanford University Technical Report No. 2 (1951).

3. Bayes, Thomas, Facsimiles of Two Papers by Bayes. Prepared under the direction of W. Edwards Deming, Washington, The Graduate School, the Department of Agriculture. Pp. xvi, 52 numbered in facsimile.

4. Black, Duncan, On the Rationale of Group Decision-Making, Journal of Political Economy, 56 (February, 1948), 23-34.

5. Black, Duncan, The Decisions of a Committee Using a Special Majority, Econometrica 16 (July, 1948), 245-261.

6. Black, Duncan, The Elasticity of Committee Decisions with an Altering Size of Majority, Econometrica 16 (July, 1948), 262-270.

7. Black, Duncan, Un approccio alla teoria delle decisioni di comitato, Giornale degli economisti e analli di economica, 7, Nuova Serie (Maggio-Giugno, 1948), 262-284.

8. Blackwell, D. and Girshick, M. A., Results presented at the Santa Monica meeting of the Institute of Mathematical Statistics, August, 1951.

9. Chernoff, Herman, Remarks on a Rational Selection of a Decision Function, Cowles Commission Discussion Paper, Statistics, No. 326A (1948).

10. Coombs, Clyde H., Social Choice and Strength of Preference. Chapter VI, infra.

11. Copeland, A. H., A "Reasonable" Social Welfare Function (mimeographed notes), University of Michigan Seminar on Applications of Mathematics to the Social Sciences, November, 1951.

12. Dalkey, Norman, Cooperative Aggregation (mimeographed notes), University of Michigan Summer Seminar on Design of Experiments on Decision Processes.

13. De Finetti, Bruno, La Prévision: Ses Lois Logiques, Ses Sources Subjectives, Annales de l'Institut Henri Poincaré, 7 (1947), 1-68.

14. De Finetti, Bruno, Recent Suggestions for the Reconciliations of Theories of Probability, Proceedings of the Berkeley Symposium on Mathematical Statistics and Probability (1950).

15. Goodman, Leo A. and Markowitz, Harry, Social Welfare Functions Based on Rankings, Cowles Commission Discussion Paper, Economics, No. 2017 (1951).

16. Goodman, Leo A. and Markowitz, Harry, Social Welfare Functions Based on Individual Rankings, American Journal of Sociology, LVIII, No. 3 (1952), 257-262, and reprinted as Cowles Commission New Series No. 67.

17. Hildreth, Clifford, Measurable Utility and Social Welfare, Cowles Commission Discussion Paper, Economics, No. 2002 (1950).

18. Hildreth, Clifford, Alternative Conditions for Social Orderings, Cowles Commission Discussion Paper, Economics, No. 2028 (1952).

19. Hurwicz, Leo, A Criterion for Decision-Making under Uncertainty, Cowles Commission Discussion Paper, Statistics, No. 355.

20. Marschak, Jacob and Radner, Roy, Criteria for Planning and Incomplete Information, Cowles Commission Discussion Paper, Economics, No. 2018 (1951).

21. Milnor, John, Games Against Nature, Project RAND Research Memorandum 679 (1951).

22. Rubin, Herman, The Existence of Measurable Utility and Psychological Probability, Cowles Commission Discussion Paper, Statistics, No. 331.

23. Savage, L. J., The Theory of Statistical Decisions, Journal of the American Statistical Association 46 (1951), No. 253, 55-67.

24. Todhunter, I., A History of the Mathematical Theory of Probability. Cambridge and London: Macmillan and Co., 1865, pp. v, 624.

25. von Neumann, John and Morgenstern, Oskar, Theory of Games and Economic Behavior. Second Edition. Princeton: Princeton University Press, 1947, pp. xviii, 641.

26. Wald, Abraham, Statistical Decision Functions. New York: John Wiley and Sons, Inc., 1950, pp. ix, 179.

CHAPTER IV

GAMES AGAINST NATURE[*]

by

John Milnor

PRINCETON UNIVERSITY

1. INTRODUCTION

The object of this paper will be to study games of the following type. A matrix (a_{ij}) is given in which a player must choose
a row. A column will be chosen by "Nature", a fictitious player
having no known objective and no known strategy. The payoff to
the player will then be given by the entry in that particular row
and column. This entry should represent a numerical utility in
the sense of von Neumann and Morgenstern. (See [3] or [1].)

It will be shown that several known criteria for playing such
games can be characterized by simple axioms. An axiomatic
procedure will also be used to criticise these criteria, and to
study the possibilities for other criteria.

(Our basic assumption that the player has absolutely no information about Nature may seem too restrictive. However
such no-information games may be used as a normal form for
a wider class of games in which certain types of partial information are allowed. For example if the information consists of
bounds for the probabilities of the various states of Nature, then
by considering only those mixed strategies for Nature which
satisfy these bounds, we construct a new game having no information. Unfortunately in practice partial information often occurs in vague, non-mathematical forms which are difficult to
handle.)

The following criteria have been suggested for such games
against Nature.

Laplace. If the probabilities of the different possible states
of Nature are unknown, we should assume that they are all equal.

[*]The preparation of this paper was sponsored in part by the
RAND Corporation. The author was a National Science Foundation fellow during 1952-53.

Thus if the player chooses the i-th row his expectation is given by the average $(a_{i1}+ \cdots +a_{in})/n$, and he should choose a row for which this average is maximized.

Wald [4] (Minimax principle). If the player chooses the i-th row then his payoff will certainly be at least $\underset{j}{\text{Min}}\, a_{ij}$. The safest possible course of action is therefore to choose a row for which $\underset{j}{\text{Min}}\, a_{ij}$ is maximized. This corresponds to the pessimistic hypothesis of expecting the worst.

If mixed strategies for the player are also allowed, then this criterion should be formulated as follows. Choose a probability mixture $(\xi_1, \cdots, \xi_m)$ of the rows so that the quantity $\underset{j}{\text{Min}}\,(\xi_1 a_{1j}+ \cdots +\xi_m a_{mj})$ is maximized. In other words play as if Nature were the opposing player in a zero sum game.

Hurwicz[1]. Select a constant $0 \leqq \alpha \leqq 1$ which measures the player's optimism. For each row [or probability mixture of rows] let a denote the smallest component and A the largest. Choose a row [or probability mixture of rows] for which $\alpha A + (1-\alpha)a$ is maximized. For $\alpha = 0$ this reduces to the Wald criterion.

Savage [2] (Minimax Regret). Define the (negative) regret matrix (r_{ij}) by $r_{ij} = a_{ij} - \underset{k}{\text{Max}}\, a_{kj}$. Thus r_{ij} measures the difference between the payoff which actually is obtained and the payoff which could have been obtained if the true state of Nature had been known. Now apply the Wald criterion to the matrix (r_{ij}). That is choose a row [or mixture of rows] for which $\underset{j}{\text{Min}}\, r_{ij}$ [or $\underset{j}{\text{Min}}\,(\xi_1 r_{1j}+ \cdots +\xi_m r_{mj})$] is maximized.

These four criteria are certainly different. This is illustrated by the following example, where the preferred row under each criterion is indicated.

$$
\begin{pmatrix}
2 & 2 & 0 & 1 \\
1 & 1 & 1 & 1 \\
0 & 4 & 0 & 0 \\
1 & 3 & 0 & 0
\end{pmatrix}
\begin{array}{l}
\text{Laplace} \\
\text{Wald} \\
\text{Hurwicz (for } \alpha > 1/4) \\
\text{Savage}
\end{array}
$$

2. AXIOMATIC CHARACTERIZATION OF CRITERIA

In this section we will consider criteria which assign to each matrix (a_{ij}) a preference relation $\gtrsim$ between pairs of rows[2] of the matrix. It will be shown that each of the four criteria of 1 is characterized by certain of the following axioms. The first five axioms are compatible with all four criteria.

1. Ordering. The relation $\gtrsim$ is a complete ordering of the rows. That is it is a transitive relation, such that for any two rows r, r' either $r \gtrsim r'$ or $r' \gtrsim r$.

2. Symmetry. This ordering is independent of the numbering of the rows and columns.
(Thus we are not considering situations where there is any reason to expect one state of Nature more than another.)

3. Strong domination. If each component of r is greater than the corresponding component of r', then $r > r'$ (shorthand for: $r \gtrsim r'$ but not $r' \gtrsim r$).

4. Continuity. If the matrices $a_{ij}^{(k)}$ converge to a_{ij}, and if $r^{(k)} > r_1^{(k)}$ for each k, then the limit rows r and r_1 satisfy $r \gtrsim r_1$.

5. Linearity. The ordering relation is not changed if the matrix (a_{ij}) is replaced by (a'_{ij}) where $a'_{ij} = \lambda a_{ij} + \mu$, $\lambda > 0$.

The following four axioms serve to distinguish between the four criteria.

6. Row adjunction. The ordering between the old rows is not changed by the adjunction of a new row.

7. Column linearity. The ordering is not changed if a constant is added to a column.

(This can be interpreted as an assertion that Nature has no prejudices for or against the player. It also asserts that the utility is linear, not only with respect to known probabilities, but also with respect to unknown probabilities of the type under consideration.)

8. <u>Column duplication</u>. The ordering is not changed if a new column, identical with some old column, is adjoined to the matrix. (Thus we are only interested in what states of Nature are possible, and not in how often each state may have been counted in the formation of the matrix.)

9. <u>Convexity</u>. If row r is equal to the average $\frac{1}{2}(r' + r'')$ of two equivalent rows, then $r \gtrsim r'$.
(Two rows are <u>equivalent</u>, $r' \sim r''$, if $r' \gtrsim r''$ and $r'' \gtrsim r'$. This axiom asserts that the player is not prejudiced against randomizing. If two rows are equally favorable, then he does not mind tossing a coin to decide between them.)

Finally we will need a modified form of axiom 6 which is compatible with all four criteria.

10. <u>Special row adjunction</u>. The ordering between the old rows is not changed by the adjunction of a new row, providing that no component of this new row is greater than the corresponding components of all old rows.

The principal results of this section are all incorporated in the following diagram, which describes the relations between the ten axioms and the four criteria. The symbol "X" indicates that the corresponding axiom and criterion are compatible. Each criterion is characterized by those axioms which are marked "⊠".

	Laplace	Wald	Hurwicz	Savage
1. Ordering	⊠	⊠	⊠	⊠
2. Symmetry	⊠	⊠	⊠	⊠
3. Str. Domination	⊠	⊠	⊠	⊠
4. Continuity	X	⊠	⊠	⊠
5. Linearity	X	X	⊠	X
6. Row adjunction	⊠	⊠	⊠	
7. Col. linearity	⊠			⊠
8. Col. duplication		⊠	⊠	⊠
9. Convexity	X	⊠		⊠
10. Special Row adj.	X	X	X	⊠

Diagram 1. X = compatibility.
Each criterion is characterized by axioms marked ⊠

Theorem 1. The Laplace criterion is compatible with all of these axioms other than axiom 8; the Wald criterion with all but axiom 7; the Hurwicz criterion with all but 7 and 9; the Savage criterion with all but 6.

The proofs are all completely trivial. Perhaps the following two examples are of interest. In the first matrix the Hurwicz criterion (for $\alpha > 0$) is not compatible with axiom 9 (convexity). In the second pair the Savage criterion is not compatible with axiom 6 (row adjunction).

$$\begin{pmatrix} 2 & 0 & 0 \\ 1 & 1 & 0 \\ 0 & 2 & 0 \end{pmatrix} \qquad \begin{pmatrix} 2 & 1 \\ 0 & 2 \end{pmatrix} \longrightarrow \begin{pmatrix} 2 & 1 \\ 0 & 2 \\ -7 & 4 \end{pmatrix}$$

Theorem 2. The Laplace criterion is characterized by axioms 1,2,3,6,7.

It is first necessary to prove the following.

Lemma 1. Assuming axioms 1,2,6 (ordering, symmetry, row adjunction) two rows which differ only in the order of their components are equivalent.

Adjoin a sequence of intermediate rows so that two consecutive rows differ only by a permutation of two components. The result now follows by an application of the symmetry axiom to each pair of consecutive rows.

The proof of theorem 2 follows. Suppose that the average of the components of r equals the average of the components of r'. Alternately perform the following two operations on the matrix:

a) Permute the elements of r and r' so that they are in order of increasing size. (Permissible by lemma 1, and axiom 6).

b) Subtract from each column the component in r or the component in r', whichever is smaller. (Permissible by axiom 7). After a finite number of steps, all of the components of r and r' will be zero. It follows that r ~ r'.

Now using axioms 3 and 6 it follows that r > r' whenever the average of the elements of r is greater than the average of the elements of r'. Thus the criterion is that of Laplace.

Theorem 3. The Wald criterion is characterized by axioms 1,2,3,4,6,8,9.

Two lemmas are first necessary.

Lemma 2. Assuming axioms 3 and 4 (domination and continuity), if each component of r is greater than or equal to the corresponding component of r', then $r \gtrsim r'$.

The proof is clear.[3]

Lemma 3. Assuming axioms 1,2,3,4,6,8, two rows which have the same minimum element and the same maximum element are equivalent.

Let $(a_1, \cdots, a_n)$ be any row having the minimum component a and the maximum component A. From lemmas 1 and 2 it follows that

$$(a, \cdots, a, A) \lesssim (a_1, \cdots, a_n) \lesssim (A, \cdots, A, a).$$

But $(a, \cdots, a, A)$ is equivalent to $(A, \cdots, A, a)$ since the matrix $\begin{pmatrix} a \cdots a \ A \\ A \cdots A \ a \end{pmatrix}$ can be obtained from the symmetrical matrix $\begin{pmatrix} a \ A \\ A \ a \end{pmatrix}$ by column duplication. Therefore any two rows having minimum element a and maximum element A are equivalent.

Proof of theorem 3. By lemma 3 it is sufficient to consider pairs (a, A) with $a \lneq A$ in place of rows. Applying the convexity axiom (9) to the matrix

$$\begin{pmatrix} a & \frac{1}{2}(a+A) & \frac{1}{2}(a+A) \\ a & a & A \\ a & A & a \end{pmatrix}$$

we have $(a, A) \lesssim (a, \frac{1}{2}(a+A))$. By repeated application of this rule, together with the continuity axiom, we have $(a, A) \lesssim (a, a)$, hence $(a, A) \sim (a, a)$. It follows easily that the criterion is that of Wald.

Theorem 4. The Hurwicz criteria are characterized by axioms 1,2,3,4,$\overline{5}$,6,8.

Again it suffices to consider pairs (a, A) with $a \leq A$. Let α be the supremum of all numbers α' such that

$$(\alpha', \alpha') \lesssim (0,1).$$

By the domination axiom it follows that $0 \lneq \alpha \lneq 1$. By continuity it follows that $(\alpha, \alpha) \sim (0,1)$. By linearity

$$(\alpha A + (1-\alpha)a, \ \alpha A + (1-\alpha)a) \sim (a, A),$$

whenever $a < A$. It follows easily that the given criterion is just that criterion of Hurwicz which corresponds to the parameter value α.

Theorem 5. The Savage criterion is characterized by axioms 1,2,3,4,7,8,9,10.

A matrix will be called normalized if it contains a row r_0 consisting entirely of zeros, and if it contains no positive components. Any given matrix can be normalized by first subtracting the maximum element from each column, and then adjoining the row r_0. By axioms 7 and 10 these operations do not change the ordering relation between the old rows. In a normalized matrix we are free, by axiom 10, to adjoin any row which contains no positive elements and to delete any row other than r_0. The proof is now completely parallel to the proof of theorem 3. It is only necessary to require that all matrices considered be normalized.

3. CRITICISM OF THE CRITERIA

There is one fundamental principle which has not yet been mentioned: that of domination (or admissibility). One strategy is said to dominate another if it is just as good in all states of Nature and definitely better in at least one. It is natural to require that the following axiom be satisfied.

3'. If r dominates r' then $r > r'$.

This axiom is not compatible with the criteria of Wald, Hurwicz, and Savage. Each of these criteria could be modified in a trivial way[4] so as to satisfy 3', but the result would violate the equally fundamental axiom of continuity. This difficulty is illustrated by the following two examples.

Example 1. Consider the family of matrices

$$\begin{pmatrix} 2 & 1 & 1 \\ 2 & 2 & k \end{pmatrix}$$

where $0 \leqq k \leqq 1$. Mixed strategies are to be allowed. In the case k = 1 the second row dominates the first. It is therefore natural to expect that the second row should be chosen exclusively for k = 1, and should be chosen with high probability for k close to 1. But according to the Wald and Hurwicz criteria ($a < 1$) the first row should be chosen whenever $k < 1$. (Compare diagram 2). In this example the Savage criterion has the expected behavior, but in the following, more complicated, example, the Savage criterion is also unsatisfactory.

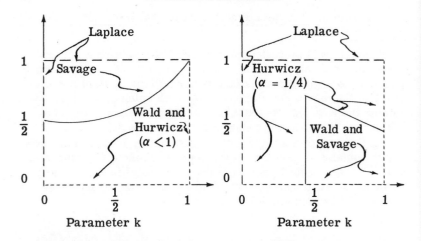

Diagram 2. Probability of choosing second row (Example 1.)

Diagram 3. Probability of choosing last two rows (Example 2.)

Example 2. Consider the matrices

$$\begin{pmatrix} 1 & 0 & 1 & 0 \\ 0 & 1 & 0 & 1 \\ 1 & 1 & k & 0 \\ 1 & 1 & 0 & k \end{pmatrix}$$

where $0 \leq k \leq 1$. For $k = 1$ the first two rows are dominated, yet according to the Wald and Savage criteria these two rows should be chosen exclusively whenever $k < 1$. (Compare diagram 3). Only the Laplace criterion gives a satisfactory solution in this example.

The Laplace criterion has been successful under all of the tests which have been made of it, with the single exception of axiom 8 (column duplication). It appears that, if we are willing to sacrifice this axiom, then the Laplace criterion is definitely the best. However in many applications it is desirable to preserve axiom 8. This is particularly true in cases where there is no clear and natural separation of the possible states of Nature into a finite number of distinct alternatives.

Thus all of the criteria under consideration seem unsatisfactory in that they fail to satisfy certain rather basic axioms.

4. POSSIBILITIES FOR OTHER CRITERIA

It has become apparent that no possible criterion can have all of the properties that one would desire. It is therefore natural to try constructing a list of those properties which are most fundamental and important, to see if at least these can be satisfied. The following is the author's attempt to construct such a list. Others would doubtlessly have given rather different lists.

Let S denote the simplex of mixed strategies over the rows of the matrix.

I. To each matrix there corresponds a non-vacuous choice set C contained in S.
(The complete ordering of 2 really gave more information than was necessary.)

II. Symmetry. C does not depend on the numbering of the rows and columns.

III. Domination. Every element of C is undominated (= admissible).

IV. Continuity. If $a_{ij}^{(k)} \longrightarrow a_{ij}$, $s^{(k)} \epsilon C(a_{ij}^{(k)})$, and $s^{(k)} \longrightarrow s$, then $s \epsilon C(a_{ij})$.

V. Row adjunction. The choice set is not changed by the adjunction of a new row which is dominated by some old row.
(Some stronger row adjunction axiom would be desirable, but at least this much seems indispensable.)

The following three axioms are also desirable, although not as basic as the first five.

VI. Column duplication. C is not changed by the adjunction of a duplicate of some column.

VII. Column linearity. C is not changed by the addition of a constant to a column.

VIII. Convexity. C is convex.
Evidently no criterion which has been mentioned so far satisfies all of these axioms.

Theorem 6. There exist criteria which simultaneously satisfy the preceding eight axioms.

First consider the following slight modification of the Savage criterion. Let S be a convex polyhedron of mixed strategies for the player, and let $p_1, \cdots, p_n$ be linear payoff functions on

S, corresponding to the n possible states of Nature. The negative regret is defined by $r_j(s,S) = p_j(s) - \underset{s' \in S}{\text{Max}}\, p_j(s')$. The Savage choice set $C(S)$ consists of the set of all strategies $s \in S$ for which $\underset{j}{\text{Min}}\, r_j(s,S)$ attains its maximum M. Instead we will consider the set $C_{\mathcal{E}}(S)$ consisting of all $s \in S$ such that

$$\underset{j}{\text{Min}}\, r_j(s,S) \geqq M - \mathcal{E}.$$

The required criteria are now constructed as follows. Choose as parameters an infinite sequence of positive numbers $\mathcal{E}_1, \mathcal{E}_2, \cdots$ which converge to zero. Define the sets $S_0 \supset S_1 \supset \cdots$ by $S_0 = S$, $S_i = C_{\mathcal{E}_i}(S_{i-1})$. As choice set $C_{(\mathcal{E}_1, \mathcal{E}_2, \ldots)}(S)$ we take the intersection of the S_i.

The axioms I through VIII may now be verified. The proofs will not be carried out, since they are rather involved (at least for domination and continuity). In any case these criteria are probably too difficult computationally to be of practical interest.

A further interesting property which is possessed by these criteria is the following. The n payoff functions are all constant on the choice set. Thus any two elements in the choice set are completely equivalent.

It is interesting to ask if there exist any simple, computable criteria which satisfy all of the preceding conditions.

FOOTNOTES

1. Suggested by L. Hurwicz in an unpublished paper.

2. For simplicity, only pure strategies for the player are considered in this section. However the results can easily be generalized to the (more natural) case where mixed strategies are allowed.

3. Lemma 2 suggests the following criterion. Define $r \gtrsim r'$ if and only if each component of r is $\geqq$ the corresponding component of r'. It may be shown that this criterion satisfies all axioms except 1, and is characterized by 2,3,4,6,7,8, together with the transitivity portion of 1.

4. Let r be preferred to r' (in the modified sense) if either $r > r'$ in the old sense (of Wald, Hurwicz, or Savage) or r dominates r'.

BIBLIOGRAPHY

1. Herstein, I. N. and Milnor, J., An Axiomatic Approach to Measurable Utility, Econometrica, 21 (1953), 291-297.

2. Savage, L. J., The Theory of Statistical Decision, Journal of the American Statistical Association, 48 (1947), 238-248.

3. von Neumann, J., and Morgenstern, O., Theory of Games and Economic Behavior, Princeton, 1944.

4. Wald, A., Statistical Decision Functions, New York, 1950.

CHAPTER V

NOTE ON SOME PROPOSED DECISION CRITERIA[*]

by

Roy Radner and Jacob Marschak

COWLES COMMISSION FOR RESEARCH IN ECONOMICS

1. SUMMARY

The purpose of this paper is to apply two currently advocated statistical decision procedures to a simple problem and show that they result in solutions that have certain undesirable properties. Each of the two procedures is a generalization or interpretation of the minimax principle. The problem consists of a game in which an individual observes and bets on the outcomes of tosses of a coin with constant but unknown probability of falling heads.

2. INTRODUCTION

2.1. The Rational Decision-Maker. In this discussion we shall consider an individual decision-maker who is rational in the following sense: if he can specify a set of "states of nature" such that for a given state n and a given strategy he knows the probability distribution of outcomes, then he will always

(1) choose some admissible strategy (when possible),[1]
(2) choose the strategy so as to maximize his expected utility, if he knows the true state of nature.

Let $U(s,n)$ be the expected utility when n is the true state of nature and the individual uses strategy s. A strategy s_0 is admissible if there is no other strategy s such that

$$U(s,n) \geqq U(s_0,n), \quad \text{for all } n, \quad \text{and}$$

[*] This research was carried out under contract with the Office of Naval Research. We are indebted to E. Lehmann for several valuable suggestions and discussions.

$$U(s,n_0) > U(s_0,n_0) , \quad \text{for some } n_0 .$$

2.2. The Minimax Principle. If the individual does not know the true state of nature then, in general, the criterion of admissibility will not be sufficient to enable him to choose a strategy; thus some further criteria are needed. Such a criterion is Wald's "minimax principle." (Cf. [8], p. 18) One interpretation of this principle is: "Minimax the negative expected utility," i.e., choose s to achieve

$$\min_{s} \max_{n} [-U(s,n)] .$$

This interpretation has been attacked by many as too pessimistic (cf. for example [7], p. 63), and it is this undesirable property which has, in part, led to the proposal of two alternative criteria which we will now consider.

2.3. The Hurwicz Criterion. The first of these, which might be considered as comprising a whole class of criteria, including the minimax principle as just stated, is a generalized form of a criterion proposed by L. Hurwicz [3]. In this generalized form it requires that a strategy be chosen which maximizes:

$$(1) \qquad H(s) = \phi \left(\operatorname{Sup}_{n} U(s,n), \operatorname{Inf}_{n} U(s,n) \right)$$

where ϕ is some fixed monotone increasing function of each of its two arguments. ϕ itself is chosen by the decision-maker and in some sense characterizes his attitude towards uncertainty. A special case (the one actually suggested by Hurwicz) is

$$(2) \qquad \phi = \alpha \operatorname{Sup}_{n} U(s,n) + (1-\alpha) \operatorname{Inf}_{n} U(s,n)$$

where α is some fixed number between 0 and 1. Here α might be regarded as a degree of optimism (cf. [4], p. 344).

We will present an example in which application of the Hurwicz criterion leads to the conclusion that at most one observation should be taken in a situation in which common sense demands that a large number of observations be taken.

2.4. The Minimax Regret Criterion. A different direction is taken by L. J. Savage, [7], who gives good reason why Wald could not have considered negative expected utility as the appropriate thing to minimax (cf. Wald [8], p. 8). Instead, Savage says the proper interpretation of the "minimax rule" is: "Choose that strategy which minimizes $\operatorname{Sup}_{n} R(s,n)$ where

(3) $$R(s,n) = \sup_{s'} U(s',n) - U(s,n) .$$

We will call $R(s,n)$ the regret function.[2] Chernoff, [2], has criticized this principle because there are cases in which, if the domain S of the player's available strategies is enlarged, a new minimax regret solution is obtained which differs from the old one, yet is contained in the original S. (This is not surprising, since the value of $R(s,n)$ for any pair (s,n) depends upon the domain S. Note that this is not true of $H(s)$.)

It is interesting to note that the idea behind Chernoff's objection has analogues in Nash's treatment of the bargaining problem (postulate 7, p. 159 of [5]) and Arrow's discussion of social welfare functions (Condition 3, p. 27 of [1]). Borrowing Arrow's terminology we shall say that in the kind of cases described above the minimax regret solution is "dependent upon irrelevant alternatives."

3. A NON-SEQUENTIAL GAME

3.1. General Description. Consider the following game: The player observes an odd number $(2k + 1)$ of tosses of a coin with a constant but unknown probability p of falling heads (and q = 1 - p of falling tails), whereupon he makes a bet on the outcome of the next toss, wins one dollar if his prediction is correct and loses one dollar if incorrect. Each toss costs the player c dollars, and he must decide in advance the (odd) number of tosses he will observe before betting. The player is also free not to enter the game at all. This last possible decision we will call the null strategy. Aside from it, any pure strategy of the player consists of a number k, which determines that he will bet after $2k + 1$ tosses, and a rule r, which determines for every set of observations (sample) which way he will bet. A mixed strategy is a probability distribution on the set of pure strategies (k,r).

We shall see that for both types of solutions there is an optimal rule r_m which requires that the player bet with the majority of previous tosses. This will be called the maximum likelihood rule. It will be shown that the Hurwicz solution has the property that for any (positive) cost c, and any ϕ, no more than one observation should be taken. In the special case of a linear ϕ [equation (2)], the solution is: if $\alpha \geq 2c$, bet after one observation, if $\alpha \leq 2c$ do not play.

The minimax regret solution is of the form: randomize between two adjacent values of k, these values being certain non-increasing functions of c; if c is less than a certain quantity, randomize between one observation and not playing. However, if we modify the game by compelling the player always to use the maximum likelihood rule, the optimal number of observations will be seen to differ from that in the solution of the more general game.

3.2. Hurwicz Solution. For any non-null strategy the expected gain cannot be more than $1 - c(N + 1)$ where N is the expected number of observations, since this is the gain if the prediction is correct with certainty. On the other hand, for any non-null strategy the expected gain for $p = \frac{1}{2}$ is $-c(N + 1)$, hence the minimum cannot be more than $-c(N + 1)$.

If the player uses the maximum likelihood rule, then the expected gain is exactly $1 - c(N + 1)$ for $p = 0$ or 1, while it is never less than $-c(N + 1)$. (If the reader is not immediately convinced of this latter statement he can examine the expected gain function in more detail in the next section.) Moreover, given that a non-null strategy is used, the smallest possible value of N is 1. Hence among non-null strategies both $\underset{n}{\text{Sup}}\ U(n,s)$ and $\underset{n}{\text{Inf}}\ U(n,s)$ are maximized by using the maximum likelihood rule and taking one observation, and no matter what the ϕ and c the optimal procedure will have the property that no more than one observation is taken. If ϕ has the linear form of (2) and if s_O is the strategy which consists of using the maximum likelihood rule after one observation with probability v and not playing with probability $1 - v$, then

$$H(s_O) = \alpha\ v(1 - 2c) + (1 - \alpha)\ v(-2c)$$
$$= v(\alpha - 2c) .$$

Thus $H(s_O)$ is maximized by taking v equal to 1 or 0 according as $\alpha \geqq 2c$ or $\alpha \leqq 2c$.

3.3 Minimax Regret Solution. This solution is not so easily obtained as the one imposed by the Hurwicz criterion, and we will only sketch the method of arriving at it.

Let $d(k,r)$ denote a joint probability distribution of k and the rule r and let $d(r|k)$ be the conditional distribution of r given k.

Denote the player's expected money gain using $d(k,r)$, given p, by $U(d(k,r),p)$; the expected money gain using $d(r|k)$, given k and p, by $U_k(d(r|k),p)$; and the null strategy by $k = -1$. Then:

$$(4) \qquad U(d(k,r),p) = \sum_{k=-1}^{\infty} f(k)\, U_k(d(r|k),p) \,.$$

Let $\bar{h}_i$ and $\bar{t}_i$ be the events of getting i heads and i tails respectively with respective probabilities $h_i(p)$ and $t_i(p)$ $(i = 0, \cdots, k + 1)$. Any $d(r|k)$ is a rule of the form:

"For given k, if $\bar{h}_j$, bet on heads with the probability η_i and if $\bar{t}_i$ bet on tails with probability $\mathcal{T}_i$."

The maximum likelihood rule r_m is defined by $\eta_i = \mathcal{T}_i = 1$. If $d(r|k)$ differs from r_m, it will do so exactly on certain events $\bar{h}_j$ (j in J) and $\bar{t}_\ell$ (ℓ in L). It is easily verified that:

$$(5) \qquad U_k(r_m,p) = (p - q) \sum_i [h_i(p) - t_i(p)] - 2(k + 1)c$$

$$(6) \qquad U_k(d(r|k),p) = U_k(r_m,p)$$
$$+ 2(p - q)\left[\sum_L t_\ell(p)(1 - \mathcal{T}_\ell) - \sum_J h_j(p)(1 - \eta_j)\right].$$

It is not hard to show that we can reject as inadmissible all strategies such that there is some k (with $f(k) \neq 0$), for which J and L are not disjoint. The set of remaining strategies we will call S.

We want that $d(k,r)$ which minimizes the supremum, with respect to p, of the regret:

$$R[d(k,r),p] = \hat{U}(p) - U[d(k,r),p], \quad \text{where}$$
$$\hat{U}(p) = \underset{d(k,r)}{\text{Sup}}\; U[d(k,r),p] \,.$$

$\hat{U}(p)$ is attained, for every p, if the player bets on heads when $p \geq \frac{1}{2}$, on tails when $p \leq \frac{1}{2}$ and pays as small a cost as possible (i.e., $k = 0$) provided the resulting expected gain is positive; otherwise it is attained by not playing. Thus:

$$\hat{U}(p) = \max\{|p - q| - 2c,\, 0\} \,.$$

Let $h(k,p)$ and $t(k,p)$ be the probabilities of majorities of heads and tails respectively.

Then for a strategy using the maximum likelihood rule, the regret is:

$$\rho(f,p) = \sum_{k=-1}^{\infty} f(k)\, \rho_k(p) \quad \text{where, for } k \geq 0,$$

$$\rho_k(p) = \begin{cases} 2(q - p) h(k,p) + 2kc, & (q - p) \geq 2c \\ 2(k + 1)c - (p - q)(h(k,p) - t(k,p)), & p - q \leq 2c \\ 2(p - q) t(k,p) + 2kc, & (p - q) \geq 2c \end{cases}$$

and

$$\rho_{-1}(p) = U(p).$$

The function $\rho(f,p)$ is symmetric in p, for all f, and has a maximum at two points, say p_1 and $q_1 = 1 - p_1$, if $c < c_0$; or at $\frac{1}{2}$, if $c \geq c_0$, where

$$\frac{1}{2} + c < p_1 < 1$$

and c_0 is defined by

$$c_0 = \sum_{k=0}^{\infty} f(k)(p_1 - q_1) t(k,p_1)$$

i.e., c_0 is the cost per observation for which the three relative maxima of $\rho(f,p)$ are equal.

Next, it can be shown that one of the minimax regret strategies uses the maximum likelihood rule. The important step in the proof of this point is the fact that (when $c < c_0$), if the regret for some strategy s at $p = p_1$ is less than $\rho(f,p_1)$ then at $p = q_1$ it is greater than $\rho(f,q_1)$, and vice versa.

It remains now to find the optimal distribution f of k, when the maximum likelihood rule is used.

Although $\rho_k(p)$ is defined only for integral values of k, it is, for every fixed p, analogous to a convex function of k, in that for every integer k (and fixed p):

$$\rho_{k+1}(p) - \rho_k(p) \leq \rho_{k+2}(p) - \rho_{k+1}(p).$$

It is shown in [6] that in such a case the only admissible strategies (using the maximum likelihood rule) are those such that f(k) is concentrated on at most two consecutive integers. Since such a distribution is determined by its mean we can express the solution by a single number $\hat{k}$, which will be a function of c. The approximate value of this function $\hat{k}(c)$ has been determined numerically for several values of c, and the results are given in Table 1 below.[3]

3.4. <u>Dependence on "Irrelevant Alternatives."</u> We shall now show that in this game the minimax regret solution "depends upon irrelevant alternatives."

Suppose we modify the above game by requiring the player to use the maximum likelihood rule. We proceed to obtain the minimax regret solution for this case.

The expected gain using $f(k)$ is given by (4) and (5). Again the negative of $U_k(r_m, p)$ is convex in k for every p, in the sense described above, and the only admissible f's are those which are zero at all but at most two consecutive values of k. As in Section 3.3, we have obtained the value of the function $\hat{k}(c)$, describing the optimal strategy, for various values of c. The results are given in Table 1.

Cost c	.001	.002	.005	.010	.020	.050
$\hat{k}$ for General Strategy Domain	13.8	8.9	4.3	2.4	1.2	0.2
$\hat{k}$ for maximum likelihood Strategy Domain	9.1	5.4	2.6	1.8	.7	

Table 1. Minimax Regret Solutions for 2 Strategy Domains

We recall that the two games considered differ only in that in the first game the player is free to use strategies which do not incorporate the maximum likelihood rule, while in the second he must use that rule. Nevertheless, in the first game the optimal strategy is shown to use the maximum likelihood rule, but with a different number of trials $2k + 1$.

4. A SEQUENTIAL GAME—THE HURWICZ SOLUTION

It is worthwhile pointing out[4] that the essential feature of the Hurwicz solution in Section 3.2 carries over to a sequential generalization of the first game. That is, if we allow the player to decide when he will make his bet after having seen any number of observations, it remains true that any optimal strategy will not involve taking more than one observation. The proof of this for general ϕ is practically the same as that for the nonsequential game.

FOOTNOTES

1. In our examples there will always be admissible strategies.

2. Savage calls this the "loss function" but economists and others are liable to confuse this with negative income.

3. Computations for this and the following section were made under the direction of J. Templeton and W. Parrish.

4. We are indebted to E. L. Lehmann for doing so to us.

BIBLIOGRAPHY

1. Arrow, K. J., Social Choice and Individual Values, New York, 1951.

2. Chernoff, H., Remarks on Rational Selection of a Decision Function, Cowles Commission Discussion Papers, Statistics Numbers 326 and 326A (mimeographed).

3. Hurwicz, L., A Class of Criteria for Decision Making under Ignorance, Cowles Commission Discussion Paper, Statistics No. 356 (mimeographed).

4. Hurwicz, L., Some Specification Problems and Applications to Econometric Methods (Abstract), Econometrica, 19 (1951), 343-344.

5. Nash, J. F. Jr., The Bargaining Problem, Econometrica, 18 (1950), 155-162.

6. Radner, R., Note on Generalized Convex Functions and the Decision Problem, Cowles Commission Discussion Paper, Statistics No. 362 (mimeographed).

7. Savage, L. J., The Theory of Statistical Decisions, Journal of the American Statistical Association, 48 (1947), 238-248.

8. Wald, A., Statistical Decision Functions, New York, 1950.

CHAPTER VI

SOCIAL CHOICE AND STRENGTH OF PREFERENCE*

by
Clyde H. Coombs
UNIVERSITY OF MICHIGAN

I. NATURE OF THE PROBLEM

The problem of constructing a mechanism to aggregate the preferences of individuals into a social preference pattern has been of concern to psychologists only implicitly. Papers explicitly concerned with the problem are usually found in the literature of economics and mathematics. Psychologists, however, in dealing with their measurement problems, have built formal mechanisms which, while never mentioning "social utility," actually constitute mechanisms for merging the preferences of the individual members of a group.

The nature of the problem of defining a social utility is described by Arrow in his recent monograph on Social Choice and Individual Values [1]. Consequently, the problem will merely be illustrated here by a hypothetical setting in which it might arise. Imagine a group of individuals who are all members of an art society which has money in its treasury to purchase some paintings. Each member of the society has his individual preferences among the paintings available in the market. The strength of an individual's preference for a painting will be referred to as the utility of an individual for a painting.

The problem facing the society is to arrive at a mechanism for merging the utilities of its members for the various paintings in order to obtain a social choice giving a decision as to which paintings are to be purchased. Because paintings vary in price it is necessary that the social preference pattern be simply ordered in order that the purchasing agent be completely instructed, regardless of the state of the market.

*This paper was prepared as part of a research project under Contract Nonr: 37400 with the Office of Naval Research. I am indebted to my research assistant, Mr. J. E. Keith Smith, for invaluable assistance throughout this research.

Defining a social choice function always involves, implicitly or explicitly, two value judgments: 1) the relative weight to be assigned to each individual in the society and 2) the relative weight to be given to each preferential vote. These value judgments are sometimes explicit in real mechanisms and always explicit in formal mechanisms. The social scientist is interested in making such value judgments explicit because they reflect the culture of the group. Also a group is in a better position to objectively select a real mechanism for arriving at a social choice function when the alternative mechanisms are visible and their respective value judgments explicit.

There are two ways in which this problem may be studied: empirically and theoretically. These two approaches correspond respectively to the left and right side of Figure 1 in "Some Views on Mathematical Models and Measurement Theory" (Chapter II). The empirical approach would be concerned with the nature and characteristics of the social utility arrived at by group processes of different kinds—as for example the group decision of a jury in which there is vocal interaction and unanimity is required, as compared with the election of a president of a professional society by a process of preferential voting. With these characteristics as a starting point a theoretician would be interested in constructing a formal model, i.e., specifying the axioms, which would deliver such a choice function.

The theoretical approach to the problem of defining a social utility would start out with a set of axioms designed to arrive at a social utility with certain characteristics. This would then constitute an "available" mechanism for a group to deliberately select for the purpose of arriving at a social utility and it might be a mechanism which describes the process already being used by some groups.

The direction of approach in this paper is a theoretical one, that of constructing a social utility which will have certain characteristics. The particular problem which has intrigued the writer is the problem of constructing a social utility which will weight preferential judgments by their "strength."

This problem is difficult because comparability of utility measures between individuals is required. Arithmetically averaging strengths of preference over individuals requires the assumption of the existence of a common unit of measurement for utility and then an actual numerical estimate of it. We shall here define a social utility which will contain the assumption of the existence of a common unit of measurement for utility between individuals, but no numerical estimate is required.

Furthermore, certain of the conditions which data must satisfy for the assumption to hold will be verifiable.

The social utility to be constructed here is derived from a theory of psychological scaling published elsewhere ([5], [6]) so only certain necessary elements of the scaling theory will be presented. To illustrate the stringent conditions which data must satisfy to permit construction of a social utility which weights strength of preference, an experiment was run and will be utilized for constructing such a social utility. These same data will provide an empirical basis for comparing this social utility with two other mechanisms commonly used by psychologists for the same implicit purpose. For all these social utilities, individuals will be weighted equally.

II. EXPERIMENTAL SETTING

The experiment conducted to illustrate the problem and the scaling theory is the following. The objets d'art to be judged consisted of a series of isosceles triangles with a base of one inch, which varied in altitude from .25 to 2.5 inches in steps of .25 inches. The individuals were presented the triangles in sets of three and asked to judge the most preferred and least preferred in each set. Every individual was presented with every set of three triangles. There were ten triangles, so there were 120 triads and there were 31 individuals making the judgments. The presentations were randomized with respect to the frequency with which any given triangle occurred in each position within triads and with respect to order in the sequence of triads.

Analysis of the data was somewhat different for each of the social utilities to be illustrated. A general scaling theory, in the context of which each of these social utilities will be compared, will next be discussed.

III. THE UNFOLDING TECHNIQUE

As much of the material required by this paper on the subject of the basic scaling theory has now been published ([5], [6]) only a brief sketch of that part of it which pertains particularly to the problem of defining a social utility will be discussed.

When an individual makes a preferential choice between two or more stimuli, the individual will be conceived as possessing an ideal and the stimuli, the objects being judged, are evaluated with respect to their relative distance from this ideal. In the context of this experiment, an individual is conceived of as having an "ideal" triangle, at any given moment, which would be preferred to all others. This ideal would correspond to a point on a continuum of "altitudes of isosceles triangles with one inch bases." This point will be designated the C value of an individual with the subscripts h, i, and j designating respectively the moment in time, the individual, and the stimulus being evaluated.

The stimulus is also conceived as possessing some degree of this same attribute, related possibly to its particular altitude, and this magnitude will be designated its Q value and will also have the subscripts h, i, and j. The difference between the Q value of the stimulus and the C value of the individual, his ideal, will be defined as his utility for the stimulus, $|P_{hij}|$. Thus, in a one dimensional case:

$$(1) \qquad |P_{hij}| = |Q_{hij} - C_{hij}|$$

and the postulate which defines the information in a comparative preferential judgment between two stimuli, j and k, may be written as follows:

$$(2) \qquad |P_{hij}| \leqq |P_{hik}| \quad \text{if and only if } j > k$$

where the symbol $>$ signifies the verbal response "preferred to".

Equation (1) constitutes an observational equation of preference[1] and the information obtained in an observation is given by equation (2). The left side of equation (1) will be referred to as the phenotypic level of behavior corresponding to the manifest observed behavior, the right side of the equation as the genotypic level, an inferred, hypothetical level of description. A set of preference data consists of a number of simultaneous equations with only certain order relations given for the terms on the left hand side. The problem is to go from the information given on the left hand side of the equation to the inferences that can be drawn about the quantities on the right hand side, constituting a solution to the simultaneous equations.

If there is a single common latent attribute underlying or generating the preferences of the individuals, the analysis of the data immediately yields this attribute in the form of order relations on the Q values, order relations on the C values, and information on metric relations.

Consider the following illustration. Suppose there were a single latent attribute with the stimuli (A, B, C, D, E) on it as in Figure 1, and the judges' ideals distributed over the entire range.

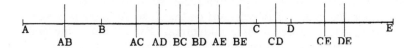

Fig. 1

This will be called a J scale or Joint scale because it has both people and stimuli on it. When an individual makes a preference judgment between any two stimuli, then, according to equations (1) and (2), he will prefer that stimulus which is nearer his ideal. If an individual says he prefers stimulus A to stimulus B, this indicates that at the time of that judgment his ideal was located to the left of the midpoint between these two stimuli. Similarly, if he says he prefers B to E, he is located to the left of the midpoint BE. Hence, the midpoints of all possible pairs of stimuli partition the continuum into segments. If an individual in the course of making all his paired comparison judgments is located in one of these segments, then these judgments would be consistent and transitive and could be completely represented by a rank order of the stimuli.

This rank order of the stimuli is called the I scale of the individual and each I scale corresponds uniquely to a segment of the J scale bounded by an adjacent pair of midpoints (except for the two end segments). An I scale may be looked upon as the J scale folded at the ideal of an individual with the stimuli ranked in order of increasing distance away from the individual. The data consist, then, of these I scales, and the J scale is obtained by unfolding them. This is the reason for the name, Unfolding Technique.

In order to unfold a set of I scales it is necessary first to order them. It is immediately apparent that every I scale in a set ends in one of two stimuli, these being the first and last on the J scale. Also, every complete set contains two I scales which begin with one of these two stimuli and end with the other and these two I scales are mirror images of each other. These immediately provide a simple ordering of the stimuli on the J scale. The remainder of the I scales are ordered between the first and last by the simple rule that every stimulus must first move to the left end of an I scale before it can move to the right. Two adjacent I scales then differ in that two adjacent stimuli are in different order. This reversal indicates the midpoint that was crossed in passing from one to the next.

Given the order of the stimuli on the J scale there is a necessary partial order on their midpoints. For example, the midpoint BC necessarily precedes the midpoint BD. The data, however, yield a simple order on these midpoints and it is this fact which provides metric information. The hypothetical data in Table 1, based on the J scale of Figure 1, indicate that the midpoint AD precedes BC. This will occur if, and only if, the distance between stimuli A and B is greater than the distance between the stimuli C and D. If the reverse were true, then the midpoint BC would precede AD and I_4 would have been CBADE.

	I-Scales	Order of Midpoints	Metric Information
I_1	ABCDE	AB	
I_2	BACDE	AC	
I_3	BCADE	AD	
I_4	BCDAE	BC	AD, BC $\implies \overline{AB} > \overline{CD}$
I_5	CBDAE	BD	BC, AE $\implies \overline{CE} > \overline{AB}$
I_6	CDBAE	AE	BD, AE $\implies \overline{DE} > \overline{AB}$
I_7	CDBEA	BE	AE, CD $\implies \overline{AC} > \overline{DE}$
I_8	CDEBA	CD	BE, CD $\implies \overline{BC} > \overline{DE}$
I_9	DCEBA	CE	
I_{10}	DECBA	DE	
I_{11}	EDCBA		

Table 1.

The I scales which lie between the first three and last three in a set are the ones which provide metric information. The metric information contained in these data, where n = 5, are given in Table 1 and illustrated by the partial order in Figure 2.

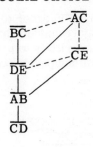

Fig. 2.

It can readily be shown that metric relations on the magnitudes of the intervals bounded by the midpoints of pairs of stimuli, follows from information about the metric relations on the distances between stimuli.[2] The results of such an analysis are contained in Table 2 which gives the information on how large each interval is in terms of the distances between stimuli, for this example. Figure 3 gives the ordering of these intervals in relative magnitude.

Interval	Magnitude
I_2	$\dfrac{\overline{BC}}{2}$
I_3	$\dfrac{\overline{CD}}{2}$
I_4	$\dfrac{\overline{AB}-\overline{CD}}{2}$
I_5	$\dfrac{\overline{CD}}{2}$
I_6	$\dfrac{\overline{DE}-\overline{AB}}{2}$
I_7	$\dfrac{\overline{AB}}{2}$
I_8	$\dfrac{\overline{BC}-\overline{DE}}{2}$
I_9	$\dfrac{\overline{DE}}{2}$
I_{10}	$\dfrac{\overline{CD}}{2}$

Table 2.

Note: $I_4 + I_6 + I_8 = \dfrac{\overline{BC}-\overline{CD}}{2} = I_2 - I_3$

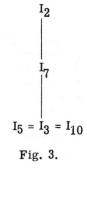

Fig. 3.

This hypothetical data has been presented in order to provide some general background on the Unfolding Technique and to indicate some of the conditions the data must satisfy to provide experimental evidence for inter-individual comparability of utility.

IV. A SOCIAL CHOICE FUNCTION BASED ON STRENGTH OF PREFERENCE

Let us now look at this model from the point of view of constructing a social utility. The mechanisms usually used for such a purpose involve the relative frequencies of the paired comparison judgments. In other words they deal with the phenotypic level of behavior. It is proposed here to construct a social utility on the inferred genotypic continuum.

A social utility may be constructed based on the value judgments of giving equal weight to each individual, but weighting each preference by its "strength," defined by equation (1). Such a social utility would be the arithmetic mean of the individuals' utilities for each stimulus. Thus, the social utility for stimulus j would be:

$$(3) \qquad |P|_{\cdot\cdot j} = \frac{1}{Nt} \sum_i \sum_h |P_{hij}|$$

These quantities cannot be <u>arithmetically</u> determined because the preferential judgments do not give the absolute magnitude of the strength of the individual's utilities for each stimulus but just their relative magnitude. Given certain conditions, however, these quantities, $|P|_{\cdot\cdot j}$, can be simply ordered over j.

The conditions required are the following:

1) The preferential judgments must satisfy the conditions for a single latent attribute, i.e., the I scales must unfold into a single quantitative J scale.
2) The judges must be distributed symmetrically on the J scale.
3) The <u>existence</u> of a common metric on this J scale must be assumed.

The first is a condition which perhaps can be relaxed and generalized to multidimensional latent attributes. The frequencies of the I scales in combination with the metric relations will provide some information relevant to the second condition. The third is a fundamental assumption which appears to be unavoidable if one requires that a social choice function weight the strength of preferences.

With these assumptions, it follows that the quantity, $|P|._{.j}$, the social utility of stimulus j, is the arithmetic mean of the absolute deviations of the individuals about stimulus j as an origin. In other words, the social utility of a stimulus is the mean deviation of the individuals about stimulus j, as the origin. From statistical theory, we know that the mean deviation will be a minimum about the median and will be increasingly large as the origin deviates from the median. Hence, the median individual will be that origin about which the quantities $|P|._{.j}$ will be a minimum for any j. So, the rank order I scale of the median individual in a distribution will be the rank order of the minimal values of $|P|._{.j}$ over j and will constitute a social utility which has the characteristic of being the least disliked. If the data satisfy the necessary conditions, which are very strict, a simply ordered social utility which weights strength of preference is then obtained.

These assumptions are very stringent. For example, if the conditions are satisfied, then if one individual's ideal is A and he dislikes B very much, and another individual's ideal is B, it necessarily follows that the second individual dislikes A very much, and in fact his dislike for A must be equal to the first individual's dislike for B.

Leo Goodman[3] has brought to the writer's attention the fact that Duncan Black [4] has pointed out that if the condition of single peakedness is satisfied (implied by equations (1) and (2)), then the first choice of the median individual is, in fact, the most preferred stimulus as obtained by the system of majority voting.

V. RESULTS OF THE EXPERIMENT

Real data usually do not result in a set of I scales which will unfold into a single quantitative J scale. This scaling theory is very vulnerable; it does not necessarily yield unidimensionality, for example, but rather sets up conditions which the data must satisfy in order to draw the inference of a unidimensional latent attribute. It is to be expected that judgments of individuals will contain error. Even in the case of a single latent attribute one can conceive of an individual vacillating or being uncertain as to precisely where he stands on the continuum. Over a number of judgments, an individual may actually have a distribution of C values or ideals and, for judgments at different times, be located at different places in such a distribution.

By using a method of collecting data which requires replication of a paired comparison, as does the method of triads, one can determine the percentage of times an individual's ideal was on either side of a given midpoint. This permits a partial reconstruction of an individual's distribution of ideals.

This experiment on the aesthetics of isosceles triangles involved 10 triangles. Hence, there are 45 midpoints and the continuum is divided into 46 intervals corresponding to a set of 46 I scales.

The ten triangles used in this experiment differed in altitude by increments of .25 inches, so the entire range of differences in altitude was 2.25 inches. This continuum, being broken into 46 intervals, means that on the average these intervals represented a physical range of .05 inches in altitude. It is perhaps to be expected then that individuals would vary over a number of adjacent intervals unless they could discriminate altitude very well and knew precisely what altitude they most preferred and didn't vary from it. It was found that practically all the subjects did vary on the continuum. Hence, for any pair of stimuli, the individual's preference was taken to be that member of the pair which was most frequently preferred. This would correspond in an ideal case to the median position of his distribution on the J scale.

This experiment was conducted with students in two graduate courses at the University of Michigan, a total of 31 students. This is clearly not enough subjects to have some in every interval of the J scale, but the results will serve as an illustration of the Unfolding Technique and the problems one has in arriving at this social utility from real data.

The preferential judgments of the individuals are summarized in Table 3. In the first column are the intervals numbered from 1 to 46. In the second column are I scales obtained in the data which all satisfy a common quantitative J scale with the stimuli in order from A to J. Each occurred with a frequency of one. In the next column are listed alternative I scales all of which satisfy the same qualitative J scale, with the stimuli ordered from A to J, but the metric relations implied are not the same as those implied by the I scales in the first column. In the column headed "Others" are listed those I scales which do not even satisfy the same qualitative J scale.

Int.	I Scales	Alternate I Scales	Others
1	ABCDEFGHIJ		JIHGFEBDAC
2			AIJHGFBEDC
3			GHFCDIEJBA
4			EDFGACBHIJ
5			AJBICHDGFE
6			GFEIHDCJBA
7			
8			
9			
10			
11			
12	CDBEFGHIJA		
13			
14		DCEFBGHIAJ	
15			
16	DCEFGBHIJA		
17	DECFGBHIJA		
18	DECFGHBIJA		
19	DEFCGHBIJA	EDFCGBHIJA	
20		DECFGHIJBA	
21	EFDCGHBIJA		
22		EDFGCHIBJA	
23			
24	EFGDHCBIJA		
25	FEGDHCBIJA		
26		EDFGHIJCBA	
27			
28			
29			
30	GFEHDICBJA		
31		FGEHDIJCBA	
32	GFEHIDCJBA		
33	GFHEIDCJBA		
34			
35		FGHIEJDCBA	
36			
37	HGFEIJDCBA	GHFIEJDCBA	
38			
39			
40	HGIFJEDCBA		
41	HGIJFEDCBA		
42			
43	IHGJFEDCBA		
44			
45			
46	JIHGFEDCBA		

Table 3

If we look at the seventeen cases in the first column (the only ones which appear to satisfy the conditions for arriving at our social utility) the I scale of the ninth individual would constitute a simply ordered social utility which weighted strength of preference. This is the I scale in the twenty-fifth interval, FEGDHCBIJA.

This mechanism for achieving a social utility has certain serious limitations. While on the one hand, some of us may find it "satisfying" to construct a social utility which weights the strengths of preferences, this has only been done for the special case in which there is a single latent attribute underlying individuals' preferences, and with strong additional assumptions. While some of the problems involved in extending this mechanism to cases with multidimensional latent attributes have been solved [3], additional problems remain, such as, for example, determining a median point in a multidimensional space [7] and also criteria for unfolding.

Let us turn next to another mechanism for arriving at a social utility.

VI. A SOCIAL UTILITY WITH VOTES WEIGHTED EQUALLY

In a study by Austin and Sleight [2] on the aesthetics of isosceles triangles, they were interested in the so-called golden ratio of altitude to base, 1.62 to 1, which is supposed to be the most aesthetically pleasing. They used twelve triangles, 52 subjects and the method of paired comparisons. They determined the per cent of times each triangle was preferred to some other, and thereby, though not explicitly, constructed a social utility. The results they reported are illustrated in Figure 4, copied from their article. The rank order of the triangles on the social utility so constructed can be read from the figure and is EFDGCHIJBKLA. (The stimuli A through J have the same designations as in the experiment reported previously; stimuli K and L are two additional triangles they used, with altitudes of 2.75 inches and 3 inches, respectively.)

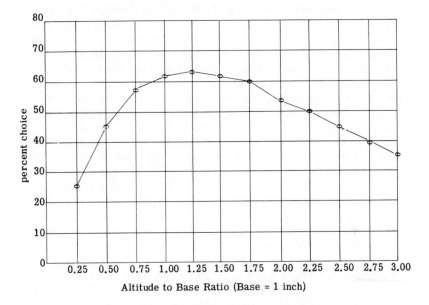

Fig. 4.   Austin-Sleight Data (N = 52)

Their data are not reported in such a manner that the Un-folding Technique could be applied to permit constructing a social utility which weighted the individual preferences by their strength. It is evident, however, that their social utility may also be obtained by folding the J scale in the neighborhood of stimulus E, and in fact is from the 26th interval of a J scale with the stimuli going from A to L.

The value judgments underlying their social utility are the following: 1) every individual is given an equal voice; 2) each preferential judgment (dyadic) is given equal weight. Such a social utility appears on experimental grounds to be a folded J scale and on theoretical grounds is sensitive to both the metric relations and the distribution of judges on the J scale. It is not yet clear whether these two effects on the social utility can be distinguished, to permit unfolding it into a J scale with metric relations.

The data from the first experiment reported here may also be used to construct a social utility based on the same value judgments as the Austin-Sleight social utility. The result of this is a social utility with the stimuli in the order FEGDHCIBJA, which is one of the possible I scales which could occur in the 26th interval of the J scale.

They make an observation about their data which is a very significant one. They observed that very few subjects had their strongest preference for the stimuli which were highest on the social utility. Most of the best-liked triangles were at the extremes. While many subjects preferred most the triangles at one extreme, many other subjects had a definite dislike for these same triangles and made first choices at the other extreme. When the data are combined into a social utility, the "average" preference for the extreme triangles drops. The result is that the social utility constitutes not necessarily the order in which the triangles are most preferred, but rather the order in which they were least disliked. The triangles in the middle of the J scale were not disliked by any of the subjects and these are the ones which come out highest on the social utility. This might provide a general characterization of the social utilities arrived at by the political mechanism of democracy when there are more than two stimuli to be ordered.

In the context of aesthetics, the so-called golden section ratio of altitude to base, 1.62 to 1, is not necessarily the most aesthetically pleasing, but rather is least aesthetically displeasing over a number of individuals. These are by no means necessarily the same thing.

VII. THE SOCIAL UTILITY OBTAINED FROM THE LAW OF COMPARATIVE JUDGMENT

We have now examined two social utility mechanisms based on different value systems and it will be of interest to examine a third which is widely used by psychologists. In 1927, Thurstone published his "Law of Comparative Judgment" [8] as a mechanism for constructing a scale from paired comparison judgments. Insofar as the formal and computational characteristics of the Law of Comparative Judgment are concerned, there is no distinction between judgments as to which of two stimuli is preferred and which of two stimuli possesses more of some property. From the point of view of the Unfolding Technique, however, these are distinctly different. It is only the first, pertaining to judgments of preference, which provides another mechanism arriving at a social utility.

In the notation of the Unfolding Technique the postulate underlying the Law of Comparative Judgment is that given by equation (2) which for this purpose can be put in the more convenient form:

(4) $|P_{hij}| - |P_{hik}| \leq 0$ if and only if $j > k$

If each of a number of individuals makes a judgment of preference between each pair of stimuli, the percentage of times $j > k$ is obtained. This corresponds, by the postulate, to the percentage of times the difference, $|P_{hij}| - |P_{hik}|$, was less than zero over h and i.

The distribution of these differences has mean $|P|_{..j} - |P|_{..k}$ and variance $\sigma^2_{|P|_{..j} - |P|_{..k}}$. Making the judgment that these differences are normally distributed, then we may write:

(5) $|P|_{..j} - |P|_{..k} = X_{jk} \, \sigma_{|P|_{..j} - |P|_{..k}}$

where X_{jk} is the normal deviate of a difference of zero. For each pair of stimuli (j, k), an observational equation may be written as above. The set of simultaneous equations so obtained is insoluble, as there are always more parameters than equations. Thurstone's Case V of this Law of Comparative Judgment eliminates the majority of the parameters by assuming that the variance of the differences is constant for all pairs (j,k). It may then be set equal to one and used as the unit of measure. Thus, one has $\binom{n}{2}$ experimentally independent observations and solves for $n - 1$ parameters: a scale value for each stimulus, with one set equal to zero to provide an origin.

When this procedure is applied to preference data, a numerical scale is obtained which may be regarded as the attribute "preferability" and the stimuli are points on this scale.

It is of interest, now, to regard this mechanism as one for arriving at a social utility. From this point of view, it is evident that the value judgments in this mechanism are as follows:

1) each individual is given an equal voice;
2) a preference judgment is weighted monotonically with its popularity.

The latter statement arises from the fact that the normal curve is used to obtain the quantity X_{jk} in the observational equations. As the percentage of judgments for one stimulus over another deviates from 50%, the normal deviate for a zero difference moves increasingly farther from the mean of the distribution and the increment in this distance attributable to each vote increases, on the average.

The data obtained in the experiment reported here on preferences for triangles could be used to secure this social utility also. Because the Method of Triads was used to collect the data instead of the Method of Paired Comparisons, each individual replicated each judgment eight times. So the eight responses of each of the seventeen judges were tabulated to determine the proportion of times one stimulus was preferred to another. The social utility so obtained is given in Figure 5. It may be noted that the order of the stimuli on the social utility is the same for the Law of Comparative Judgment solution and for the social utility secured by weighting each vote equally. This will not always be the case but will be dependent upon the distribution of the judges' ideals on the J scale.

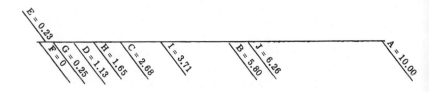

Fig. 5. Law of Comparative Judgment Solution
to Triangle Data.

It is evident from this development that the social utility arrived at by Austin and Sleight has some of the characteristics associated with the judgment that the distribution of differences, $|P_{hij}| - |P_{hik}|$, is rectangular in contrast to normal. It has probably been noted that the designation of the shape of this distribution of differences, both here and for the Law of Comparative Judgment, was referred to as a judgment and not as an assumption. The reason for this is that in the context of defining a social choice function, there is no natural "reality" but one which is constructed by the decisions and value judgments of the group. The shape of this distribution of differences simply corresponds to a value judgment on the relative weights which should be given to individual preference judgments to merge them into a social utility.

VIII. IMPLICATIONS FOR EXPERIMENT

It is evident that as wide a variety of social utilities can be formally constructed as there are varieties of value judgments on the weighting of individuals themselves and the weighting of the individual preference judgments.

A problem of interest to the social scientist is to match the live mechanisms of particular groups with one or more of the various formal mechanisms in order to make explicit the value judgments that characterize certain operational procedures that may be used to arrive at a social utility.

For example, it would be instructive to analyze the implicit value judgments underlying determination of a social utility by a jury, in which unanimity must be obtained and there is open discussion. This could be studied in contrast to those obtaining for a legislative group, with discussion, but not requiring unanimity on the social utility.

It would be interesting to know how the way political leaders decide on order of importance of items in the party platform differed from the mechanism that characterizes the jury. Other variants, and experimental problems, are numerous and obvious.

FOOTNOTES

1. As the quantity $|P_{hij}|$ increases, the individual dislikes the stimulus more.

2. Cf. Chapter VII of [6].

3. Personal communication.

BIBLIOGRAPHY

1. Arrow, K. J., Social Choice and Individual Values. New York, 1951.

2. Austin, T. R., and R. B. Sleight, Aesthetic Preference for Isosceles Triangles, Journal of Applied Psychology, 35 (1951), 430-431.

3. Bennett, J. F., The Dimensionality of a Set of Rank Orders, Unpublished Ph.D. Thesis, University of Michigan, 1951.

4. Black, Duncan, On the Rationale of Group Decision-Making, Journal of Political Economy, 56 (1948), 23-34.

5. Coombs, C. H., Psychological Scaling without a Unit of Measurement, Psychological Review, 57 (1950), 145-158.

6. Coombs, C. H., A Theory of Psychological Scaling, Engineering Research Bulletin No. 34, University of Michigan Press, 1952.

7. Haldane, J. B. S., Note on the Median of a Multivariate Distribution, Biometrika, 35 (1948), 414-415.

8. Thurstone, L. L., A Law of Comparative Judgment, Psychological Review, 34 (1927), 273-286.

CHAPTER VII

ALTERNATIVE CALCULI OF SUBJECTIVE PROBABILITIES

by

Stefan Vail

UNIVERSITY OF MICHIGAN

1. THE NEED FOR AN INVENTORY OF ALTERNATIVE CALCULI

The traditional theory of choice states that an individual's behavior under uncertainty may be explained on the basis of two intervening magnitudes, utility and subjective probability, and that an exact analogue of the mathematical theory of probability can handle the problems of behavior under uncertainty.

If we think that the traditional calculus oversimplifies reality and provides a spurious norm, we ought to review other existing calculi and other existing norms or invent new, richer but workable concepts with which to axiomatize theories of choice under uncertainty.

An inventory of alternative calculi will serve to locate the exact area of a given experimental or theoretical contribution; it may itself suggest further theories and further experiments; and it may make some contribution to the metaphysics of probability.

The concepts that we are seeking are not merely "additional variables," "influencing" utility and subjective probability. They may have to be entirely different constructs, exhibiting the logical properties neither of utility nor of subjective probability.

2. THE HORIZON OF CHOICE

This section is a digression. Its purpose is to set apart the question of the horizon of choice, which is usually bound up with many theories of choice under uncertainty.[1]

When a situation involves numerous alternative choices or numerous outcomes, we might find it fruitful to use a concept of "summarization" or "polarization" into a more compact and graspable set, perhaps—I would venture—typically into a dilemma. Dilemmas arise in fact all too frequently out of logically more complex situations, (for instance in multi-party politics, 3-and-more-person games, arguments, attitudes) so that their genesis deserves special attention. This polarization might be characterized by two seemingly antithetical axioms: first, that the derived set is highly dependent on the composition of the parent set and, second, that once the derived set has crystallized, choice is independent of the alternatives blacked out. In addition we might have axioms to describe which of the candidate alternatives enter the derived set; for example: I) The derived set consists of the extreme elements of the parent set; II) The derived set consists of two alternatives representing the "average value" of the set of favorable alternatives and the "average value" of the set of unfavorable alternatives. Either axiom would explain the tendency toward the dilemma.

When to each alternative choice is associated a set of possible outcomes—say in the form of an interval—the ordering of the choices presents additional problems. We will need a device, such as an indifference map, which permits a complete ordering of the alternatives. An indifference map with metric relations between indifference-sets is equivalent to a utility function.

3. AN INVENTORY OF CALCULI

A calculus of uncertainty is a set of rules governing a process, whether conscious or unconscious, that transforms real or imagined uncertainty into decisions. Under the term "decisions" are subsumed such diverse activities as sorcery, gambling, and the laying down of the principles of a mathematical theory of probability.

We may first divide uncertainty calculi into those involving 'mechanical choice" versus those that embody "genuine decisions."

3.1. Mechanical choice. Mechanical choice is a very widespread phenomenon, because it is economical of time and free of the agony of indecision. Some of it is conscious, as, for instance, the reliance on rules of thumb, magic or sorcery. Unconscious mechanical choice is exemplified by carry-on-as-usual activity and by behavior in a learning situation. All uncertainty calculi tend in the course of an individual's life to be replaced by some mechanical process; the crowning example of such a mechanical process is an elaborate theory of mathematical probability and the theories of statistical decision which it supports.

We will leave behind sorcery and the use of rules of thumb, merely noting that they seem to be quite widespread even among literate, sophisticated people, even when the stakes are important, and even when other calculi (such as subjective or objective odds) are available. We possess no predictive theories for this sort of behavior.

Of learning we have several well-developed theories, usually cast in stochastic terms, with the two great virtues of being operational and predictive. These theories of learning are weak in two respects: first, they cannot explain the differential effects of different outcomes unless we superimpose on the learning theory a utility theory; second, learning theories are self-contained, that is, they do not predict when and how a given individual ceases to act according to the learning pattern, say, upon having an insight: e.g. if he thinks the stochastic process to which he is exposed is random, if he looks for a pattern, or if he suspects foul play.

The factors likely to upset the stable process of mechanical choice are: a new context, a new problem, a new insight, or a high degree of realism of the decision situation and the relentless approach of a deadline for action.

We possess no detailed theory (except what can be borrowed from the theories of the "threshold"), concerning the manner in which a mechanically choosing individual is forced to make genuine decisions. He is presumed to act "as usual" unless something "important" has happened, is perceived, and demands a new decision.

Theorists and experimenters recognize that behavior varies considerably with the degree of realism of the choice situation, and we possess comparative sets of observations to substantiate this guess. If we possessed a measure of this effect, in terms of, say, the frequency distributions of a certain set of responses to a given choice situation we could, of course, use this information to refine or interpret other data. A more interesting project, however, would be to determine to what extent people sincerely trying are in effect unable to make genuine decisions when they don't have to; whether they shift into different sorts of subjective probability calculi when they play for keeps, or for chips, in imagination only, or in other values of the degree of realism.

Formally akin to the degree of realism is the question of the deadline or of the revocability of a decision. If t is the interval of time between the present and the deadline we might expect a priori results analogous to the effects of the degree of realism of the previous paragraph. Here, however, we would have more

possibilities than in the former case, because nearly every decision situation has to undergo a sequence of phases with respect
to the deadline. If there is, as time passes, a tendency to re-
evaluate the choice, the pattern of the swerving itself will often
influence the final choice. How often did our deadlines not catch
us unawares in a last minute antithesis to which we had not
"really" meant to commit ourselves?

   3.2. Genuine decision. (A) Subjective probability functions.
The various concepts to be defined, e.g. "degree of belief,"
"psychological probability" or "perception of frequency" all
refer to contemplated events, more precisely, to propositions
concerning contemplated events.

   A point to be made at the outset is that these events do not
have to be contemplated as occurring in the future. Thus, our
area of study will include not only the case of a gambler betting
on a horse to run tomorrow, but also the case of a student who
answers "yes" or "no" to the question whether "Moscow is to
the east of Constantinople," and also the case of a scholar who
decides to accept that "the writer of Shakespeare's plays and
Francis Bacon were the same person."

   (a) Existence of a belief function. An individual is usually assumed capable of vaguely ordering outcomes as "more likely"
and "less likely." And we will have to make different further
assumptions for the individuals who ascribe to nature passivity,
constancy, and randomness and for those who animate nature
into a friend or into an adversary. The individual who considers
nature passive (likelihoods unaffected by his own aspirations or
actions) is not necessarily better informed or more rational than
the superstitious kind, for the former may, for example, fall
prey to the fallacy that a run of heads must be restituted by tails
in the next toss, or he may magnify (or simply like better) certain odds. The individual who sees nature as an ally or as an
adversary, though possibly tragically misinformed, may be able
to make choices that appear perfectly rational when we view his
situation—as he does—as a game of strategy.

   (b) Determinateness of the belief functions. Whatever denominations people give to odds, "none," "slim," "questionable,"
"even," "fair," "good," "excellent," and so forth, are usually
postulated as simply ordered and as invariant with respect to
the constitution of the set of events to which they are ascribed.
However much haziness veils the boundaries of that coarse
grained classification, we ordinarily expect asymmetry, and

transitivity to be satisfied. In a more general postulation we should expect them to be satisfied in probabilistic terms,[2] with the requirements becoming less and less rigid as the number of alternatives increases.

In addition to the ordering postulates it might prove useful on occasion to postulate concerning "metric relations" that whenever we are given an n-fold classification of odds, it is easier to distinguish between classes removed from each other by r places if they are astride the equal-odds class, than if they are both on the same side of the equal-odds class. Such a "bunching" could be used to derive the tendency toward the dilemma, noted several paragraphs ago.

(c) The nomenclature of the belief function. We should not, in general, expect the terminology to mean the same things and to retain its simply ordered properties over heterogeneous events which are unrelated to each other in ordinary decision situations, and the same can be said, in particular, about the relation that these denominations bear to numerical odds.

3.3. Genuine decision. (B) Probabilities—subjective, objective and mathematical. The accompanying table is a schematic representation of the relations between the concepts that this section discusses.[3]

Classification of Concepts

Number of Occurrences	Single Occurrence Event $n = 1$	Repetitive Event		
		$1 < n < \infty$	∞	
1. Mathematical	A/	B/ μ	C/ μ	
2. Psychological	D/ β_1	E/ $\psi\mu$ ψf β_n	F/ $\psi\mu$ β_∞	J/ pro-theory of μ
3. Objective	G/	H/ f	I/	

The rows bear the labels: mathematical, psychological, objective; the columns refer to the number of occurrences of an event. The cells are named A through J. Entry J is outside the row-column scheme of classification.

I assume that we understand what is meant by events similar in relevant respects; this notion, or the notion of a set, or something equivalent is indispensable to the classical approach to the mathematical theory of probability. On this basis, suitable definitions of a "measure of a set," "ratio of measures," etc. allow us to fill cells B and C in the table. Let us call this entity μ or "mathematical probability" or "theoretical probability."

If we want to make entries in A we will discover that to be satisfactory, they have to be defined in terms of the entry μ: we seek "relevant characteristics" of the single-occurrence event in question, which will enable us to assign this event to one or more classes of the kind that underlie μ.

Let us skip for a while the second row of cells and enter an f in cell H. This f stands for the objective relative frequency of an empirical event; it presupposes knowledge whether the event did in fact happen, a suitable operative definition of time intervals and an objective method for counting occurrences and non-occurrences. It is clear that we cannot fill in cells G and I.

For the second row of cells one can think of several a priori distinct conceptual entities:

a. The psychological pattern which dictates that we postulate such-and-such properties for μ ; the thing which makes us confident that some particular set of axioms for a theory of mathematical probability provide the best model of the world around us; the process which enables even a child to state with assuredness that for a fair coin μ (heads) = μ (tails). I call this process a "pro-theory concerning μ."

b. Sometimes the faculty for discerning proper values for μ, ("proper" in accordance with the principles provided by the pro-theory) is dimmed by haste, by inability to perform complicated computations, or by forgetting essential data of the problem. For example, it may be, for some people, very hard to say whether μ (either a spade, or a king, or a queen, or a jack in a single drawing for a pack of 52 cards) is greater or less than, or equal to μ (a black card in a single drawing from a similar pack).

Let us denote these estimates of μ, '$\psi\mu$' and call them "perception of mathematical probability μ." In general $\psi\mu$

will be not only a function of μ, but a function of the particular event E, whose μ is under consideration; it will be a function of the wording of the problem, of time allotted to its solutions, and so forth. Part of my experimenting (reported in the appendix) relates to this function ψ.

c. Given an event with objective frequency f, we will call ψf the perception of this frequency, or the impression we obtain by being exposed to the occurrence of a finite repetitive event. Experiments by Lawrence, Estes, and Bush and Mosteller deal with this entity.

d. Now it may happen that an individual has certain confidence in the occurrence of an event. This confidence may or may not have arisen from a conscious attempt to calculate the μ (if any) of the event, or to observe the f (if any) of the event. Let the letter β stand for this degree of belief, and, let us mark in our table β_1, β_n, β_∞ for we have a priori no way of knowing whether the same laws apply to all β's regardless of the index. It seems that interesting problems in economics (such as business investment decisions, occupational choice, large household expenditures) fall under β_1 or β_n with n a rather small integer.

A scheme such as the above is too transparently formal to be readily acceptable. We must convince ourselves of its usefulness.

It may be objected to the column-wise classification that the classes are not correlative: Column 1 is of a different sort than the other columns because statements concerning truly "unique" events are not statements about probability. This is precisely why no symbol associated with our ordinary mathematical theory of probability has been entered in Column 1. Truly unique events cannot be reduced to intersections of sets of repetitive events. It is certain that Column 1 differs very radically from the other two in terms of our ordinary mathematical theory of probability; but from the point of view of the experience of unsophisticated people it is Column 3 that differs most radically in kind, simply because it concerns something ideal and beyond experience. The column-wise classification was meant as a reference device, until we have empirical reasons to believe one or both of these distinctions superfluous.

We may ask, is not the comparison between statements belonging to Column 1 and those belonging to Column 3 somewhat irrelevant? Coin-tossing, even if it happens only once, still belongs to Column 3; whereas guessing what the capital of Iraq is belongs to Column 1. Column 1 contains statements about sets containing a unique element for which probability is inapplicable almost by definition.

Strictly speaking, the tossing of this penny, now, by me, etc., is a unique event, a set consisting of one element. Strictly speaking, it belongs to Column 1, and if you maintain that it really belongs to Column 3, you do so because you happen to think that this, now, and me are irrelevant "accidents"; your theory of probability tells you to abstract therefrom. Now, it would be interesting to find whether certain people do in fact think of all instances of coin-tossing as so many one-element sets while other kinds of people think in more generic terms, pooling all such instances into an infinite set belonging to Column 3.

Similarly the distinction between $\psi\mu$ and ψf, aside from that suggested by purely verbal analogy from the distinction between μ and f themselves can in certain cases prove of real behavioral significance. Because a person equipped with a pro-theory or with a theory concerning μ might or might not be able to obtain (by computation, or by any other process allowable by his pro-theory or theory) values for μ "correct" or "distorted" with respect to criteria defined by his theory. Now, quite independently of his ability on this score, his perception may or may not distort the objectively measurable f's.

Whether as a rule people distinguish between the $\psi\mu$ and ψf in practice so as to justify a hair-splitting task of classification should be settled empirically. However, my impression is that many people are vaguely aware that observable chance events approximate the "true mathematical odds" perhaps only "in the long run"; some people are not at all surprised to observe "runs" of luck (significant fluctuations in f as a function of the number of trials) and yet their confidence in the appropriateness of their favorite probability calculus remains unshaken. For such people we may say that they do distinguish frequency from probability, and it would be reasonable to expect them to exhibit corresponding differences in behavior.

3.4. Choice on the basis of μ, $\psi\mu$, β, f or ψf. Now that we possess a large assortment of indicators of uncertainty we must ask the further question, how are these indicators transformed into choice?

First we must acknowledge the possibility that choice is independent of the indicators' "intrinsic" value. To the extent that people simply like certain odds better than others and choose actions accordingly, they fail to utilize the "intrinsic" (say the order, the metric, the numerical) uncertainty properties of the indicator. If, as Ward Edwards[4] has reported, the phenomenon

of pure preference for some odds is widespread, it will over-
whelm the subtler effects of many true calculi.

There exist numerous true calculi of indicators of uncertainty.
Alongside the indicator of uncertainty they carry a second indicator, of goodness, (utility). All such theories contain an additional device, the "indifference map" which establishes "exchange
ratios" between utilities and probabilities.[5] Choice maximizes
the "psychological product" of these indicators.

These theories (with the exception of Shackle's, op. cit.) contain "Boolean postulates" that permit easy reductions of the
probability of complex (alternative, conjunctive) events into
simple probabilities, and permit a direct application of the laws
of mathematical probability to subjective probabilities.

With these comments I shall leave aside the discussion of the
traditional two-parameter calculi. They are developed into well
known axiomatic structures rich in theorems and in normative
implications. Let us return to our classificatory table. What
about the column-wise distinctions?

Does it make any appreciable difference in behavior whether
the event contemplated is believed to belong to the $n = 1$, $n = 2$,
$n = 3, \cdots$ etc. class?

I think the answer to this is an unqualified yes. The distinction between values of n helps make sense out of "nonsensical"
behavior in most experimental games. Almost all critics of the
Mosteller-Nogee application of the von Neumann approach to
the measurement of utility have remarked that the choices made
by the subjects between the odds offered by the experimenters
would have been different if the experimenters had warned the
subjects that their choice would actually be enforced once,
twice, $\cdots$, n times. It would be interesting to measure how
fast the inconsistency (upon replication) in the choice "odds A
vs. odds B" decreases as the number of contemplated plays increases (provided the odds A and B are not mathematically
equivalent). We may postulate that for sufficiently large n the
(objective) probability that a certain individual will adopt a pure
strategy will exceed a given amount. Believers in reincarnation
should be expected to approximate pure strategies for quite low
values of n, because such people expect to play the same game
a large, or perhaps an infinite, number of times and hence expect their long-run luck to approximate the true odds. The con-
vergence to pure strategy will, of course, be less rapid for believers in reincarnation with strong time preference.

4. DIAGNOSIS AND MEASUREMENT

Empirical research in the field of uncertainty has to solve three distinct problems:

(1) Diagnosis—how to devise crucial tests that will tell us which calculus is used by a given subject in a given circumstance. Without ruling out introspection and interviews, we should prefer tests based on the logical properties of the calculi.

(2) Identification—whether it is possible to separate a belief function from measurements of a total situation that involves other psychological unknowns (say, a utility function).

(3) Measurement—having assumed a particular calculus, or having diagnosed it and certified its identifiability, how to obtain estimates and confidence limits for its parameters, and how to test its axioms or theorems. The pilot experiment reported in the appendix describes one possible procedure for obtaining a measure of the perception of mathematical probability.

APPENDIX

The pilot experiments summarized[6] in this report attempt to throw some light on the following problems: (1) the existence of a probability calculus; (2) whether such a calculus has the nature of a psychological probability function; (3) the shape of this function; (4) factors which cause behavior to deviate from what such a function implies.

Experimental design. The subject was supposed to perceive—with or without distortion—mathematical probabilities μ_i, given implicitly in terms of propositions E_i. Depending on whether E_i occurred, or failed to occur, one or the other of two sides of a bet would win. For each bet (about sixty for each value of i) the subject said which side he preferred to take. As the stakes and/or prizes varied for the same bet, the subject might change his side on the bet. Some of these bets were straight bets (x cents to y cents), while others involved gains only, and still others losses only. If the subject is assumed to maximize his (tentatively assumed linear) utility for money, weighted by his perception of the mathematical probabilities of the E_i, the levels over the stake-prize field at which he reverses his choice determine a real number $\psi\mu_i$ $(0 \leqslant \psi\mu_i \leqslant 1)$ for each i. This is identified as the "perception of the mathematical probability μ_i."

Subjects. Four Santa Monica High School students were the subjects. They were paid for their time at a flat rate, plus anything they won from the experimental bets.

Conclusions. The following conclusions are to be considered firm for their limited sample in spite of certain inadequacies in the execution of the pilot experiment:

1. The utility function can without violence to observation be assumed as linear for the prize ranges investigated $0¢$ to $+13¢$.
2. An ordinary bet, gambling without possibility of loss, and gambling without possibility of gain give rise to qualitatively different responses and contradict the hypothesis that choice is based on a simple psychological "product" of utility and the perception of probability.
   (a) If the choice is between evils, the lesser loss is chosen regardless of the relative odds of the two evils.
   (b) If the choice is between two positive prizes, the surer prize is chosen regardless of the magnitudes of the two prizes.
3. A function ψ can be derived for straight bets with a high level of significance for each subject.
4. The functions thus derived agree in three out of four cases with independently derived metrics over the continuum μ, and with independent tests in which the subjects rank-ordered the events E_i according to their probabilities.
5. All subjects underestimate probability $1/6$, two overestimate probability $1/4$, and three overestimate very markedly probabilities exceeding $1/4$.

FOOTNOTES

1. Examples: (a) the postulates restricting the commodity field over which utilities at any one time are defined, N. Georgescu-Roegen: "The Theory of Choice and the Constancy of Economic Laws," in Quarterly Journal of Economics, LXIV (Feb. 1950); (b) the gambler-indifference map, G. L. S. Shackle, Expectation in Economics, Cambridge, 1952; (c) the minimax principle in games and in statistical decision functions. All these are special kinds of functions mapping what I call the parent set onto the derived set of alternative courses of action. They have nothing to do with uncertainty.

2. See, e.g., Karl Menger's "Probabilistic Theories of Relations", Proc. Nat. Acad. Sci. U.S.A., 37 (1951), 178-180.

3. This scheme of classification has its origins in C. H. Coombs, "The Measurement of Psychological Probabilities and Their Interactions with Utility for Consequences and for Risk", Working Memo 2, Michigan Project, July 9, 1952.

4. "Probability Preferences in Gambling Behavior", Amer. J. Psychol., 66 (1953), 349-364.

5. It is not usually realized that this conception leads to an objectionable logical regress: for in addition to the utility which, along with probability, defines the field of indifference, we must have second-order super-utilities, more "ultimate" than the first, corresponding to the contours of the indifference map.

6. Full discussion of these experiments will be found in Working Memos 15, 27, 33 and 35 (hectographed) of the Seminar on the Design of Experiments on Decision-Making Processes, Santa Monica, 1952.

CHAPTER VIII

A FORMAL STRUCTURE FOR
MULTIPLE-CHOICE SITUATIONS

by

Robert R. Bush,* Frederick Mosteller, *Gerald L. Thompson*
HARVARD UNIVERSITY, DARTMOUTH COLLEGE

1. INTRODUCTION

A large class of problems in experimental psychology involves choice situations. An animal or person is periodically
presented with a choice of alternative courses of action, e.g., a
rat can turn right or left in a maze, or a person chooses one of
several answers on a questionnaire as the "correct" one. The
possible choices are ordinarily well defined in an experiment.
In many such experiments on conditioning and learning the
same choice situation is presented to the subject repeatedly for
many trials and the psychologist is interested in the sequence of
choices actually made by the subject.

When one looks at the data from learning experiments involving choice situations, systematic changes in the behavior of
the subject are usually observed. These changes take place, one
assumes, as a result of the treatment used by the experimenter.
For example, the experimenter may reward one response and
punish another. The rewards and punishments may assume
various forms in different experiments—a pellet of dog chow
may be rewarding to a hungry rat, but a nod of approval may be
equally effective for an "ego-involved" human subject. The
events which alter behavior may be the mere execution of a response, i.e., a "practice effect" may be present in some experiments; there may be a tendency to be consistent. In a rather
general sense, then, what characterizes the experiments we are

*The work of the first two authors named was partly supported
by the Laboratory of Social Relations, Harvard University; the
work of the third was done in part at Princeton University with
support of the Office of Naval Research. Seniority of authorship
is not implied by the order of the names.

discussing is a set of possible courses of action and certain events which alter the subject's tendency to choose those courses of action. In the mathematical system we are about to present, these two notions will play a central role.

The work to be described below is an outgrowth of the work by Bush and Mosteller on mathematical models for learning [1,2,3] and related work by Estes [4], Miller and McGill [6] and Flood [5]. In this paper no attempt will be made to apply the mathematical system to experimental data. Instead, we have chosen to present the mathematical structure in as general terms as we consider feasible and leave the applications to future papers. The reader is referred to the literature for a few applications of special cases [3,4,6].

2. THE ELEMENTS OF THE SYSTEM

As primitives in the mathematical system we choose a set a of alternatives and a set σ of outcomes. The set a will contain r mutually exclusive and exhaustive alternatives A_j, and these alternatives will correspond to classes of responses of real organisms in an experimental situation. In an experimental study of the behavior of rats in a simple T-maze, for example, we would distinguish two alternatives: turning right (A_1) and turning left (A_2). We assume that the set a is presented to the organism on each of a series of trials and that on each trial the organism chooses or performs one of the A_j. Whenever an alternative A_j occurs it will have some outcome O_k and σ is the set of the s possible outcomes. In general, an outcome O_k will correspond to some change in the organism's environment, a stimulus change, a reward or punishment, but we will include no change as a possible outcome. In the T-maze experiment mentioned above we would distinguish two outcomes: finding food (O_1) and not finding food (O_2).

In terms of our two primitives, alternatives and outcomes, we will define what we shall call events. Corresponding to each alternative-outcome pair, (A_j, O_k) we will have an event E_{jk}. We denote the set of the E_{jk} by $\mathcal{E}$. A more general formulation would include events E_i which are not identified with alternative-outcome pairs, but we will not consider such a generalization here. We further define a set π of conditional probabilities π_{jk}. If alternative A_j occurs on trial n, then π_{jk} is the (conditional) probability that outcome O_k occurs and hence that event E_{jk} occurs. We will assume that these π_{jk} are constant; they will correspond to probabilities which the experimenter controls. Since some outcome must follow each alternative,

$$(1) \qquad \sum_{k=1}^{s} \pi_{jk} = 1 \, .$$

It is convenient to regard all O_k as possible outcomes of every alternative A_j; if an O_k cannot follow A_j, then $\pi_{jk} = 0$ for such impossible events. The above described concepts characterize, for our purposes, the environment of an organism, i.e., represent an abstract experimental situation. In fact we shall call $[\alpha, \mathcal{E}, \pi]$ a representation of the experimental situation.

We now need to ascribe certain properties to the organism. For any trial n ($n = 0, 1, \cdots$) we let the organism possess a probability vector $p(n)$ whose components are the probabilities of occurrence of the alternatives A_j on trial n. Some event E_{jk} will occur on trial n and this event will change the probability vector to $p(n+1)$. For each event E_{jk} we define an operator T_{jk} such that if E_{jk} occurs on trial n,

$$(2) \qquad p(n+1) = T_{jk} \, p(n) \, .$$

We then assume that the operators T_{jk} are linear and so we represent them by $r \times r$ stochastic matrices. For our purposes a stochastic matrix has non-negative elements, and columns which separately sum to unity. (Usually it is the rows that sum to unity, but we are using a different convention.) The vectors $p(n)$ will be written as column vectors and so the T_{jk} operate upon the $p(n)$ from the left. We next place some further restrictions on the operators T_{jk}.

3. THE COMBINING OF CLASSES

Because the identification between real classes of behavior and alternatives in the model is, to a certain extent, arbitrary, we should like to have the behavior of the organism be invariant under changes in these identifications. In this section we shall formulate the "combining classes" condition and then give some interpretations. When this condition is imposed, it will be possible to combine alternatives that have the same set of outcome probabilities without altering the basic features of the system. For example, if rats are being conditioned to bar-pressing, one might define two classes of bar-pressing; presses from the right and presses from the left. If these two classes were to be

"treated" the same way, i.e., were to have the same consequences for the rat, then we would like to be able to combine
these classes on any trial without changing our behavioral predictions. We will now make this idea precise.

We shall consider two representations of the same abstract
experiment and shall denote these by $[a, \mathcal{E}, \pi]$ and $[a^*, \mathcal{E}^*, \pi^*]$.

Let $a_0 = \{A_{j_1}, \cdots, A_{j_h}\}$ be a subset of $a = \{A_1, \cdots, A_r\}$.

Define a composite alternative A_0 to be chosen if and only if
one of the alternatives A_{j_γ} in a_0 is chosen.

Let $a^* = \{A_0\} \cup (a - a_0)$, i.e., the set consisting of all alternatives A_j which are in a but not in a_0 together with the alternative A_0. Since the alternatives A_{j_γ} are mutually exclusive
the probability of A_0 being chosen at the nth trial is

(3) $\Pr\{A_0\} = p_{j_1}(n) + \cdots + p_{j_h}(n) = p_0(n)$.

We should like to define the composite event $E_{ok} = (A_0, O_k)$
to occur if and only if one of the events $E_{j_\gamma k} = (A_{j_\gamma}, O_k)$ occurs,
but this leads to a further consideration. Note that the uncondi-
tional probability that one of the $E_{j_\gamma k}$ occurs at trial n is
$\sum_{\gamma=1}^{h} p_{j_\gamma}(n)\, \pi_{j_\gamma k}$. In order that A_0 could be treated as an ordinary alternative, this expression would have to be equal to
$p_0(n)$ times the probability that O_k occurs following the choice
of alternative A_0. But the latter probability depends on which
alternative A_{j_γ} has been chosen given that A_0 is chosen. Hence
the concept   "the probability of O_k given A_0" is well defined
only if $\pi_{j_\gamma k}$ is a constant for all γ and for each k. Let $\mathcal{E}^* =$
$\{(A_0, O_1), \cdots, (A_0, O_s)\} \cup \{(A_j, O_k) \mid A_j \in (a - a_0)\}$ that is,
each of the composite events E_{ok} together with the events which
are not composite events. We shall say that $[a, \mathcal{E}, \pi]$ and
$[a^*, \mathcal{E}^*, \pi^*]$ are equivalent representations of the same abstract
experiment if and only if $\pi_{j_\gamma k} = \pi_{ok}$ for $\gamma = 1, \cdots, h$ and each
value of k, that is, if and only if the alternatives A_{j_γ} receive
the same treatment.

In most experimental arrangements of interest to us the conditional probabilities π_{jk} are at the disposal of the experimenter.
Therefore, we assume that any two representations of an abstract experiment can be made equivalent by an appropriate
choice of the π_{jk}.

In the representation $[\mathcal{a}, \mathcal{E}, \pi]$ of the experiment there are r alternatives and in the representation $[\mathcal{a}^*, \mathcal{E}^*, \pi^*]$ of the experiment there are $r - h + 1$ alternatives. Consider, for example, the case in which the first $(r-1)$ alternatives are combined, i.e., $\mathcal{a}_0 = \{A_1, \cdots, A_{r-1}\}$, $\mathcal{a}^* = \{A_0, A_r\}$. In this case the probability vector

(4)
$$\begin{pmatrix} p_1 \\ \vdots \\ p_r \end{pmatrix} \text{ is replaced by the vector } \begin{pmatrix} p_0 \\ p_r \end{pmatrix}.$$

This change can be thought of as a linear transformation of the r-dimensional probability vectors (which form an $(r-1)$ dimensional simplex Σ_{r-1}, the space over which the probability vector can vary after the restrictions $\Sigma p_j = 1$ and $0 \le p_j$ are imposed) onto a one-dimensional sub-simplex Σ_1 of itself. This is a linear transformation which sends

(5)
$$\begin{pmatrix} p_1 \\ \vdots \\ p_r \end{pmatrix} \text{ onto the vector } \begin{pmatrix} p_0 \\ 0 \\ \vdots \\ 0 \\ p_r \end{pmatrix},$$

where we have arbitrarily placed p_0 in the first row (it could have been placed in any one of the first $r-1$ rows). The only difference between (4) and (5) is the addition of $r-2$ rows of zeros in the second vector of (5) and the correspondence (isomorphism) between the two is obvious. For this example, the matrix of the singular linear transformation (5) is given by

(6)
$$C = \begin{pmatrix} 1 & 1 & \cdots & 1 & 0 \\ 0 & 0 & \cdots & 0 & 0 \\ \cdot & \cdot & \cdots & \cdot & \cdot \\ 0 & 0 & \cdots & 0 & 0 \\ 0 & 0 & \cdots & 0 & 1 \end{pmatrix}$$

The mathematical term for this kind of a linear transformation is <u>projection</u>.

To each pair of equivalent representations of an abstract experiment there is a projection matrix C similar to the one shown in (6). For each operator T_{jk} define the projected operator

$T^*_{jk} = C\ T_{jk}$, and for each probability vector p define the projected probability vector $p^* = C\ p$. The star operation is equivalent to left multiplication by a projection matrix C.

We shall say that the operators T_{jk} (abbreviated T in the following) satisfy the <u>combination of classes requirement</u> if and only if, for each pair $[\alpha, \mathcal{E}, \pi]$ and $[\alpha^*, \mathcal{E}^*, \pi^*]$ of equivalent representations of the experiment with associated projection matrix C, each operator T satisfies

(7) $\qquad T^* p^* = (T\ p)^*$ that is, $(CT)C\ p = C(T\ p)$,

for all p in Σ_{r-1}. Since matrix multiplication is associative this condition will hold for all p if and only if

(8) $\qquad\qquad\qquad CTC = CT.$

We wish to have the operators T_{jk} independent of the π_{jk} and so we are at liberty to choose the π_{jk} so that any two representations of an experiment are equivalent. Hence we require that equation (8) be satisfied by <u>all</u> projection operators C. The foregoing arguments are summarized in the

<u>Definition</u>: A stochastic matrix operator T satisfies the combination of classes requirement if and only if equation (8) is satisfied for all projection matrices C.

To see what restriction this places on the operators,[1] let $\|t_{\gamma\delta}\|$ be the matrix of an operator T, and consider the projection matrix C in equation (6). Then computing the right and left sides of (8) we have:

$$CT = \begin{pmatrix} \sum\limits_{\gamma=1}^{r-1} t_{\gamma 1} & \sum\limits_{\gamma=1}^{r-1} t_{\gamma 2} & \cdots & \sum\limits_{\gamma=1}^{r-1} t_{\gamma r} \\ 0 & 0 & \ldots & 0 \\ \cdot & \cdot & \ldots & \cdot \\ \cdot & \cdot & \ldots & \cdot \\ \cdot & \cdot & \ldots & \cdot \\ 0 & 0 & \ldots & 0 \\ t_{r1} & t_{r2} & \cdots & t_{rr} \end{pmatrix}$$

$$CTC = \begin{pmatrix} \sum\limits_{\gamma=1}^{r-1} t_{\gamma 1} & \sum\limits_{\gamma=1}^{r-1} t_{\gamma 1} & \cdots & \sum\limits_{\gamma=1}^{r-1} t_{\gamma 1} & \sum\limits_{\gamma=1}^{r-1} t_{\gamma r} \\ 0 & 0 & \cdots & 0 & 0 \\ \cdot & \cdot & \cdots & \cdot & \cdot \\ \cdot & \cdot & \cdots & \cdot & \cdot \\ \cdot & \cdot & \cdots & \cdot & \cdot \\ 0 & 0 & \cdots & 0 & 0 \\ t_{r1} & t_{r1} & \cdots & t_{r1} & t_{rr} \end{pmatrix}$$

These two matrices will be equal if and only if $t_{r\delta} = t_{r1}$ for $\delta = 1, \cdots, r-1$. When $t_{r\delta} = t_{r1}$ for $\delta = 1,2, \cdots, r-1$, the last rows are identical at once, and the first rows are identical because each column must sum to unity. If we take the other subsets of $r-1$ alternatives and combine them we will obtain projection matrices similar to the one in (6) and applying them to equation (8) we find that in order that any subset of $r-1$ alternatives can be combined it is necessary that the $t_{\gamma\delta}$ should be equal for all $\delta \neq \gamma$, i.e.,

(9) $t_{\gamma\delta} = t_{\gamma}$ for $\gamma \neq \delta$, $\gamma, \delta = 1,2, \cdots, r$.

Conversely if (9) is satisfied then any subset or $r-1$ or fewer alternatives can be combined in the desired way.

These results imply that when the combining classes condition is satisfied we can write the matrix of any operator T as follows:

$$T = \begin{pmatrix} 1 - \sum\limits_{\gamma \neq 1} t_{\gamma} & t_1 & \cdots & t_1 \\ t_2 & 1 - \sum\limits_{\gamma \neq 2} t_{\gamma} & \cdots & t_2 \\ \cdot & \cdot & \cdots & \cdot \\ t_r & t_r & \cdots & 1 - \sum\limits_{\gamma \neq r} t_{\gamma} \end{pmatrix}$$

$$= (1 - \sum\limits_{\gamma=1}^{r} t_{\gamma}) I + \begin{pmatrix} t_1 & t_1 & \cdots & t_1 \\ t_2 & t_2 & \cdots & t_2 \\ \cdot & \cdot & \cdots & \cdot \\ t_r & t_r & \cdots & t_r \end{pmatrix},$$

where I is the r x r identity matrix. Setting $\alpha = 1 - \sum_{\gamma=1}^{r} t_\gamma$
and $\lambda_\gamma = t_\gamma/(1-\alpha)$, for $\alpha \neq 1$, we have

$$T = \alpha I + (1-\alpha) \begin{pmatrix} \lambda_1 & \lambda_1 & \cdots & \lambda_1 \\ \cdot & \cdot & \cdots & \circ \\ \lambda_r & \lambda_r & \circ \cdots & \lambda_r \end{pmatrix}$$

Note that $\sum_{\gamma=1}^{r} \lambda_\gamma = 1$ and that $0 \leq \lambda_\gamma$ and therefore λ is itself

a probability vector. Let Λ be the r x r matrix, each of whose columns is the vector λ. This leads to

Theorem 1. If a stochastic matrix operator T satisfies the combination of classes requirement, as given by equation (7) above, then T can be written in the form

(10) $$T = \alpha I + (1-\alpha)\Lambda .$$

From this theorem we immediately obtain the following three corollaries:

Corollary 1. If $\alpha < 1$, then λ is the unique fixed point of both Λ and of T, while if $\alpha = 1$ then every probability vector is a fixed point of T.

The first part of this corollary follows from the fact that for any probability vector p we have $\Lambda p = \lambda$, because the components of p sum to unity and all the entries in a row of Λ are identical. Moreover, if $\alpha < 1$ then $T p = p$ if and only if $p = \lambda$. When $\alpha = 1$ then from equation (10) above we see that T reduces to the identity operator I.

Corollary 2. When an operator T satisfies equation (10) above then the nth iterate of T is given by

(11) $$T^n = \alpha^n I + (1-\alpha^n) \Lambda$$

and when in addition $|\alpha| < 1$ then $p(n) = T^n p(o)$ converges (in the topology of Σ_{r-1}) to λ.

Equation (11) follows from the fact that $\Lambda^n p = \lambda$ for $n = 1, 2, \cdots$ which is a consequence of $\Lambda p = \lambda$ and $\Lambda \lambda = \lambda$. The convergence for $|\alpha| < 1$ is immediate from the definition of p(n) and equation (11).

Corollary 3. Two operators T_1 and T_2 which satisfy $T_i = \alpha_i I + (1-\alpha_i)\Lambda_i$ have a commutator $T_1 T_2 - T_2 T_1$ given by

(12) $$T_1 T_2 - T_2 T_1 = (1-\alpha_1)(1-\alpha_2)(\Lambda_1 - \Lambda_2),$$

and T_1 and T_2 commute if and only if $\alpha_1 = 1$ or $\alpha_2 = 1$ or T_1 and T_2 have the same fixed point.

It is readily shown that $\Lambda_1 \Lambda_2 = \Lambda_1$ and $\Lambda_2 \Lambda_1 = \Lambda_2$, and then a simple computation gives equation (12). The two operators commute if and only if their commutator is the zero operator and the three conditions which cause this to be so may be seen immediately from equation (12); when $\Lambda_1 = \Lambda_2$ then $\lambda_1 = \lambda_2$.

In order that the operator T in equation (10) should have non-negative elements the parameters α and λ_i must satisfy the inequalities $0 \le \alpha + (1-\alpha)\lambda_i \le 1$ and $0 \le (1-\alpha)\lambda_i \le 1$ for all i. Since the λ_i are non-negative, the above inequalities require that α satisfy

(13) $$\max_{\gamma} \left(\frac{\lambda_\gamma}{\lambda_\gamma - 1} \right) \le \alpha \le 1.$$

[If some $\lambda_\gamma = 1$, then $\lambda_\gamma / (\lambda_\gamma - 1)$ is to be interpreted as $-\infty$.]

If p is any probability vector and T is a matrix of the form (10), then $Tp = \alpha p + (1-\alpha)\lambda$. If α is non-negative then p is sent by T to a point Tp on the line segment between p and λ. It can be shown that the only linear operators which possess this interpolation property are of the form (10). We shall insist upon this property for all events E_{jk}, i.e., for all j and k,

(14) $$T_{jk} = \alpha_{jk} I + (1-\alpha_{jk})\Lambda_{jk}.$$

Another interpretation of the combining of classes restriction is the following. If p is any probability vector and C is any projection operator of the form (6) we have the following diagram:

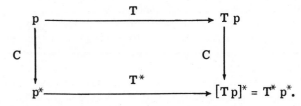

Hence if $p(0)$, $p(1)$, $p(2)$, $\cdots$ is any sequence in the representation $[\alpha, \mathcal{E}, \pi]$ and $p(0)^*$, $p(1)^*$, $p(2)^*$, $\cdots$ is any sequence in the representation $[\alpha^*, \mathcal{E}^*, \pi^*]$ then we have

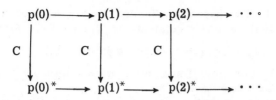

Hence if the combining of classes condition holds or if each of the operators is as in (14) then any sequence in the representation $[\alpha^*, \mathcal{E}^*, \pi^*]$ is a projection of a sequence in the representation $[\alpha, \mathcal{E}, \pi]$.

4. TRAPPING THEOREMS

Now that we have developed the general form of the event operators, given by equation (14), we will show that the probability vector p(n) is contained within specified regions in the limit as $n \to \infty$. Because a vector cannot be moved out of these regions by any of the T_{jk}, we call the statements about the regions the "trapping theorems." In the first part of this section we shall consider the operators to be indexed by a single subscript i; thus we have operators

$$T_i = \alpha_i I + (1-\alpha_i) \Lambda_i,$$

where $i = 1, \cdots t$. For any subset X of Σ_{r-1} hereafter denoted by Σ, let $T_i(X)$ be the set of images of points of X after one application of the operator T_i. The following lemma exhibits the properties of the operator T_i. (For simplicity we drop the subscript i in the statement of the lemma.)

Lemma. If $T = \alpha I + (1-\alpha)\Lambda$ and $\alpha \neq 0$ then T has the following properties:

(a) T is one to one and continuous,
(b) T sends closed (open) sets into closed (open) sets,
(c) T sends hyperplanes onto parallel hyperplanes.
If $\alpha = 0$ then T maps every vector onto the vector λ.

Proof. (a) If $Tp = Tp'$ then $\alpha p + (1-\alpha)\lambda = \alpha p' + (1-\alpha)\lambda$ so that $\alpha(p-p') = 0$. Since $\alpha \neq 0$ we have $p = p'$. The continuity is obvious.
(b) The inverse mapping to T is $T^{-1} = \frac{1}{\alpha} I + (1-\frac{1}{\alpha})\Lambda$ which is continuous and therefore T sends closed sets into

closed sets. A similar statement holds for open sets.

(c) Let $h = (h_1, \cdots, h_r)$ by a row vector, x a (column) probability vector and d a real number. Then consider the hyperplane $H = \{x \mid hx = d\}$. We have, for any point x on H

$$h(Tx) = \alpha \; hx + (1-\alpha) \; h \lambda = \alpha d + (1-\alpha) \; h \lambda = d'$$

where d' is a real constant. Then T(H) is the hyperplane $H' = \{x \mid hx = d'\}$ and so H' is parallel to H.

If $\alpha = 0$ then $T = \Lambda$ and $Tp = \Lambda p = \lambda$ for all p in Σ. This completes the proof of the lemma.

It follows as a corollary to this lemma that the image under T_i of any polyhedron is again a polyhedron. In particular $T_i(\Sigma)$ is a simplex with faces parallel to the faces of Σ.

If $\alpha_i = 1$ then T_i is the identity operator and $T_i(\Sigma) = \Sigma$; hence this case might be interpreted as no learning. If $\alpha_i = 0$ then, as seen above, $T_i(\Sigma) = \lambda_i$, a point in Σ, and so this case might be interpreted as one trial learning. If $0 < \alpha_i < 1$ then each point p in Σ is moved by T_i to an interior point on the line segment between p and λ_i, so that this might be considered uniform learning; the smaller α_i, the more rapid the learning. If $\alpha_i < 0$ then each point p in Σ is moved by T_i to a point on the line through p and λ_i which lies on the opposite side of λ_i from p.

In Figure 1 we illustrate graphically the sets Σ, $T(\Sigma)$ and $T^2(\Sigma)$ for the case r = 3. In Figure 1(a) the operator[2] is $Tp =$

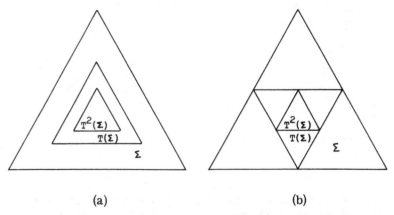

(a)   (b)

Fig. 1. The simplex Σ and its first two images, $T(\Sigma)$ and $T^2(\Sigma)$, for the case of three alternatives (r = 3). In Fig. 1(a) we have taken $\alpha = 1/2$ and $\lambda = (1/3, 1/3, 1/3)$; in Fig. 1(b), $\alpha = -1/2$ and $\lambda = (1/3, 1/3, 1/3)$.

$1/2 \, p + 1/2 \, (1/3, 1/3, 1/3)$, that is, $\alpha = 1/2$ and $\lambda = (1/3, 1/3, 1/3)$. In Figure 1(b) the operator is $Tp = -1/2 \, p + 3/2(1/3, 1/3, 1/3)$, i.e. $\alpha = -1/2$ and $\lambda = (1/3, 1/3, 1/3)$.

Regardless of the choice of the initial vector $p(0)$ in Σ we can say that after the first step in the process

$$(15) \qquad p(1) \, \epsilon \bigcup_{i=1}^{t} T_i(\Sigma) = S_1 \quad \text{(set-theoretical union).}$$

S_1 is closed since by the lemma each $T_i(\Sigma)$ is closed and so S_1 is the union of closed sets.

A possibly weaker statement than this one is

$$(16) \qquad p(1) \, \epsilon \bigvee_{i=1}^{t} T_i(\Sigma) = C_1 \quad \text{(convex union),}$$

where the symbol $\displaystyle\bigvee_{i=1}^{t} T_i(\Sigma)$ means the smallest convex set

containing the union of the sets $T_i(\Sigma)$. Since this union is closed, C_1 is closed. Figure 2(a) shows the set S_1 and Figure 2(b) the set C_1 for an example with $r = t = 3$ and two of the α_i positive and one negative.

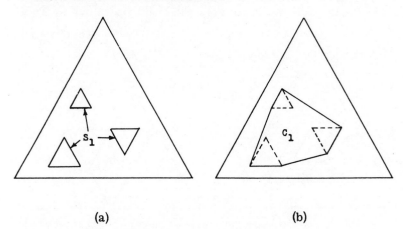

(a)   (b)

Fig. 2. The set-theoretic union, S_1, and the convex union, C_1, of the sets $T_i(\Sigma)$ for $r = t = 3$. Two of the α_i are positive and one is negative.

The corresponding statements at the end of the nth trial are:

$$(17) \qquad p(n) \, \epsilon \, \bigcup_{i=1}^{t} \, T_i(S_{n-1}) = S_n$$

$$(18) \qquad p(n) \, \epsilon \, \bigvee_{i=1}^{t} \, T_i(C_{n-1}) = C_n \, .$$

S_n and C_n are closed for the same reasons that S_1 and C_1 were closed. The sets S_n and C_n provide bounds on the location of the probability vector on the nth trial. If the α_i are small in magnitude these may be quite useful bounds.

Since each $|\alpha_i| \leq 1$, the sequences of sets which obtain, namely $\{S_0, S_1, S_2, \cdots\}$ and $\{C_0, C_1, C_2, \cdots\}$ where $S_0 = C_0 = \Sigma$, are monotone decreasing and have limits. Hence we define

$$(19) \qquad S = \lim_{n \to \infty} \, S_n = \bigcap_{n=0}^{\infty} S_n \, ,$$

$$(20) \qquad C = \lim_{n \to \infty} \, C_n = \bigcap_{n=0}^{\infty} C_n \, .$$

Note that both S and C are closed sets since each member of each sequence is closed. Since $C_n \supset S_n$ for every n, $C \supset S$.

We next define recursively two more sequences of sets $\{R_n\}$ and $\{B_n\}$ with which we shall be concerned. Let

$$(21) \qquad R_0 = \bigvee_{i=1}^{t} \lambda_i = B_0 \, ,$$

$$(22) \qquad R_n = \bigcup_{i=1}^{t} T_i(R_{n-1}) \, ,$$

$$(23) \qquad B_n = \bigvee_{i=1}^{t} T_i(B_{n-1}) \, .$$

Since $T_i(\lambda_i) = \lambda_i$ the sequence $\{B_n\}$ is monotone increasing so that we can define

$$(24) \qquad B = \lim_{n \to \infty} \, B_n = \bigcup_{n=0}^{\infty} B_n \, .$$

In this case B need not be closed. For example, let $r = t = 2$ and consider the two operators, T_1 and T_2, where $T_1 p = -\frac{1}{2} p + \frac{3}{2}(1/3, 2/3)$ and $T_2 p = -\frac{1}{2} p + \frac{3}{2}(2/3, 1/3)$. It is not hard to show that for these two operators B is the one-dimensional simplex of probability vectors except for the vectors $(1,0)$ and $(0,1)$, and is therefore an open set.

The sequence $\{R_0, R_1, \cdots\}$ is in general not monotonic. The following example[3] shows that this sequence need not converge. Let $r = t = 2$ and consider the following two operators: $T_1(p) = (1,0)$ and $T_2(p) = -p + 2(1/2, 1/2)$. It is not hard to show that the limit inferior of the sequence $\{R_n\}$ consists of three points and the limit superior of the whole simplex Σ_1. Hence we define

$$(25) \qquad R = \lim_{n \to \infty} \sup R_n = \bigcap_{m=1}^{\infty} \bigcup_{n=m}^{\infty} R_n.$$

R need not be closed for the same reason that B was not necessarily closed.

With this notation we can state the "weak" trapping theorem. A slightly stronger version of it will be given later (Theorem 4).

Theorem 2. If $|\alpha_i| < 1$ for $i = 1, \cdots, t$ then $C = \overline{B}$ (where $\overline{B}$ is the closure of B). When $0 \le \alpha_i < 1$ for all i, then $C = B_0$.

Proof. If all α_i are zero then $C_1 = C_2 = \cdots = C = B_0 = B_1 = B_2 = \cdots = B$, and the theorem is trivially true. Hence we assume that at least one α_i is non-zero. Let $\alpha = \max_i |\alpha_i|$; then $0 < \alpha < 1$. We also assume that $B_0 \subset \Sigma$ (proper containing) or there is nothing to prove, because if $B_0 = \Sigma$, then $B_n = C_n = \Sigma$ for $n = 1, 2, \cdots$.

First we show that $C \supseteq \overline{B}$. We know $C_0 \supseteq C_1 \supseteq \cdots \supseteq C_n \supseteq \cdots$ and $B_0 \subseteq B_1 \subseteq \cdots \subseteq B_n \subseteq \cdots$. Since $C_0 \supseteq B_0$ it follows by induction that $C_n \supseteq B_n$. Let $m \ge n$; then $C_n \supseteq C_m \supseteq B_m$. Hence for every n, $C_n \supseteq B_m$ for all $m \ge n$. Furthermore $C_n \supseteq B_m$ for $m < n$, and so $C_n \supseteq \bigcup_m B_m = B$ for every n; therefore $C = \bigcap_{n=1}^{\infty} C_n \supseteq B$, and since C is closed $C \supseteq \overline{B}$.

Next we show that $C \subseteq \overline{B}$. We will do this by first showing that as n gets large, the extreme points of C_n get arbitrarily close to $\overline{B}$, and then using convexity. Since each C_n is a convex polygon it is spanned by a finite number of extreme points. Let $\mu_1, \cdots, \mu_r$ be the extreme points of $C_0 = \Sigma$. Then since the operators T_i are linear, C_1 will be spanned by a subset of the points $\mu(1) = T_i(\mu_j)$ for $i = 1, \cdots, t$ and $j = 1, \cdots, r$. In general, C_n will be spanned by a subset of the points $\mu(n) = T_{i_n} \cdots T_{i_1}(\mu_j)$ for $i_n, \cdots, i_1 = 1, \cdots, t$ and $j = 1, \cdots, r$.

Observe that

$$(26) \qquad T_{i_n} \cdots T_{i_1}(\Sigma) \supset \bigcup_i T_{i_n} \cdots T_{i_1}(\lambda_i).$$

Let δ be the diameter of Σ. (The diameter of a set X is the longest line segment that it contains; symbolically $\delta = \underset{x,y \in X}{\text{g.l.b}}\, d(x,y)$, where $d(x,y)$ is the distance between x and y.)
Then the diameter of $T_{i_n} \cdots T_{i_1}(\Sigma)$ is $\leq \delta\, \alpha^n$ which can be made arbitrarily small by taking n large.

Since each of the r points on the right hand side of (26) belongs to B we have $d[\mu(n), \overline{B}] \leq$ diameter of $T_{i_n} \cdots T_{i_1}(\Sigma) \leq \delta\, \alpha^n$. Hence the extreme points of C_n get arbitrarily close to B. Since the extreme points of C are not necessarily those of any C_n and are not necessarily finite in number, we introduce the sets $E_n = \{z \mid d(z, \overline{B}) \leq \delta\, \alpha^n,\ \text{with } z \in \Sigma\}$. Since C_n is convex the above argument shows $E_n \supseteq C_n$ and we already have shown that $C_n \supseteq \overline{B}$. Since $\delta\, \alpha^n \to 0$ the sets E_n are monotone decreasing and we have

$$(27) \qquad \lim_{n \to \infty} E_n = \bigcap_{n=1}^{\infty} E_n = \lim_{n \to \infty} E_n = C = \overline{B}$$

which is the first part of the theorem. When $0 \leq \alpha_i < 1$ we have $B_0 = B_1 = \cdots = B = \overline{B}$ and the second part of the theorem follows.

The weak form of the trapping theorem was concerned with the sets C and B. Correspondingly, the strong form of the trapping theorem is concerned with the sets R and S.

Theorem 3. If $\alpha_i < 1$ for $i = 1, \cdots, t$, then $S = \overline{R}$, where $\overline{R}$ is the closure of R. Moreover, if at least two of the λ_i are not equal, and if $\alpha_i \neq 0$ for all i, then S is a perfect set.[4]

Proof. From the definitions we have $S_n \supseteq R_n$ and, since S_n is a decreasing sequence $S_n \supseteq R_m$ for $n \leq m$. Hence

(28) $$S = \bigcap_{n=1}^{\infty} S_n \supseteq \bigcap_{n=1}^{\infty} \bigcup_{m=n}^{\infty} R_m = R \ .$$

Since S is closed we also have $S \supseteq \overline{R}$.

Suppose $x \in S$, then $x \in S_n$ for every n. Then for each n there exists a set of integers $i_n, \cdots, i_1$ such that $x \in T_{i_n} \cdots T_{i_1}(\Sigma)$. By (26) and (21) we see that $T_{i_n} \cdots T_{i_1}(\Sigma)$ contains points of $\overline{R}$, namely the $T_{i_n} \cdots T_{i_1}(\lambda_i)$. Hence $d(x, \overline{R}) < \delta \alpha^n$ for every n, i.e., $x \in \overline{R}$. This proves $S = \overline{R}$.

If $\alpha_i \neq 0$ for all i and at least two of the λ_i are not equal, we must show that S is a perfect set, i.e., we must show that if x is a point of S then it is a limit point of S. Let U be an open spherical neighborhood with center at x and diameter d. To show that x is a limit point of S it is clearly sufficient to show that every such neighborhood contains points of S other than x. As before, let $\alpha = \max_i |\alpha_i|$ and let δ be the diameter of Σ. Choose an N so large that $\delta \alpha^n < d/2$ for $n \geq N$. Now $x \in S \subset S_n$ for every n, and S_n consists of the union of sets of the form $T_{i_n} \cdots T_{i_1}(\Sigma)$. Choose $n > N$; then for some $i_n, \cdots, i_1$ we have $x \in T_{i_n} \cdots T_{i_1}(\Sigma) \subset U$, since the diameter of $T_{i_n} \cdots T_{i_1}(\Sigma)$ is at most $\delta \alpha^n < d/2$. Now $T_{i_n} \cdots T_{i_1}(\Sigma)$ contains points of S, namely the images of the points $\lambda_1, \cdots, \lambda_t$ under these operators. Since at least two of these points are distinct and since the lemma implies that the operators are one to one, the neighborhood U contains at least two points of S. Hence the set $U - \{x\}$ contains at least one point of S and therefore x is a limit point of S.

We return now to the double-subscript indexing of the operators and drop any assumptions on the α's. Recall that, if on the nth trial, alternative j is chosen and outcome k occurs, then the operator

(29) $$T_{jk} = \alpha_{jk} I + (1 - \alpha_{jk}) \Lambda_{jk}$$

is applied to the probability vector p(n). If $\alpha_{jk} = 1$ then T_{jk} is the identity operator; hence if $0 < \pi_{jk}$ then there is positive probability that the extreme point $\mu_j = (0, \cdots, 0, 1, 0, \cdots, 0)$ (the 1 occurs at the jth place) will not be moved on that trial. For the operators T_{jk} with $\alpha_{jk} < 1$, or $\alpha_{jk} = 1$ and $\pi_{jk} = 0$, Theorem 2 still applies. We can restate Theorem 2 as follows:

Theorem 4. Consider the following sets.

(a) Let W be the convex set spanned by the vectors μ_j for which there is an operator T_{jk} with $\alpha_{jk} = 1$ and $0 < \pi_{jk}$.

(b) Let B be the set defined as in equations (21), (23), and (24) where the operators T_{jk} considered are those for which $\alpha_{jk} < 1$, or for which $\alpha_{jk} = 1$ and $\pi_{jk} = 0$.

(c) Let C be defined as in equations (16), (18), and (20).

Then $C = \overline{B} \cup W$. When $0 \le \alpha_i < 1$ for all i then $C = B_0 \cup W$.

Verbally this theorem states that asymptotically the probability vector will be "trapped" either in the convex subspace W or in the convex subspace $\overline{B}$. However, with probability 1 the probability vector will be trapped in $\overline{B}$.

By similar reasoning one can restate Theorem 3 as follows:

Theorem 5. Consider the following sets.

(a) Let W be defined as in Theorem 4.

(b) Let R be defined as in equations (21), (22), and (25) for those operators T_{jk} such that $\alpha_{jk} < 1$ or such that $\alpha_{jk} = 1$ and $\pi_{jk} = 0$.

(c) Let S be defined as in (15), (17), and (19) for the same set of operators as in (b).

Then $S = \overline{R} \cup W$. Moreover, if $\alpha_{jk} \ne 0$ for each j and k, and W contains more than one point, then S is a perfect set.

Again the probability vector will be trapped in $\overline{R}$ with probability 1.

Negative values of α have been of little interest in experimental applications. If the α's are non-negative then Theorem 3 can be modified as follows: If the α's are non-negative and $\alpha_{jk} + \alpha_{j'k'} < 1$ for all j, k, j', and k', and if the λ_{jk} span an n-dimensional convex set, then S is a (generalized) n-dimensional Cantor set.

The strength of the above theorems depends upon the size of the parameters α_{jk} and the location of the fixed points of the operators. If the α's are small and the fixed points lie in the interior of the simplex Σ then the theorems are very powerful, but if the α's are close to unity and the fixed points are at the extreme points of the simplex then the theorems (especially Theorem 2) may very well be vacuous. It is also clear that Theorem 2 could be obtained as a consequence of Theorem 3 but that the proof is no easier than the independent proof given.

5. THE EQUAL ALPHA CASE

In Section 3 we restricted the operators T_{jk} to the form given by equation (14). We now introduce another major restriction on these operators as a special case. We require that

$$(30) \qquad \alpha_{jk} = \alpha, \quad j = 1, 2, \cdots r; \quad k = 1, 2, \cdots s .$$

This restriction greatly simplifies further mathematical considerations. Furthermore, the resulting model is of interest in some psychological applications.

We will now discuss some of the sequential aspects of the problem. We begin with an initial vector $p(0)$. On trial 0 we will apply one of the rs operators

$$(31) \qquad T_{jk} = \alpha I + (1-\alpha)\Lambda_{jk}$$

to $p(0)$ to obtain a vector $p(1)$. On trial 1 we will again apply one of these operators, etc. On trial n, then, there will be $(rs)^n$ possible (not necessarily distinct) vectors $p(n)$. We shall label these possible vectors with a subscript $i = 1, 2, \cdots, (rs)^n$. Corresponding to each such vector $p_i(n)$ will be a sequence of vectors for trials 0 to n. Let the probability of occurrence of the ith sequence be P_{in}. Therefore, on any finite trial n, the $p_i(n)$ form a multivariate distribution in the original r-dimensional space and P_{in} is the density associated with $p_i(n)$. The jth component of these vectors $p_i(n)$ will have a <u>marginal</u> <u>distribution</u>, and this marginal distribution will have a <u>mean</u> value, called the jth <u>marginal</u> <u>mean</u>. The r marginal means will form a vector V_n. Because of the linear-combination properties of vectors, V_n is the same as the mean vector defined by

$$(32) \qquad V_n = \sum_{i=1}^{(rs)^n} P_{in}\, p_i(n) .$$

With this definition and the operators T_{jk} we can develop a recursive formula for these vectors of marginal means. On trial n, one of rs events E_{jk} occurs. The probability that E_{jk} occurs is $p_{i,j}(n)\, \pi_{jk}$ where $p_{i,j}(n)$ is the jth component of $p_i(n)$, i.e., is the probability of occurrence of alternative A_j on trial n when the ith sequence has occurred, and where π_{jk} is the conditional probability of outcome O_k, given A_j. The vector of marginal means on trial n+1 is then

$$(33) \qquad V_{n+1} = \sum_{i=1}^{(rs)^n} P_{in}\left\{\sum_{j=1}^{r} \sum_{k=1}^{s} p_{i,j}(n)\, \pi_{jk}\, T_{jk}\, p_i(n)\right\} .$$

Now when we apply T_{jk} of equation (31) to $p_i(n)$ we have

(34) $$T_{jk} p_i(n) = \alpha \, p_i(n) + (1-\alpha) \, \lambda_{jk} .$$

Using this result in equation (33) and recalling that $\sum\limits_k \pi_{jk} = 1$ and $\sum\limits_j p_{i,j}(n) = 1$, we have

(35) $$V_{n+1} = \sum_{i=1}^{(rs)^n} P_{in} \left\{ \alpha \, p_i(n) + (1-\alpha) \sum_{j=1}^{r} \sum_{k=1}^{s} p_{i,j}(n) \, \pi_{jk} \, \lambda_{jk} \right\} .$$

We then define an average vector $\bar{\lambda}_j$ by

(36) $$\bar{\lambda}_j = \sum_{k=1}^{s} \pi_{jk} \lambda_{jk}$$

and consider the sum $\sum\limits_j p_{i,j}(n) \, \bar{\lambda}_j$. If we form an $r \times r$ matrix $\bar{\Lambda}$ by letting its jth column be $\bar{\lambda}_j$, we have

(37) $$\sum_{j=1}^{r} p_{i,j}(n) \, \bar{\lambda}_j = \bar{\Lambda} \, p_i(n) .$$

Thus, equation (35) becomes

(38) $$V_{n+1} = \sum_{i=1}^{(rs)^n} P_{in} \left\{ \alpha \, p_i(n) + (1-\alpha) \, \bar{\Lambda} \, p_i(n) \right\}$$

but from definition (32) we get

(39) $$V_{n+1} = \alpha \, V_n + (1-\alpha) \, \bar{\Lambda} \, V_n .$$

Hence, we can obtain the vector V_{n+1} by applying to V_n an operator $\bar{T}$ defined by

(40) $$\bar{T} = \alpha \, I + (1-\alpha) \, \bar{\Lambda}.$$

This expected or average operator $\bar{T}$ will have a unique fixed point x provided that the equation $\bar{T}x = x$ has a unique solution. But we see that this requires that

$$\bar{T}x = \alpha \, x + (1-\alpha) \, \bar{\Lambda} \, x = x ,$$

or

(41) $$\bar{\Lambda} x = x .$$

Thus, $\bar{T}$ will have a unique fixed point if and only if $\bar{\Lambda}$ has a unique fixed point. Moreover, the fixed point of $\bar{T}$, if it exists, is the fixed point of $\overline{\Lambda}$. The requirement of a unique fixed point is identical to the requirement that the vector equation

$$(42) \qquad\qquad (\overline{\Lambda} - I) x = 0$$

have a unique non-trivial solution x, and this in turn requires that the matrix $(\overline{\Lambda} - I)$ have rank r-1. Moreover, if $\overline{T}$ has a unique fixed point z and if x is any point in Σ_{r-1} then the point $x(n) = T^n x$ will converge (in the topology of Σ_{r-1}) to z.

For some purposes it is convenient to write out the components of the vector of marginal means. Let us denote the νth component of the fixed point by $V_{\infty,\nu}$ and the νth component of $\overline{\lambda}_j$ by $\overline{\lambda}_{j,\nu}$. Then equation (41) gives

$$(43) \qquad\qquad \sum_{j=1}^{r} \overline{\lambda}_{j,\nu} V_{\infty,j} = V_{\infty,\nu},$$

or using the definition (36)

$$(44) \qquad\qquad \sum_{j=1}^{r} \sum_{k=1}^{s} \pi_{jk} \lambda_{jk,\nu} V_{\infty,j} = V_{\infty,\nu}.$$

These equations, along with the condition that

$$(45) \qquad\qquad \sum_{\nu=1}^{r} V_{\infty,\nu} = 1$$

may be solved for the asymptotic marginal means, $V_{\infty,\nu}$.

We now place one further restriction on the $\lambda_{jk,\nu}$ which seems reasonable in experimental applications. We assume that if all alternatives are treated alike, i.e., if

$$(46) \qquad\qquad \pi_{jk} = \pi_k \qquad \begin{cases} j = 1,2,\cdots, r \\ \\ k = 1,2,\cdots, s \end{cases}$$

then the asymptotic marginal means are all equal, i.e.,

$$(47) \qquad\qquad V_{\infty,j} = \frac{1}{r} \qquad\qquad j = 1,2,\cdots, r$$

This restriction simply means that if all alternatives have the same set of outcome probabilities, then, on the average, no alternative will be preferred to any other in the limit. We further assume that the λ_{jk} do not depend upon the π_{jk}, i.e., the limit point of any operator T_{jk} is independent of the conditional probabilities of applying that operator. When we introduce equations (46) and (47) in (44) we have

$$(48) \qquad \sum_{j=1}^{r} \sum_{k=1}^{s} \pi_k \, \lambda_{jk,\nu} = 1 \; .$$

We want this equation to hold for all values of the π_k consistent with the condition that

$$(49) \qquad \sum_{k=1}^{s} \pi_k = 1$$

and so we must have

$$(50) \qquad \sum_{j=1}^{r} \lambda_{jk,\nu} = 1 \; .$$

This condition is useful in applications where the alternatives are symmetrically defined, e.g., when the experimental design is such as to eliminate effects of position preferences.

6. THE EQUAL ALPHA CASE WITH TWO ALTERNATIVES AND TWO OUTCOMES

In this section we will apply the analysis of the preceding section to the case of two alternatives, A_1 and A_2, and two outcomes O_1 and O_2, to illustrate how the mathematical system might be used to describe a simple experiment. We shall use condition (50) and so we have

$$(51) \qquad \lambda_{1k,\nu} + \lambda_{1k,\nu} = 1 \qquad \begin{cases} k = 1,2 \\[2ex] \nu = 1,2 \end{cases}$$

Further, since λ_{jk} is a probability vector

$$(52) \qquad \lambda_{jk,1} + \lambda_{jk,2} = 1 \qquad \begin{cases} j = 1,2 \\[2ex] k = 1,2 \end{cases}$$

We now make a further restriction on the $\lambda_{jk,\nu}$. We assume that outcome O_1 is associated with "reward" and O_2 with "non-reward," [so that if $\pi_{11} = 1$ and $\pi_{21} = 0$ (A_1 is always "rewarded" and A_2 is never "rewarded") then $V_{\infty,1} = 1$]. Equation (44) gives for these special conditions,

$$\lambda_{11,1} = 1$$
(53)
$$\lambda_{11,2} = 0 .$$

Equations (51) then give

$$\lambda_{21,1} = 0$$
(54)
$$\lambda_{21,2} = 1 .$$

These equations along with equations (44) and (45) then allow us to solve for $V_{\infty,1}$ and obtain

$$\text{(55)} \qquad V_{\infty,1} = \frac{1 - \pi_{21}}{2 - \pi_{11} - \pi_{21}} .$$

This result was obtained earlier by Estes in unpublished work. The interpretation of equation (55) for two choice situations with risk is clear; it gives the asymptotic mean proportion of choices of alternative A_1 in terms of the probability π_{11} of reward of A_1 and the probability π_{21} of reward of A_2. For example, if $\pi_{11} = 0.7$ and $\pi_{21} = 0.2$, then $V_{\infty,1} = 0.73$. Thus, the equal alpha case predicts that the organism will not learn to choose the favorable side all the time. Furthermore, there is evidence in some experimental situations that indicates that this result is approximately correct.

7. APPLICATIONS OF THE SYSTEM

In applying the mathematical system described above to the analysis of experimental data, a number of problems arise. First of all, one must set up identifications between elements of the mathematical system and observables in an experiment; the alternatives and outcomes in the model must be given empirical referents. Any rules for making such identifications are outside the mathematical system but are crucial in making use of it. Secondly, there are serious problems in statistical estimation of parameters, such as the α_{jk} and the components of the λ_{jk}, from experimental data. Most standard statistical techniques are not easily applied to such a stochastic process.

Most of the applications of the system have been to problems with but two alternatives. Bush and Mosteller [3] describe the use of two special cases when $r = 2$, one to data on the avoidance training of dogs and the other to data from two-choice experiments on rats and humans. Estes has applied a mathematical model which is essentially equivalent to the one described in this paper to a number of experiments but most of his work is still unpublished. Miller and McGill [6] present a model, which they show is a special case of this system, and apply it to data on rote learning. Finally, Flood has used the system for studying the behavior of people in a nine-choice punch-board experiment [5]. In these several studies, the estimation procedures have involved either fitting the data to the marginal means in the model or using standard maximum likelihood procedures. None of these procedures utilize all the information contained in the data and hence there is a need for better estimation techniques.

APPENDIX

Since the manuscript of this paper was written a more general development of the combining of classes condition has been found which we present here. The original manuscript was shown to L. J. Savage who then proved the following theorem: To satisfy the combining of classes condition in three or more dimensions, a continuous stochastic operator S must be of the form $Sp = \alpha p + (1-\alpha)\lambda$, where α is a suitably chosen scalar and λ is a probability vector. In this appendix we prove a slightly more general theorem without using the assumption of continuity, and so extend the theorem to arbitrary stochastic operators.

In the following, we will always imply that probability vectors and operators are r-dimensional, where r is finite and $r \geq 3$.

Definition 1. By a stochastic operator S we shall mean an operator which sends probability vectors into probability vectors, i.e., $Sp = p'$ where p and p' are probability vectors.

Definition 2. A projection of a probability vector $p = (p_1, p_2, \cdots, p_r)$ into the probability vector p' is obtained by choosing a non-empty sub-set σ of elements of p and replacing all but one of them by zeros and that one by the sum of the elements in the sub-set, while maintaining unchanged the elements of p not in σ. Any stochastic operator C that projects probability vectors is a projection operator and can be represented by an rxr matrix.

Clearly there are a finite number of projection operators corresponding to the finite number of sets σ.

Definition 3. A stochastic operator S is said to satisfy the combining of classes condition if and only if

(1) $$CSCp = CSp$$

for all projection operators C and all probability vectors p.

Lemma 1. If S satisfies the combining of classes condition and p and p' are probability vectors such that $Cp = Cp'$, then,

(2) $$CSp = CSp' .$$

In particular we have, for the components $S_j p$ of Sp

(3) $$\sum_{j \in \sigma} S_j p = \sum_{j \in \sigma} S_j p'$$

where σ is the set defining C.

Proof. If $Cp = Cp'$ then $CSCp = CSCp'$ and application of (1) to both sides shows that $CSp = CSp'$, which is (2). Expression (3) is obtained by reading off the proper component of the vectors in (2).

Lemma 1 says that if the projections of two r-dimensional vectors on a sub-simplex are equal, then the projections of their images on that sub-simplex are equal.

Lemma 2. If S satisfies the combining of classes condition then $Sp = (\gamma_1(p_1), \gamma_2(p_2), \cdots, \gamma_r(p_r))$ where the γ_i are functions sending I into I (I is the unit interval, $\{x | 0 \leq x \leq 1\}$).

Proof. Let $\sigma = 1, \cdots, i-1, i+1, \cdots, r$ and let C be the projection operator defined for this σ. Let p be a fixed probability vector; then for all probability vectors p' with $p_i' = p_i$ we have $\sum_{j \in \sigma} p_j = \sum_{j \in \sigma} p_j' = 1 - p_i$ so that $Cp = Cp'$. Lemma 1 now implies that (3) holds, so that

$$S_i p = 1 - \sum_{j \in \sigma} S_j p = 1 - \sum_{j \in \sigma} S_j p' = S_i p' .$$

Since p' was an arbitrary vector satisfying $p_i' = p_i$, and p fixed, this shows that $S_i p$ depends only on p_i, and defines a single-valued function $\gamma_i(p_i) = S_i p$. This function γ_i maps I into I because S is a stochastic operator so $0 \leq p_i \leq 1$ implies $0 \leq \gamma_i(p_i) \leq 1$.

Lemma 3. Let x be any point in I; then there exists a function γ sending I into I such that

$$(4) \qquad \gamma_i(x) = \gamma(x) + \gamma_i(0)$$

for $i = 1, \cdots, r$. Moreover, if x, y and $x + y$ belong to I, then

$$(5) \qquad \gamma(x + y) = \gamma(x) + \gamma(y).$$

Proof. Consider two probability vectors p and p' such that $p = (p_1, p_2, p_3, \cdots, p_r)$ and $p' = (p_1 + p_2, 0, p_3, \cdots, p_r)$. Then

$$(6) \quad 1 - \sum_{j=3}^{r} \gamma_j(p_j) = \gamma_1(p_1) + \gamma_2(p_2)$$
$$= \gamma_1(p_1 + p_2) + \gamma_2(0).$$

Setting $p_1 = 0$ and $p_2 = x$ in this equation we have

$$\gamma_1(x) - \gamma_1(0) = \gamma_2(x) - \gamma_2(0) = \gamma(x)$$

thus defining the function γ sending I into I. By repeating the argument for other pairs of indices we obtain (4).

Now let x, y and $x + y$ belong to I; setting $x = p_1$, $y = p_2$, substituting (4) into (6) and simplifying, we obtain (5). This completes the proof of Lemma 3.

We want to show that γ is a linear operator, i.e., that equation (5) above is satisfied and in addition

$$\gamma(cx) = c\,\gamma(x)$$

for all x in I and all real constants c such that cx is in I. We will prove that this latter requirement is met by showing that $\gamma(x) = \beta x$ where β is a constant in I.

Lemma 4. If γ is a function sending I into I and $\gamma(x + y) = \gamma(x) + \gamma(y)$ for x, y and $x + y$ in I, then $\gamma(x) = \beta x$ for some non-negative constant β.

Proof.[5] Let $\gamma(1) = \beta \geq 0$. Then $\beta = \gamma(\frac{1}{2} + \frac{1}{2}) = 2\gamma(\frac{1}{2})$ so that $\gamma(\frac{1}{2}) = \frac{\beta}{2}$. By induction $\gamma(\frac{1}{n}) = \frac{\beta}{n}$. Now for $n \geq 2$,

$\gamma(\frac{1}{n} + \frac{1}{n}) = 2\gamma(\frac{1}{n}) = \frac{2\beta}{n}$ and, by induction, $\gamma(\frac{m}{n}) = \frac{m\beta}{n}$ if $m \leq n$.

Suppose now that the assertion is false, namely, suppose that there exists an x such that $\gamma(x) = \beta x + a$, where a is a positive real number. (For a negative an analogous argument holds.) Observe that $\gamma(x) = \gamma((x - y) + y) = \gamma(x - y) + \gamma(y)$ so that $\gamma(x - y) = \gamma(x) - \gamma(y)$, if $x \geq y$. Hence, for all rational p such that $x \pm p$ belongs to I, we have

$$\gamma(x \pm p) = \gamma(x) \pm \gamma(p) = \beta(x \pm p) + a .$$

Since $a > 0$ there exists a positive integer N such that $Na > 1$. In the open interval $0 < z < \frac{1}{N}$, choose any point $y = x \pm p$, with p a rational number. Such a point exists since the points of the form $x \pm p$ are dense in I. The point Ny belongs to I since $Ny < N\frac{1}{N} = 1$. By induction one can show that $\gamma(Ny) = N\gamma(y)$. Moreover

$$\gamma(Ny) = N\gamma(y) = N[\beta y + a] \, Na > 1$$

contradicting the fact that γ sends I into I. This contradiction establishes the lemma.

<u>Theorem 1.</u> A stochastic operator S (for $r \geq 3$) satisfies the combining of classes condition if and only if it has the form

$$(7) \qquad Sp = \alpha p + (1-\alpha)\lambda$$

where λ is a probability vector and α is a suitably chosen constant.

<u>Proof.</u> The "if" part of the theorem follows easily by showing that an operator of the form (7) satisfies the combining of classes condition.

For the "only if" part, observe that Lemmas 3 and 4 show that

$$(8) \qquad \gamma_i(x) = \beta x + \gamma_i(0) .$$

Define a constant α by means of the equation

$$(9) \qquad \sum_{i=1}^{r} \gamma_i(0) = 1 - \alpha .$$

We now have two cases to consider, namely $\alpha \neq 1$ and $\alpha = 1$.

Case 1. $\alpha \neq 1$. In this case we set $\lambda_i = \dfrac{\gamma_i(0)}{1-\alpha}$ and note that $\Sigma\lambda_i = 1$.

Then we have from (8) that $\gamma_i(x) = \beta x + (1-\alpha)\lambda_i$. Let p be a probability vector; then

$$
\begin{aligned}
1 = \Sigma\gamma_i(p_i) &= \Sigma(\beta p_i + (1-\alpha)\lambda_i) \\
&= \beta \Sigma p_i + (1-\alpha) \Sigma\lambda_i \\
&= \beta + (1-\alpha)
\end{aligned}
$$

so that $\beta = \alpha$. Thus $\gamma_i(p_i) = \alpha p_i + (1-\alpha)\lambda_i$ and the operator must be of the desired form (7).

Case 2. $\alpha = 1$. Equation (9) then implies that $\Sigma\gamma_i(0) = 0$ and, since each $\gamma_i(0)$ is non-negative, this means that $\gamma_i(0) = 0$ for all i. Let p be a probability vector; we have

$$
1 = \Sigma\gamma_i(p_i) = \Sigma\beta p_i = \beta\Sigma p_i = \beta
$$

so that $\beta = \alpha = 1$. Then $\gamma_i(p_i) = p_i$, i.e., $Sp = p$, and hence S is the identity operator which can be written in the form (7) by setting $\alpha = 1$.

This completes the proof of the theorem.

For the case r = 2, equation (1) is satisfied for all operators and imposes no restriction. Hence Theorem 1 cannot be proved if n = 2. Analogous situations occur in other parts of mathematics in which the lower dimensional cases are atypical. However, it is frequently convenient to assume the operators have the form of (7) also when r = 2.

FOOTNOTES

1. In the appendix we generalize the combining of classes requirement to apply to all stochastic operators and then demonstrate that Theorem 1 below is still valid.

2. For typographical convenience we write all vectors as row vectors, but it is clear from the context when a column vector is meant.

3. This example was provided by H. Raiffa.

4. A perfect set is a closed set which has no isolated points, that is, one in which every point is a limit point.

5. The essential idea of this proof was suggested to us by R. L. Davis.

BIBLIOGRAPHY

1. Bush, R. R., and Mosteller, F., A mathematical model for simple learning, Psychol. Rev., 58 (1951), 313-323.

2. Bush, R. R., and Mosteller, F., A model for stimulus generalization and discrimination, Psychol. Rev., 58 (1951), 413-423.

3. Bush, R. R., and Mosteller, F., A stochastic model with applications to learning, Annals Math. Stat., 24 (1953), 559-585.

4. Estes, W. K., Toward a statistical theory of learning, Psychol. Rev., 57 (1950), 94-107.

5. Flood, M. M., An experimental multiple choice situation, paper presented to Institute of Mathematical Statistics, East Lansing, Mich., Sept., 1952.

6. Miller, G. A., and McGill, W. J., A statistical description of verbal learning, Psychometrica, 17 (1952), 369-396.

CHAPTER IX

INDIVIDUAL BEHAVIOR IN UNCERTAIN SITUATIONS: AN INTERPRETATION IN TERMS OF STATISTICAL ASSOCIATION THEORY

by

W. K. Estes

INDIANA UNIVERSITY

INTRODUCTION

Group decision processes depend upon the behavior of individuals. For this reason it is to be expected that theories developed in social sciences and theories developed in experimental psychology will not be unrelated. Inspection of certain of the more formalized theories of group behavior, e.g., theories of games and economic behavior, reveals that these theories include, explicitly or implicitly, assumptions concerning characteristics of individual behavior. It is an attractive possibility that the descriptive laws or principles of behavior that enter theories of group behavior as axioms may be deducible from theories of individual behavior.

We note that in a game or an economic situation the individual is called upon to predict or to attempt to control uncertain events. The sequence of events may be random or it may follow a pattern about which the individual has initially incomplete information. We shall discuss in this paper two sets of experiments that have been carried out with adult human subjects (college students) in highly simplified experimental situations. The first set will bring out certain aspects of the behavior of an individual in attempting to predict correctly the outcomes of a series of situations when the alternative outcomes occur in a random sequence (the individual not being informed that the sequence will be random). The second set of experiments will bring out certain aspects of the behavior of an individual in attempting to produce an event by choosing on each trial some one of a set of alternative responses, the different responses having different probabilities (initially unknown to the individual) of producing the event. In each case we will show how the data can be handled in terms of a statistical theory of associative learning.

It is contemplated that these simplified experiments may provide basic paradigms which can be progressively modified in the direction of situations directly relevant to utility theory and game theory. It will also be of interest to consider possible relationships between the model that accounts for the data of these experiments and models that are developed in connection with other decision processes.

CASE I: PREDICTION OF AN UNCERTAIN EVENT

The experiments to be considered in this section all have the same basic design. The activity studied is similar in some respects to that involved in predicting the results of roulette games or horse races; there are two important simplifications, however. In these experiments the outcome of the situation has no utility for the individual (except that of being right or wrong in his guess) and the information available to the individual is restricted to what he can obtain from observing a series of replications of the situation.

In any one experiment, the subject is run for a series of trials. All trials in the series begin with a signal, S. In some experiments S has been onset of a light, in some the onset of a tone, in some simply a verbal signal from the experimenter. A short time (2-5 seconds) following the signal S, one of a set of alternative outcomes, $E_1, E_2, \cdots, E_n$, occurs and terminates the trial. Immediately after the onset of S on each trial the subject writes down his prediction as to which of the events $E_1, E_2, \cdots, E_n$ will occur on that trial; then he is permitted to observe which event actually does occur. The subject is given no information about the conditions of the experiment except that some one of the E_j will follow the signal S on each trial; he is instructed to do his best to make a good score (in terms of correct predictions), and to make a prediction on each trial regardless of how uncertain he may feel about the outcome. The events $E_1, E_2, \cdots, E_n$ actually occur at random with probabilities $\pi_1, \pi_2, \cdots, \pi_n$. No communication between subject and experimenter is permitted once the series of trials has begun. Trials are spaced at intervals of about five seconds ordinarily.

The theory that has been applied to this situation with some success is a statistical model for associative learning that has been developed during the last five years by the writer and others. In this theory the behaviors available to the subject on any experimental trial are categorized into mutually exclusive and exhaustive classes (in the present experiment alternative predictions concerning the E_j) by means of experimental criteria. It is assumed that the change in probability of any response class on a given trial depends upon the momentary environmental situation and upon the state of the individual as defined in the model. When the model is interpreted in terms of the present experiment, it turns out that the rate of learning (systematic change in probability of making a given prediction) depends upon the characteristics of the momentary environmental situation but that over a considerable series of trials the probability of making a given prediction tends to a stable asymptotic distribution with the asymptotic mean, for a group of similar individuals run under like conditions, being independent of the momentary environmental situation, in the present experiment, the nature of the signal, S. The dependence of $\bar{p}_j$, the mean probability (for a group of like individuals) of predicting event E_j, upon n, the number of previous trials in the series, is given by the equation

$$(1) \qquad \bar{p}_j(n) = \pi_j - \frac{1}{N\bar{\theta}} \sum_{i=1}^{N} \theta_i [\pi_j - F_{i,j}(0)][1 - \theta_i]^n$$

where the θ_i represent the probabilities of occurrence on any trial of the N environmental determiners comprising the situation at the beginning of the trial, π_j represents the probability of the outcome E_j on any trial, and $F_{i,j}(0)$ represents the initial probability that the ith element in the set of environmental determiners would, taken alone, lead to a prediction of outcome E_j. This equation is derived from certain primitive assumptions concerning the learning process. The assumptions are given in references [3, 4].

Since the stable course of action arrived at by the individual over a series of trials is the feature of the situation that is apt to be of most interest in relation to group decision processes, we shall consider only the asymptotic distribution of p_j in this paper. It can be seen from inspection of equation (1) that the asymptotic value of $\bar{p}_j$ is independent of the initial state and also of the distribution of θ_i. Therefore we can conveniently simplify the model for our present purposes by assuming all of the θ_i equal to some value θ, which amounts empirically to assuming that all aspects of the environmental situation obtaining at the beginning of each trial are equally likely to affect the subject. Then the difference equations leading to equation (1) in the theory reduce to the following set of linear transformations:

(2)   (a) If E_j occurs on trial n, then

$$p_j(n+1) = p_j(n) + \theta(1 - p_j(n))$$

(b) If E_j fails to occur on trial n, then

$$p_j(n+1) = p_j(n) - \theta p_j(n)$$

(c) If E_j occurs with probability π_j, then on the average

$$\bar{p}_j(n+1) = \bar{p}_j(n) + \theta(\pi_j - \bar{p}_j(n))$$

and we have asymptotically,

(3)   (a) $\bar{p}_j(\infty) = \pi_j$

and   (b) $\sigma^2_{p_j}(\infty) = \pi_j(1 - \pi_j)\theta/(2 - \theta)$

It will be noted that the equations (2) and (3) can be obtained from the linear operator model of Bush and Mosteller [1] if suitable restrictions are imposed upon the parameters.

Data from two experiments of the sort under consideration are summarized in Figure 1 below.

The bottom curve represents data collected by James H. Straughan and the writer at Indiana University. Subjects were 30 college students. The signal, S, was a pattern of four lights which flashed for one second at the beginning of each trial. The outcomes E_1 and E_2 were the appearance or non-appearance of a single light two seconds after the signal pattern. The trials on which E_1 appeared were determined in advance of the experiment by a random number table with $\pi_1 = .25$ and $\pi_2 = .75$. Each point on the curve represents the mean relative frequency of predictions of E_1 in a block of 10 trials. The three upper curves represent data from a very similar experiment conducted by Jarvik [7] at the University of California, with π_1 equal to .60, .67, and .75 for three groups of subjects respectively. In Jarvik's experiment the signal at the start of each trial was utterance of the word "now" by the experimenter and the two alternative outcomes, E_1 and E_2 were utterance of the word "check" or the word "plus," respectively, by the experimenter. The Jarvik data are plotted in terms of mean relative frequencies

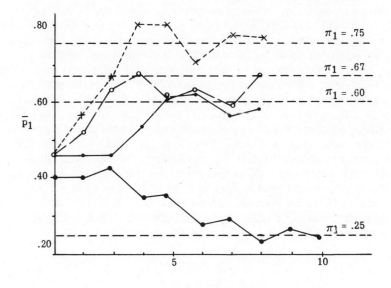

Fig. 1. Data from prediction experiments plotted in terms of mean proportion of E_1 predictions per trial block.

of "check" predictions over blocks of 11 trials. It will be seen that in all cases the mean value of p_1 levels off in the neighborhood of the predicted asymptote by the end of 60 to 80 trials. The agreement of theory and experiment in this instance is especially interesting in view of the fact that the theoretical predictions of $p_1(\infty)$ utilize no degrees of freedom from the data. Similar experiments by Humphreys [6], who originated the experimental design, and Grant [5] report data which are in accord with theoretical predictions insofar as asymptotic means are concerned. The Jarvik, Humphreys, and Grant papers do not report individual data or variance estimates.

The reader may be concerned at this point over the fact that the experimental curves cited represent group performance. The terminal mean probabilities of E_1 predictions by groups of subjects agree with the theory in all instances, but according to the theory, not only group means but also mean response probabilities of individual subjects should approach π_1 asymptotically.

We cannot tell from the group data whether this feature of the theory is verified. A mean response probability, $\bar{p}_1$ (n), equal to π_1 could arise if the values of p_1 (n) tended to cluster around π_1, but it could also arise if the proportion π_1 of the subjects in a group ended up at p_1 (n) = 1 while the remainder went to p_1 (n) = 0. As a matter of fact, inspection of individual data from a number of experiments run in the writer's laboratory shows that the latter possibility can be rejected. To illustrate this point, we have plotted in Figure 2 the records of each of a group of four subjects run in one of these experiments under somewhat better controlled conditions than the group studies. The values plotted are proportions of E_1 predictions per ten-trial block. According to theory, these individual curves, regardless of initial value, should tend to approach π_1 = .85, the relative frequency of E_1, as learning progresses. Three of the four records certainly do this; the fourth record is in some doubt, not having stabilized anywhere by the end of 120 trials.

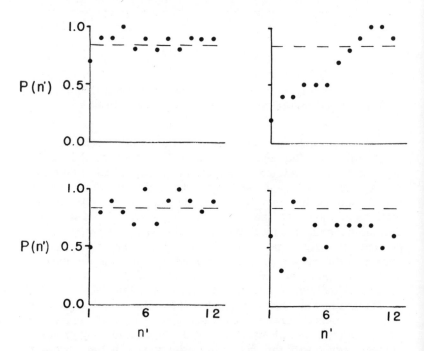

Fig. 2. Individual records from a prediction experiment plotted in terms of proportion of E_1 predictions, P(n'), per block of ten trials, n'.

It may be noted that during the later trial blocks, the plotted values for these subjects tend to fluctuate around the .85 level rather than remaining constant. This asymptotic variability is also in accordance with theory. Since the theoretical asymptotic probability of E_1 predictions is .85, the standard deviation of proportions of E_1 predictions per block of ten trials at the asymptote will be expected to be approximately (neglecting a covariance term)

$$\sqrt{\frac{.85 \times .15}{10}} = .113$$

In the case of the experiment represented in the lowest curve of Figure 1, the inter-subject variability around the mean curve decreases steadily throughout the series of trials. In the last two blocks of trials over 60 per cent of the subjects have p_1 values (i.e., proportions of E_1 predictions) in the range .1 to .3 as compared with 33 per cent in the first block, and the proportions of zero and one values do not increase at all during the series.

It will be noted that the course of action adopted by the subjects in these experiments does not maximize the expected frequency of correct predictions. Take, for example, a series with π_1 equal to .25. The subjects settle down to a relatively steady level at which they predict E_1 on 25 per cent of the trials. This behavior secures the subject an expected percentage of correct predictions

$$(25 \times .25 + 75 \times .75)\% = 62.5\%$$

whereas the "pure strategy," in the von Neumann and Morgenstern sense, of predicting the more frequently occurring event on all trials would yield an expectation of 75 per cent correct predictions.

It would be of interest in connection with the broader problem of decision processes to modify the design of these experiments on prediction by introducing systematic variation in the information available to the subject and in the utility attached to the outcomes $E_1, E_2, \cdots, E_n$.

CASE II: ATTEMPTING TO CONTROL AN UNCERTAIN EVENT

A group of experiments which are closely related, in terms of the theory, to those described above, study the behavior of the individual in attempting to control an uncertain event. In one variation of this experiment, two telegraph keys are available to the subject and he is required to choose one or the other on each trial. On a panel in front of the subject there is mounted a lamp globe. The subject is told that on each trial one key is "correct" and one key is "incorrect" in accordance with some scheme or plan that is entirely unknown to him except for what he can learn during a series of trials, and is led to believe that whenever he chooses "correctly," the light on the panel will flash. Actually the light is operated by a device programmed by means of a random number table so that the light flash will follow choices of key #1 with probability π_1 and choices of key #2 with probability π_2.

As in Case I, a theoretical account of this experiment can be derived from the statistical model [3,4]. For purposes of the present discussion we will give here simply the end result of the derivations. If we again simplify the model by assuming that all components of the situation S have equal probabilities of influencing the individual's response, then the changes in response probability on any trial are described by the linear transformations given in the table below. Let $p_1(n)$ represent the probability of choosing key #1 on trial n.

Key Chosen	Outcome	Expected Change in p_1
1	E_1	$p_1(n+1) = p_1(n) + \theta(1 - p_1(n))$
1	E_2	$p_1(n+1) = p_1(n) - \theta p_1(n)$
2	E_1	$p_1(n+1) = p_1(n) - \theta p_1(n)$
2	E_2	$p_1(n+1) = p_1(n) + \theta(1 - p_1(n))$

Then under the conditions stated above, we obtain for the expected change in mean probability of choosing key #1

$$(4) \qquad \bar{p}_1(n+1) = \theta(1 - \pi_2) + (1 - 2\theta + \theta\pi_1 + \theta\pi_2)\,\bar{p}_1(n)$$

And for the asymptotic mean

$$(5) \qquad \bar{p}_1(\infty) = \frac{1 - \pi_2}{2 - \pi_1 - \pi_2}$$

The data reproduced in Figure 3 are taken from an experiment conducted at Indiana University by Marvin H. Detambel [2]. Detambel ran four groups of college students under the conditions described above with the following values of π_1 and π_2

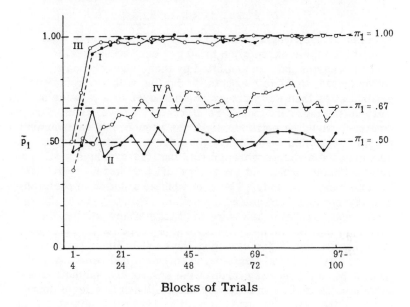

Fig. 3. Mean proportion of E_1 predictions per four-trial block in Detambel's two-key, contingent reinforcement experiment.

Group	π_1	π_2	Theoretical Asymptote, $\bar{p}_1(\infty)$
I & III	100	0	1.0
II	50	50	0.5
IV	50	0	0.67

Predicted values for asymptotic mean probabilities of choosing key #1 are readily computed from equation (5) and the values for Detambel's groups are included in the table just above. In the case of Group IV, which has $\pi_1 = 0.5$ and $\pi_2 = 0$, we see that the course of action to which the subjects tend over a series of trials is far from the "pure strategy" which would be the best solution to the situation from the standpoint of maximizing successes. Over the last half of the series the subjects, on the average, select key #1 approximately 67 per cent of the time, in accordance with theoretical expectation. Under the conditions of the experiment, this course of action yields as the expected percentage of successes

$$67 \times .50 + 33 \times 0 = 33.5\%$$

whereas by selecting key #1 on all trials the subjects would have raised their expectation to 50 per cent successes.

The behavior pattern exhibited by these subjects may be better suited, in some respects, to dealing with environmental uncertainties than the strategy of going over to a p value of unity on the more frequently reinforced response. The "pure strategy" would be optimal only if the sequence of environmental events constituted a stationary time series. Actually in this experiment the subjects were not told that the π values would remain constant throughout the series and they had no sound basis for inferring constancy. The compromise solution of the problem arrived at by the subjects would be advantageous if the environmental probabilities were to change at any point in the series so that the formerly unfavorable response became the more favorable. If, for example, the probability of reinforcement on key #2 in the Detambel experiment had been changed from zero to .75 halfway through the series, the subjects would soon have shifted their response probabilities to a level appropriate to the new situation, whereas a "rational" subject operating under a "pure strategy" of selecting key #1 on all trials would not have discovered that the balance of probabilities had changed. It is very doubtful, however, that many individuals in these experiments work out a solution at a verbal level. Probably long experience with environmental uncertainties has developed relatively stable habits of response to reinforcement and non-reinforcement. In this situation it appears that the subject proceeds as though failure of reinforcement on one key means that the other response would have been correct on the given trial, although as the experiment is conducted this actually is not generally true. Subjects might eventually change their behavior pattern, but under experimental conditions they give little evidence of doing so even over series of considerable length.

Both types of experiment seem to support the conclusion that in a simple decision process the human subject tends to behave in accordance with the principles of associative learning and not, in general, in the most rational manner as "rational" is conventionally defined. The suggestion arises, then, that in formulating theories of group decision processes it may be worth while to draw upon the principles of individual behavior revealed by experimental-theoretical research of the kind described here rather than to depend upon common sense notions concerning characteristics of individual behavior.

BIBLIOGRAPHY

1. Bush, R. R. and Mosteller, F., A linear operator model for learning. In preparation.

2. Detambel, M. H., A re-analysis of Humphrey's "Acquisition and extinction of verbal expectations." M.A. Thesis, Indiana University, 1950.

3. Estes, W. K., Toward a statistical theory of learning. Psychol. Rev., 57 (1950), 94-107.

4. Estes, W. K. and Burke, C. J., Theory of stimulus variability in learning. Psychol. Rev., 60 (1953), 276-286.

5. Grant, D. A., Hake, H. W., and Hornseth, J. P., Acquisition and extinction of a verbal conditioned response with differing percentages of reinforcement. J. exp. Psychol., 42 (1951), 1-5.

6. Humphreys, L. G., Acquisition and extinction of verbal expectations in a situation analogous to conditioning. J. exp. Psychol., 25 (1939), 294-301.

7. Jarvik, M. E., Probability learning and a negative recency effect in the serial anticipation of alternatives. J. exp. Psychol., 41 (1951), 291-297.

CHAPTER X

ON GAME-LEARNING THEORY
AND SOME DECISION-MAKING EXPERIMENTS

by

Merrill M. Flood

COLUMBIA UNIVERSITY*

1. INTRODUCTION

The theory of games [14] provides a general mathematical model that may sometimes be used to approximate a real situation. Most often, in real cases, the situation is much too complicated to permit formulation even conceptually as a formal game. In the few cases that can be so formulated, it is almost always impractical to attempt gathering the necessary data or to do the elaborate calculations required for a solution.

The non-constant-sum case, even with two players, remains unsolved in the sense of von Neumann-Morgenstern. There are theoretical proposals that dispose reasonably well of the two-person case, and of many other broad special cases; we have discussed some of these in another paper [8].

In this paper we investigate game-like situations in which the players are limited biologically in their choices of moves. These limitations are reflected in the method of play of the formal game and stem from the notion that animal organisms seem to learn by some sort of conditioning process that alters the probability that

*This work was done while the author was with The RAND Corporation, under Project RAND of the Department of the Air Force, and the results were presented in July 1952 at the Santa Monica conference on decision-making. The present paper is a condensation of an earlier memorandum [9], and was prepared at Columbia University while the author was with the Behavioral Models Project of the Office of Naval Research. Grateful thanks are also due to Dr. D. R. Fulkerson for a careful reading of the manuscript, and for many helpful comments during the course of the work.

some one of several mutually exclusive alternatives will be selected in each new instance.

This approach was suggested to us by the work of R. F. Bales and A. S. Householder [1], [2] on the group interaction process, and is closely connected with the work of R. R. Bush and C. F. Mosteller [4] on mathematical models for learning. We have profited from discussions with all four of these men. There is also an interesting philosophical discussion of stochastic learning models in a recent paper by D. M. MacKay [12], and a stimulating essay by E. G. Boring [3] on "robotology"; both of these latter papers seem to support our methodological viewpoint.

2. GENERALITIES

The approach used in this paper is applicable to situations involving more than two organisms, but we shall concentrate somewhat on the two-player case. A player could in fact be a group of people, or a component of personality within one individual, but we only touch upon such interpretations. Since our main object is to treat some one case of real behavior, we shall usually be content with a discussion in terms of a special real-life situation, leaving broader interpretations to the reader.

The connection with game theory is the correspondence between the notion of choice of a strategy for a game in normal form and the notion of individual choice of course of action in biological activity. A very fundamental case, and perhaps the simplest one, is the problem of choosing whether or not to act in a situation where there appears to be only one choice: acting or not acting. For example, in experiments like those of B. F. Skinner [13] with rats, the choice at some moment is whether or not to press a bar. For a human example, the choice might be whether or not to accept a particular offer for a new position. In these examples, and in most real-life situations, the organism somehow reduces its range of alternatives to a relatively small number from which it feels it must choose.[1] It is this recognized field of choices, whether they are considered to be conscious or unconscious alternatives, that corresponds to the set of strategies listed in the normal form of the formal game.

In what follows, we shall try to use such terms as "game", "strategy", "move", and "player" from game theory only with the meaning attached formally by von Neumann and Morgenstern [14]; for other purposes we shall use alternative words such as "situation", "plan", "act", and "subject".

3. THE PROBLEM

The games in which we shall be interested are defined in terms of expectation functions:

$$V_i^j \equiv V_{i_1 i_2 \cdots i_n}^j \quad \text{for} \quad (i_k = 1, 2, \cdots, m_k; \ j = 1, 2, \cdots, n).$$

A play of the game consists of simultaneous independent choices of specific values i_k^0 for the i_k by the n players. The quantity $V_{i^0}^j$ is the expectation for player j, where the units for $V_{i^0}^j$ relate to a measure of the utility attached by player j to the payments he receives. The functions V_i^j are real-valued.

The actual payment to player j, when the choice of pure strategies is i on a play, is a quantity x given by the distribution function $P_i^j(x)$ whose mean value is V_i^j Of course $|x|$ is bounded, so that

$$P_i^j(x) = 0 \quad \text{if} \quad |x| > \bar{b}_i^j .$$

Our problem is to select a good method of play that can be used by player ℓ when his information about the structure of the game is knowledge only of

$$m_\ell \quad \text{and a bound} \quad \bar{b}^\ell \geq \max_i \ \bar{b}_i^\ell > 0,$$

and where his information about the distribution functions $P_i^j(x)$ is gained entirely from his experience while playing the game.

It is customarily assumed [14] in the process of passing from the normal to the extended form of a game, that only the mean values V_i^j of these distributions affect the situation; we could even assume without essential loss of generality, therefore, that the variance of $P_i^j(x)$ is zero so that x only assumes the value V_i^j. Furthermore, since the problem is essentially unchanged if the utility measure x is subjected to a linear transformation we could also take $\bar{b}^j = 1$ and suppose that $P_i^j(x) = 0$ if $x < 0$ or $x > 1$.

The experience gained by player j in N plays of the game consists of a record of his own choices $i_j(t)$, and receipts $r_j(t)$ for $t = 1, 2, \cdots, N$. The central problem is to find a rule of play that will tend to maximize total receipts in a sequence of plays where the player is given some information about the number of plays before he starts on a sequence; we are intentionally vague at this point about the exact nature of the rule of play and about the advance information concerning the length of sequence.

We shall be interested in what follows, then, only in the game whose normal form has the expectation functions

$$0 \leq V_i^j \leq 1 .$$

We shall be especially concerned with one extended form of this game in which there is one chance move for each player and the actual payments are always unity or zero, whence the probability of a unit-payment to player j is V_i^j if the players choose the pure strategies i. We have noted that any game can be reduced to this form by suitable linear transformations on the utility measures of the individual players, provided only that there are known finite bounds on the possible payments; use was also made of the assumption that games in extended form are equivalent if their normal forms are identical.

4. THE GAME-LEARNING MODEL

The type of rule of play, that is investigated here, is represented for player j by the relation

$$p^j(t + 1) = M^{jh}p^j(t) \quad \text{for } h = 0, 1, 2, \cdots, 2m_j + 1,$$

where $p^j(t)$ is an $m_j + 1$ dimensional probability vector and the M^{jh} are given square stochastic matrices whose elements are non-negative real numbers that sum to unity in each column. The components $p_i^j(t)$, for $i = 0, 1, 2, \cdots, m_j$, are the probabilities that player j selects value i for i_j on play t; $p_0^j(t)$ has a special significance to be discussed later.

We now describe how the appropriate operator M^{jh} is chosen after play t. The matrices M^{jh} are first separated into two classes of $m_j + 1$ members each, denoted R^{jk} and P^{jk} for $k = 0, 1, 2, \cdots, m_j$, and either $R^{j \, i_j(t)}$ or $P^{j \, i_j(t)}$ is selected; the choice between these two matrices is made with probability $r_j(t)$ in favor of $R^{j \, i_j(t)}$. In the special case in which $r_j(t)$ is always 0 or 1, we can write the rule of play in the form:

$$p(t + 1) = \left\{ r_j(t) R^{j \, i_j(t)} + (1 - r_j(t)) P^{j \, i_j(t)} \right\} p^j(t).$$

We have defined a method of play that can be used by any player after he has made his initial strategic choice $p^j(0)$, and after specific values have been assigned for the elements of M^{jh}; in actual practice he will need to know m_j and $\bar{b}^j$ also.

5. THE FUSION GAME-LEARNING MODEL

We shall now consider a special parametric form for the matrices M^{jh}. For convenience, we shall henceforth omit the designation of the player when this leads to no ambiguity.

We set:

$$R^i_{\alpha\beta} = (1 - b^i - c^i)\delta_{\alpha\beta} + c^i \delta_{\alpha i} + b^i \delta_{\alpha 0}, \text{ and}$$

$$P^i_{\alpha\beta} = (1 - a^i)\delta_{\alpha\beta} + a^i \delta_{\alpha i},$$

for $(i, \alpha, \beta = 0, 1, 2, \cdots, m)$, where a^i, b^i, and c^i are in the closed interval $[0, 1]$ and $\delta_{\alpha\beta}$ is one or zero according as $\alpha = \beta$ or not. This special form of the more general Markov game-learning process was developed by Bush and Mosteller [6] so as to fit data obtained in a number of learning experiments with rats; they have named it the "fusion model."

We shall be interested in the case in which all but one player, say number 1, choose constant strategies p^j, but where player 1 uses the fusion model. This means that the probability that player $j > 1$ will select the value i for i_j is p^j_i on each play, and for player 1 it is $p^1_i(t)$. Since these choices are all made independently it follows immediately that the expectation of player 1, if he chooses the value x for i_1 on play t, is:

$$G_x = \sum_{i_2=1}^{m_2} \cdots \sum_{i_n=1}^{m_n} V_{xi_2\cdots i_n} P^2_{i_2} P^3_{i_3} \cdots P^n_{i_n}.$$

We may suppose, without loss of generality, that:

$$G_{m_1} \geq G_{m_1-1} \cdots \geq G_1.$$

It follows that player 1 could do no better than to choose

$$p^1_i(t) = \delta_{im_1}$$

so that his expectancy on each play is G_{m_1}. We shall be interested in comparing his expectation when he makes use of the fusion model with this maximum possible expectation G_{m_1}; of course, his success with the fusion model may also depend upon his choice of the starting vector $p^1(0)$.

The component $p^j_0(t)$ is interpreted in the game situation as the probability that no choice will be made by player j at time t.

This feature can be introduced mathematically into the game model by defining:

$$V_i^j = 0 \text{ if any component of i is zero,}$$

where the range of i_k has been extended to include zero. This augmentation of the original game problem will be used whenever the fusion game-learning model is under discussion.

6. A SPECIAL FUSION MODEL

We shall now consider a specialization of the fusion model in which a^i, b^i, and c^i are positive and independent of i; we denote their common values a, b, and c. We shall also suppose that the quantities G_x, for $x = 1, 2, \cdots, m$, are distinct and non-zero, and that $G_0 = 0$.

The expected value of p^{t+1}, given p^t, is:

$$Qp^t = \left\{ \sum_{\alpha=0}^{m} p_\alpha (G_\alpha R^\alpha + [1-G_\alpha] P^\alpha) \right\} p^t .$$

This can be rewritten to yield the following relation for the kth component of the expected value of p^{t+1}:

$$E(p_k^{t+1}) = p_k^t + (a-b-c) \sum_{\alpha=0}^{m} p_\alpha^t G_\alpha p_k^t + (c-a) G_k p_k^t + b \sum_{\alpha=0}^{m} p_\alpha^t G_\alpha \delta_{k0},$$

for $k = 0, 1, 2, \cdots, m$.

It follows easily that a vector V^h satisfies the equation $QV = V$ if and only if it is the unit vector e_0 or has the following form:

$$V_0^h = \frac{b}{b+c-a}, \text{ and } V_i^h = (1-V_0^h)\delta_{hi} \text{ for } (h, i = 1, 2, \cdots, m).$$

Bush and Mosteller [5] have called the matrix Q the "expected operator" and they have made use of the vectors V^h in discussing the asymptotic behavior of p^t.

Rather little is known concerning this asymptotic behavior, and still less is known about methods for estimating the parameters in the fusion model from experimental data, so we shall have to resort to Monte Carlo computational methods in our exploration of the properties of the fusion model. For this purpose, we shall turn to some numerical examples.

7. A RAT EXPERIMENT

The rat Su must choose one of two rooms. Five seconds after a warning bell the rat is either rewarded (fed) or punished (shocked) by the experimenter Ex, and Su does not see what the result would have been had Su chosen the other room on that particular trial.

Ex rewards or punishes according to a rule prescribed in advance. The experimental situation may be summarily described as a two-person game. The payoff matrix for Su is:

Ex Su		Places food in:	
		Room 1	Room 2
Sits in:	Room 1	1	-y
	Room 2	-y	1

At the moment, we are not interested in the payoff matrix for Ex but shall simply suppose that Ex has chosen a strategy (π_1, π_2) such that Ex places the food in Room i $100\pi_i$ per cent of the time. The expected payoff for Su is then $V(p_1) = p_1(2\pi_1-1)(1+y) + (1-\pi_1-y\pi_1)$, where y is non-negative and p_i denotes the proportion of the time Su sits in Room i. Now in this situation, even if Su had superior human intelligence, game theory would give Su little real help in choosing a strategy because there is no meaning to attach to the notion of payoff matrix for Ex. Even if there were a payoff matrix for Ex, the game would probably be non-constant sum and the value of y would vary from Su to Su as well as from time to time, and be difficult to estimate. Nevertheless, a rat or a human found in this situation does behave in some fashion, and our scientific problem is to explain and predict actual behavior as well as possible.

Before turning to the game-learning theory approach, it may be instructive to discuss the situation in the usual manner, from the standpoint of rationality. For example, if $\pi_1 = 1/2$, it does not matter what Su does, since the result is independent of his choices. If $\pi_1 \neq 1/2$, then Su should choose $p_1 = 1$ or $p_1 = 0$ according as $\pi_1 > 1/2$ or $\pi_1 < 1/2$. On the other hand, if Su feels that its past behavior (including its biological characteristics) may be analyzed intelligently by an Ex that strives to minimize the payoff to Su by choosing a time-dependent strategy in terms of past behavior of Su, then Su should somehow protect against this unwanted result by concealing its pattern of behavior from Ex (perhaps by randomization as proposed in the theory of games). These dynamic cases are entirely outside the scope of present formal game theory, of course, and are the principal cases of interest here.

The basic assumption from learning theory is that Su varies its behavior according to the pattern of its past experience. The special mathematical form assumed here for this effect is the special fusion model of section 6, with m = 2. The matrices R^{1i} and P^{1i} are, therefore:

$$R^{11} = \begin{pmatrix} 1-c & b & b \\ c & 1-b & c \\ 0 & 0 & 1-b-c \end{pmatrix}, \quad R^{12} = \begin{pmatrix} 1-c & b & b \\ 0 & 1-b-c & 0 \\ c & c & 1-b \end{pmatrix}$$

$$P^{11} = \begin{pmatrix} 1-a & 0 & 0 \\ a & 1 & a \\ 0 & 0 & 1-a \end{pmatrix} \quad P^{12} = \begin{pmatrix} 1-a & 0 & 0 \\ 0 & 1-a & 0 \\ a & a & 1 \end{pmatrix}$$

$$P^{10} = \begin{pmatrix} 1 & a & a \\ 0 & 1-a & 0 \\ 0 & 0 & 1-a \end{pmatrix}$$

R^i is used after Room i is chosen when the food was placed there, and P^i is used after Room i is chosen when the food was not placed there. Of course, Ex, as player 2, may be represented by the relations:

$$p^2(0) = \begin{pmatrix} 0 \\ \pi_1 \\ 1-\pi_1 \end{pmatrix}, \text{ and } R^{2i} = P^{2i} = \begin{pmatrix} 1 & 0 & 0 \\ 0 & 1 & 0 \\ 0 & 0 & 1 \end{pmatrix}$$

The π_i correspond exactly to the G_i of section 5. In this case, Ted Harris has shown (see [9]) that the asymptotic value of $p^1(t)$ is

$$e_0 = \begin{pmatrix} 1 \\ 0 \\ 0 \end{pmatrix} \text{ if } 0 < \pi_1 < 1$$

whatever the value of $p^1(0)$; indeed, the probability is 1 that there will eventually be an unbroken sequence of applications of P^O that terminates the process.

Monte Carlo computations were made for this model with numerical values for the parameters, chosen in agreement with estimates by Bush and Mosteller [6] on the basis of data from learning experiments with rats, as follows:

$$a=b=d=0.01, \quad c=0.10.$$

These computations were made for a rather careless assortment of values for $p^1(0)$ and π_1, and the main results are shown in Tables 1A-1G. All the computed cases show a strong tendency for p_0 to seek an equilibrium near the value 0.1, and it is interesting also that p_2 seemed always to go to zero when $\pi_1 > 0.5$; this constitutes a tendency toward optimal behavior since only choice of Rooms 1 and 2 represent actual decisions by the rat under our interpretation of the fusion model.

TABLE 1

Stat-rat Strategies

1A: $\pi_1 = 0.5$

t	p_0	p_1	p_2
0	100	450	450
5	95	555	350
10	94	450	456
30	91	512	397
50	108	446	446

1B: $\pi_1 = 0.5$

t	p_0	p_1	p_2
0	0	500	500
5	19	579	402
10	46	617	337
30	86	673	241
60	106	806	90
90	97	869	33
115	97	897	4

1C: $\pi_1 = 0.5$

t	p_0	p_1	p_2
0	900	50	50
5	895	58	47
10	900	53	46
30	900	52	48
60	692	281	25
90	355	374	271
120	193	472	335
150	111	589	299
180	139	722	139
210	97	762	141
240	98	866	36

TABLE 1 (Continued)

1D: $\pi_1 = 0.51$

t	p_0	p_1	p_2
0	800	100	100
5	717	196	87
10	717	202	80
30	398	337	265
60	337	497	165
90	148	606	247
120	116	815	69
150	98	893	9
180	115	623	262
210	98	371	31
240	88	906	6

1F: $\pi_1 = 0.9$

t	p_0	p_1	p_2
0	900	100	0
5	735	265	0
10	744	256	0
30	593	406	0
60	126	874	0
90	106	894	0
120	90	908	0
150	111	889	0
180	92	908	0
210	98	902	0
240	101	898	0

1E: $\pi_1 = 0.55$

t	p_0	p_1	p_2
0	800	100	100
5	721	193	86
10	656	262	81
30	411	439	151
60	239	715	45
90	118	875	7
120	98	901	1

1G: $\pi_1 = 1.0$

t	p_0	p_1	p_2
0	114	100	786
5	109	96	795
10	104	179	715
30	107	716	177
60	99	892	8
90	107	892	1

8. HUMAN SUBJECTS

All that has been said about the game-learning model is applicable in the analysis of experimental data with human subjects. There may be a considerable advantage in using human subjects since the conditions of the experiment can be explained to them easily, and because their choices are made quite rapidly. Some very tentative trials were run in order to gain some experience with the experimental situation, as a first step toward a design of more conclusive trials.

In the first series the subject Su was asked to call "head" or "tail" in an attempt to match the random choice made by Ex with fixed probability π_1. The success of Su was compared with that of the special fusion model (stat-rat) used in section 7, where random numbers were used to yield $\pi_1 = 0.55$. The number of trials was too small to permit any quantitative conclusion to be drawn, but it seemed likely that a more extensive series of trials would be worth while. The scheme was discontinued in favor of more promising ones to be discussed next.

The general 3x3 zero-sum symmetric game, which has no pure strategy as a solution, is represented by a three-parameter payoff matrix for its normal form:

$$V = \begin{pmatrix} 0 & u & -v \\ -u & 0 & w \\ v & -w & 0 \end{pmatrix}$$

where u, v, and w are positive. The solution of this game is the unique mixed strategy:

$$\frac{1}{u+v+w} (w, v, u).$$

There were three trials in each of which a subject played a 3x3 zero-sum symmetric game against the stat-rat, as defined numerically for the special fusion model in section 7. For these trials:

(a) The absolute values for u, v, and w were taken directly from a table of random numbers;
(b) The subject was not told the payoff matrix but was told the exact method used to select it;
(c) The subject was told that he was playing against a rat in mathematical form.

The three payoff functions were:

Subject	u	v	w	Solution
RF	-6	6	8	Col. 2
MD	6	-8	7	Col. 1
MF	6	10	-4	Col. 3

These three games each have a pure strategy for a solution, as shown in the final column of the table just preceding. The results of the three trials are summarized in Table 2. The trend in the stat-rat's mixed strategy is shown for each game in Table 2, along with an estimate of the mixed strategy in use by the subject based on the average of his ten choices centered at the play listed. Again the data are too scanty to justify careful analysis, or quantitative conclusions, and this type of trial was discontinued in favor of a more promising one to be discussed next.

TABLE 2

3x3 Symmetric Games

	RF game		MD game		MF game	
	RF	Stat-rat	MD	Stat-rat	MF	Stat-rat
No. of plays	19	19	25	25	20	20
No. of wins	6	13	5	20	10	10
Percentage wins	32	68	20	80	50	50

Through Play	Frequency of Use of Solution*					
1	—	.33	—	.33	—	.33
6	.3	.45	.4	.61	.8	.55
10	.4	.58	.5	.68	1.0	.66
15	.8	.72	.6	.70	1.0	.70
20	—	.76	.7	.74	—	.80
25	—	—	—	.74	—	—

*For the stat-rat the frequency through play x is computed as the ratio of

$$p_{Sol}^X + (1-p_O^X),$$

and for the subjects it is one-tenth the number of wins in the ten plays centered at play x.

There are really two rather different types of problems involved thus far in our discussions of game-learning situations in which the payoff functions are unknown:

(a) (Static) Those situations in which it is assumed that the opponents of the main player choose and use a fixed mixed strategy for the duration of a sequence of plays,

(b) (Dynamic) Those situations in which it is assumed that the opponents of the main player may vary their strategic behavior during the sequence in a manner that somehow takes account of the results they obtain on earlier plays.

The static case, with known payoff functions, is the usual one considered [14] whereas our interest centers here on the dynamic case with essentially unknown payoff functions. The static case always reduces to one in which there is a set of numbers G_x, in the closed interval $[0, 1]$, that represents the payment expectation if our main player chooses pure strategy x on a given play—and the numbers G_x remain constant for the sequence of plays; the dynamic case takes the same form except that the numbers G_x may vary in some manner that is dependent upon the choices made by our main player in preceding plays. The game-learning model is equally applicable in either the static or the dynamic case.

The game of Morra [7] is a convenient one for our purposes both because it is of handy size (9x9) and because it has been completely solved. The static case was examined experimentally for Morra by having two subjects and the stat-rat play the game knowing only that it was 9x9 and symmetric, and that their opponent would not be using a game-theoretic solution. Subject BC had no knowledge of game theory and Subject RB is a mathematician who is expert in game and decision theory. Actually, a fixed pure strategy, not in the solution mixture, was used in opposing the subjects and the stat-rat; it is represented by the following set of values for G_x that were used against BC and the stat-rat, those for RB being 2/3 as great:

$$G_x = (.500, .500, .833, .250, .250, .500, .500, .500, 1.000).$$

The results of play are summarized in Table 3. The data are still too skimpy to permit any conclusions to be drawn.

There is no particular reason, in the static case at least, why the experimental values chosen for G_x should come from a game that has a well-known extended form. Consequently, we have come to the following type of experiment as the most promising one to use in obtaining data on the behavior of human subjects to be used in estimating parameters in the fusion models and thus eventually to test the hypothesis that this mathematical model represents human learning behavior. The G_x are chosen from a random-number table and the subject then is asked to play a number of times fixed in advance in an effort to maximize his total number of wins; RB and AM, both experts in the relevant mathematical theories, served as subjects for trials in which there were 1,000 plays and:

$$G_x = (.04, .03, .25, .61, .64, .33, .44, .44, .75, .41).$$

TABLE 3

Static Morra

	RB	BC	Stat-rat 1	Stat-rat 2
No. of plays	67*	372*	29	43
No. of wins	24	213	14	21
Percentage wins	40	57	48	49
Through Play	Frequency of Use of Solution			
1	—	—	.100	.100
5	.1	.2	.077	.186
10	.6	.1	.058	.155
20	.5	.1	.030	.260
30	—	.1	.017	.304
60	—	.1	——	——
90	—	.1	——	——
120	—	.2	——	——
150	—	.2	——	——
210	—	.2	——	——
270	—	.1	——	——
330	—	.2	——	——
360	—	.0	——	——

*The subject announced at this point that he would continue playing pure strategy No. 9 indefinitely, and so had in effect "solved" the game. RB made this tentative decision after 32 plays and used the other 35 simply to confirm his decision.

The results are given in Table 4; it seems unlikely that the stat-rat would match this performance, but it would probably take a good many trials to give a statistically significant test of this conjecture.

One static-nine game has been played by the stat-rat with ten replications. In this play, $p_\alpha^0 = 0.1$ for $\alpha = 0.1, \cdots, 0.9$, and the values for G_x chosen from the random-number table were:

$$G_x = (.097, .510, .433, .274, .442, .364, .503, .929, .256)$$

This was the first IBM machine run and the computations were carried to eight decimal places for two hundred steps each. In nine out of the ten cases, the value of p^{200} was essentially such that $p_8^{200} = 0.9$, $p_0^{200} = 0.1$; in other words, the stat-rat had reached the optimum strategy in 200 trials. In the tenth case the value of p^{200}, if rounded off at the third decimal place, was essentially $p_6^{200} = 0.9$, $p_0^{200} = 0.1$; in other words, the stat-rat had reached a very poor strategy in 200 trials. Other details of this run of static-nine are given in Table 5, including the "winning rate" w^t which represents the expectation on the first decision after time t, where:

$$w^t = \frac{\sum\limits_{i=1}^{9} p_i^t G_i}{\sum\limits_{i=1}^{9} p_i^t}.$$

TABLE 4

Static-10-Game

	RB	AM
No. of plays	1,000	1,000
No. of wins*	719	715
Percentage wins	71.9	71.5
No. of last play before deciding permanently on strategy 9	133	204

*Based on expectation after decision to play strategy 9

TABLE 5

Static-9 Game

Item	Average excl. Game 9	Game Number									
		1	2	3	4	5	6	7	8	9	10
Time at which winning rate first exceeded:											
.84	59	41	29	58	88	98	65	72	58	—	26
.90	81	97	41	88	99	111	76	92	68	—	36
Winning rate at time:											
50	70	87	84	73	44	58	62	59	74	36	92
100	91	90	93	92	90	82	93	91	93	36	93
200	93	93	93	93	93	93	93	93	93	36	93
Percentage wins in:											
100 decisions	71	63	85	72	57	57	75	65	75	38	86
200 decisions	82	80	89	83	75	75	83	80	83	38	91
p_0^{100}	.100	.106	.091	.092	.106	.101	.093	.104	.096	.095	.110
p_0^{200}	.097	.090	.100	.092	.105	.105	.100	.092	.091	.093	.098
No. of thinking steps for 200 decisions:	23	23	25	15	29	27	18	22	21	14	29

The dynamic case is perhaps the most interesting one experimentally, especially where a fusion model is pitted against a human subject. Before going too far with such a program, it will be necessary to develop a better mathematical understanding of the models in order to design the experiments so as to permit statistical significance tests to be applied; this point has been discussed by Bush and Mosteller [5], and they and others are gradually developing some of the mathematical tools that are needed. We have some of these experiments under way with human subjects, using Morra and other games of about this complexity for the purpose. It would be interesting also to run some trials of exactly the same sort with real rats (e.g., playing Morra against the stat-rat).

9. AGAINST THE STAT-RAT

We have seen how the stat-rat is able to play any game with known bounds on the payments, even though we have not been able to settle the question concerning its degree of skill at games. We shall now be interested in how best to exploit this knowledge of the procedure used by the stat-rat in playing games when we are its opponent. Of course, if we know the expectation functions and have computed the solution of the game, then we can guarantee at least a certain minimum result by choosing the game-theoretic solution; our object is to do better than this safe solution guarantees, and we also should like to know how to play when we do not know the expectation functions or the theoretical solution.

As a special case, consider the ordinary game of matching pennies. We start with the reasonable assumption that the initial vector for the stat-rat is:

$$p^1(0) = \begin{pmatrix} .45 \\ .45 \\ .1 \end{pmatrix}.$$

To make the game quite definite, in our usual notation, we note that the game is usually represented by the expectation functions:

$$\overline{V}^1_{i_1 i_2} = 2\delta_{i_1 i_2} - 1, \text{ and } \overline{V}^2_{i_1 i_2} = 1 - 2\delta_{i_1 i_2}$$

We transform this game into an equivalent one, in the sense that linear transformations on the individual utility functions leave the solutions invariant, by setting:

$$V^1_{i_1 i_2} = \frac{1}{2} (\overline{V}^1_{i_1 i_2} + 1) = \delta_{i_1 i_2}, \text{ and}$$

$$V^2_{i_1 i_2} = \frac{1}{2} (\overline{V}^2_{i_1 i_2} + 1) = 1 - \delta_{i_1 i_2}.$$

No chance move is really needed, in this special case, since the values of $V^j_{i_1 i_2}$ are all zero or one. Finally, we specify that

there is to be a sequence of N plays, and our problem is to choose a method of play that will maximize our expected payments against the stat-rat. Since we can compute the $p^1(t)$ for the stat-rat at each stage, except for the steps when p_0^1 has effect, it is not difficult to find a method of play that gives us an average expectation in excess of that obtained if we play strategies 1 and 2 with equal frequencies. Such a good strategy would be for us always to play the strategy that is less likely to be chosen by the stat-rat. We shall not pursue this very simple example further, except to note that it becomes immediately more difficult if we do not know $p^1(0)$ or if the expectation functions are represented in the equivalent form:

$$\theta V_{i_1 i_2}^j \quad \text{where} \quad 0 < \theta < 1.$$

11. SUMMARY

This is a preliminary paper. In it we have shown how a player can "learn", during the course of a sequence of plays of a game, to improve his strategy. The fusion model developed by Bush and Mosteller to explain observed behavior of rats in experimental learning situations was used as the basis for both a theoretical and experimental investigation of the efficiency of this type of learning process in learning to play games. The experiments discussed here were with human subjects, and their game-learning performance was compared with that of the "stat-rat" represented by the fusion model with numerical values of the parameters estimated to fit experimental data for rats.

The theoretical models accept basic assumptions of von Neumann-Morgenstern game theory and Bush-Mosteller learning theory, including:

(a) Games with identical normal forms are equivalent, and this equivalence is independent of the probability distribution functions associated with chance moves.

(b) Games that differ only by linear transformations of the individual payoff functions are equivalent.

(c) Learning is a Markov process.

Equivalence here means that the games have the same solutions.

The experimental results consist of Monte Carlo computations for the stat-rat, contests between stat-rat and a human subject, and comparisons of performance of stat-rat and a human subject when playing the same static game. Very limited data indicate that:

(a) The stat-rat usually learns a good strategy when a constant mixed-strategy is played against him. In Morra and the other games played the stat-rat seemed to settle on essentially the best strategy within 200 trials or so.

(b) A person proficient at games would win against the stat-rat in Morra.

(c) The stat-rat does reasonably well in a static game, in comparison with the human subject, but a statistician would certainly defeat the stat-rat.

More extensive experiments are in progress, and it is hoped that these may provide the data necessary to estimate parameter values for human subjects and eventually to test the adequacy of this type of Markov process for description of human learning. It seems very unlikely now that such a Markov process will be adequate.

FOOTNOTE

1. This process has been most systematized for the art of decision by military commanders [10], [11].

BIBLIOGRAPHY

1. Bales, Robert F., Interaction Process Analysis, Cambridge, Addison Wesley Press, 1951.

2. Bales, R. F., Flood, M. M. and Householder, A. S., Some Group Interaction Models, RM-953, The RAND Corporation.

3. Boring, E. G., Mind and Mechanism, Amer. J. Psychology, 59 (1946), 173-192.

4. Bush, R. R., and Mosteller, C. F., A Mathematical Model for Simple Learning, Psych. Rev., 58 (1951), 313-323.

5. Bush, R. R., and Mosteller, C. F., A Linear Operator Model for Learning, (presented 27 December 1951) (the Institute of Mathematical Statistics).

6. Bush, R. R., and Mosteller, C. F., A Comparative Study of Three Models for Simple Learning, Memorandum VI, 21 December 1950 (Unpublished).

7. Dresher, Melvin, Theory and Applications of Games of Strategy, (Unpublished) The RAND Corporation.

8. Flood, M. M., Some Experimental Games, RM-789, The RAND Corporation.

9. Flood, M. M., On Game Learning Theory, RM-853, The RAND Corporation.

10. Haywood, O. G., Jr., Military Doctrine of Decision and the von Neumann Theory of Games, RM-528, The RAND Corporation.

11. Haywood, O. G., Jr., Military Decision and the Mathematical Theory of Games, Air Univ. Quarterly Review, 4 (1949), 17-30.

12. MacKay, D. M., Mindlike Behavior in Artefacts, The British Journal for the Philosophy of Science, 2 (1951), 105-121.

13. Skinner, B. F., The Behavior of Organisms, Appleton-Century-Crofts, 1938.

14. von Neumann, John, and Morgenstern, Oskar, Theory of Games and Economic Behavior, Princeton, 1944.

CHAPTER XI

REPRESENTATION OF A PREFERENCE
ORDERING BY A NUMERICAL FUNCTION*

by

Gerard Debreu

COWLES COMMISSION FOR RESEARCH IN ECONOMICS

1. INTRODUCTION

It has often been assumed in economics that if a set X (usually in the finite Euclidean space of commodity bundles) is completely ordered by the preferences of some agent, it is always possible to define on that set a real-valued order-preserving function (utility, satisfaction). This is easily seen to be false.[1]

The particular case where there exists on X (the set of prospects) a certain algebra of combining (corresponding to the combination of probabilities) has been rigorously and extensively studied by J. von Neumann and O. Morgenstern [7], J. Marschak [6], I. N. Herstein and J. Milnor [5].

But, rather paradoxically, the general case, which is more basic and simpler, has received little attention from economists. H. Wold's study [8] indeed seems to be the only rigorous one; its assumptions are however restrictive.

This note gives conditions under which a complete order

*Based on Cowles Commission Discussion Paper, Economics 2040 (April, 1952). This article has been prepared under contract Nonr-358(01), NR 047-006 between the Office of Naval Research and the Cowles Commission for Research in Economics, to be reprinted as a Cowles Commission Paper.

I am grateful to staff members and guests of the Cowles Commission and very particularly to I. N. Herstein for their comments. I owe to P. R. Halmos reference [4]. My greatest debt is to L. J. Savage who suggested, in the course of a valuable discussion that Cantor's postulate $x < z_i < y$ (see Lemma II) might be weakened to $x \leqq z_i \leqq y$.

(denoted by $\leqq$) can be represented by a numerical function. The most common preference ordering in economics is that of bundles of n commodities, i.e., of points of an n-dimensional Euclidean space. We shall however treat the problem in a more general frame since this involves no additional mathematical cost.

The familiar case of a set in a finite Euclidean space is covered by the following proposition which is a very special application of theorem II below:

Let X be a completely ordered subset of a finite Euclidean space. If for every x' ϵ X the sets $\{x \epsilon X | x \leqq x'\}, \{x \epsilon X | x' \leqq x\}$ are closed (in X), there exists on X a continuous, real, order-preserving function.

The assumption that the set $\{x \epsilon X | x' \leqq x\}$ is closed (in X) is equivalent to the more intuitive assumption: let (x^k) be any sequence of points in X having a limit $x° \epsilon$ X, if for all k, x^k is at least as good as x', then $x°$ is at least as good as x'.

2. TWO REPRESENTATION LEMMAS

A complete ordering on X is, to be precise, a binary relation, denoted $\leqq$, satisfying

1) Given any two elements x, y of X; $x \leqq y$ and/or $y \leqq x$
2) Given three elements of X such that $x \leqq y$, $y \leqq z$ then $x \leqq z$.

From this relation can be derived two new ones:

  $x \sim y$ (x indifferent to y) if $x \leqq y$ and $y \leqq x$
  $x < y$ (y better than x) if $x \leqq y$ and not $y \leqq x$.

The quotient set $X/\sim$, i.e., the set of indifference classes in X, will be denoted by A.[2] The trivial case where all elements of X are indifferent (i.e. where A has just one element) will always be excluded.

  The interval $[x', y']$ is the set $\{x \epsilon X | x' \leqq x \leqq y'\}$.
  The interval $]x', y'[$ is the set $\{x \epsilon X | x' < x < y'\}$.

A real-valued function $\phi(x)$ defined on X is said to be order-preserving if $x \leqq y$ is equivalent to $\phi(x) \leqq \phi(y)$.

A natural topology on X is a topology[3] for which the sets $\{x \epsilon X | x \leqq x'\}$, $\{x \epsilon X | x' \leqq x\}$ are closed for all x' ϵ X.

Lemma I. Let X be a completely ordered set whose quotient A is countable. There exists on X a real, order-preserving function, continuous[3] in any natural topology.

Rank the elements of A; it is clearly possible to construct by induction on the rank an order-preserving function ψ taking A into some finite real interval. Let $\lambda = \underset{a \epsilon A}{\text{Inf}}\ \psi(a)$, $\mu = \underset{a \epsilon A}{\text{Sup}}\ \psi(a)$.

If α' satisfies $\lambda < \alpha' < \mu$ and $\alpha' \notin \psi(A)$, four cases may occur: the set $\{\alpha\ \epsilon\ \psi(A)|\alpha < \alpha'\}$ (1) may, or (2) may not, have a largest element; and the set $\{\alpha\ \epsilon \psi(A)|\alpha' < \alpha\}$ (1') may, or (2') may not, have a smallest element. We wish to eliminate the gaps of type (1-2'), (2-1') and (2-2'); this can easily be done by means of a non-decreasing step function $\Theta(\alpha)$, the height of each step being equal to the length of the corresponding gap. The new function $\phi^*(a) = \psi(a) - \Theta[\psi(a)]$ is still order-preserving and $\phi^*(A)$ has no gaps of the unwanted types. Denote by $a(x)$ the indifference class a to which x belongs; we finally define $\phi(x) = \phi^*[a(x)]$. To show that ϕ is continuous in any natural topology on X consider a number α', $\lambda < \alpha' < \mu$ and the set $X_{\alpha'} = \{x \epsilon X|\ \phi(x) \leqq \alpha'\}$.

1) If $\alpha' \epsilon \phi(X)$, let $x' \epsilon X$ be such that $\alpha' = \phi(x')$. $X_{\alpha'} = \{x \epsilon X|x \leqq x'\}$ and is therefore closed.

2) If $\alpha' \notin \phi(X)$ and if the set $R_{\alpha'} = \{\alpha\ \epsilon\ \phi(X)|\alpha < \alpha'\}$ has a largest element α'', $X_{\alpha'} = X_{\alpha''}$ which is closed by 1).

3) If $\alpha' \notin \phi(X)$ and if the set $R_{\alpha'}$ has no largest element, then the set $R^{\alpha'} = \{\alpha\ \epsilon\ \phi(X)|\alpha' < \alpha\}$ has no smallest element since $\phi(X)$ has no gap of type (2-1'). Thus $X_{\alpha'} = \bigcap_{\alpha\ \epsilon\ R^{\alpha'}} X_{\alpha}$

and $X_{\alpha'}$ is closed as an intersection of closed sets.

Similarly one proves that for any number α' the set $X^{\alpha'} = \{x \epsilon X|\alpha' \leqq \phi(x)\}$ is closed. It follows that the inverse image by ϕ of any closed set of the real line R is a closed set of X.

Lemma II. Let X be a completely ordered set, $Z = (z_0, z_1, \cdots)$ a countable subset of X. If for every pair x,y of elements of X such that $x < y$, there is an element z_i of Z such that $x \leqq z_i \leqq y$, then there exists on X a real, order-preserving function, continuous in any natural topology.

The assumption made is a weakening of the postulate $(x < z_i < y)$ used by G. Cantor in [3].

Take first the quotient sets $X/\sim = A$ and $Z/\sim = C$. C is clearly countable and plays for A the role that Z played for X. If A has a smallest and/or a largest element, we can assume, without any loss of generality, that they are contained in C.

Define a new equivalence relation[2] among elements of A by: aFb if and only if <u>between a and b there is a finite number of elements of A</u>. The binary relation F is indeed reflexive, symmetric and transitive. Equivalence classes for F are denoted by $[a]_F$, $[b]_F$, $\cdots$

Every equivalence class is clearly countable. Moreover an equivalence class $[c]_F$ containing more than one element of A contains an element of C and thus the equivalence classes $[c]_F$ form a countable set. Summing up, C' the union over these classes $[c]_F$, is countable and so is $D = C \cup C'$.

Construct now on D the function ϕ^* as in the proof of Lemma I. ϕ^* is extended from D to A as follows. Let $a \epsilon A$ and $a \notin D$; the set $D_a = \{d \epsilon D | d < a\}$ has no largest element. To see this consider any $d' \epsilon D_a$. Since $a \notin D$, $a \notin C'$ and there is an infinity of elements of A between d' and a, there is therefore an infinity of elements of C, i.e. of D, between d' and a. Similarly the set $D^a = \{d \epsilon D | a < d\}$ has no smallest element. As a consequence the values $\underset{d \epsilon D_a}{\text{Sup}} \phi^*(d)$ and $\underset{d \epsilon D^a}{\text{Inf}} \phi^*(d)$ are not taken on. Moreover these two values are equal since $\phi^*(D)$ has no gap of the (2-2') type; they define $\phi^*(a)$. The function $\phi^*(a)$, and therefore the function $\phi(x) = \phi^*[a(x)]$, are clearly order-preserving and, since $\phi(X) = \phi^*(A)$ has no gaps of types (1-2') or (2-1'), $\phi(x)$ is continuous in any natural topology on X (the proof is the same as for Lemma I).

3. TWO REPRESENTATION THEOREMS

Before stating Theorem I we recall two definitions. A (topological) space X is <u>separable</u> if it contains a countable subset whose closure is X. A (topological) space X is <u>connected</u> if there is no partition of X into two disjoint, non-empty, closed sets.

<u>Theorem I</u>. Let X be a completely ordered, separable, and connected space. If for every $x' \epsilon X$ the sets $\{x \epsilon X | x \leqq x'\}$ and $\{x \epsilon X | x' \leqq x\}$ are closed, there exists on X a continuous, real, order-preserving function.[4]

This theorem can easily be derived from the results of S. Eilenberg [4]. It will be proved here as an immediate consequence of Lemma II. A much more direct proof could assuredly be given: the motivation for the two lemmas is Theorem II.

Call Z the countable set dense in X and consider a pair x', y' of elements of X such that $x' < y'$. The sets $\{x \in X | x \leqq x'\}$ and $\{x \in X | y' \leqq x\}$ are disjoint, non-empty and closed, they cannot exhaust X which is connected, therefore the open interval $]x', y'[$ is not empty, and it must contain an element $z_i \in Z$. The theorem is proved since the topology on X is a natural topology.

The assumption of connectedness is however very strong. We give a second theorem where it is removed at the cost of a slightly stronger separability assumption.

A topological space X is perfectly separable if there is a countable class (S) of open sets such that every open set in X is the union of sets of the class (S).

We remark that a separable metric space is perfectly separable, that a subspace of a perfectly separable space is perfectly separable.

Theorem II. Let X be a completely ordered, perfectly separable space. If for every $x' \in X$ the sets $\{x \in X | x \leqq x'\}$ and $\{x \in X | x' \leqq x\}$ are closed, there exists on X a continuous, real, order-preserving function.

Choose an element in each non-empty set S; they form a countable set Z".

Consider then the pairs a', b' of elements of A such that $a' < b'$ and the interval $]a', b'[$ is empty. The set of those pairs is countable. To see this, associate with each such pair a set $S_{b'}$ as follows: take two elements x', y' in the indifference classes a', b' respectively. The set $\{x \in X | x < y'\}$ is open and therefore there exists a set $S_{b'}$ in the class (S) such that $x' \in S_{b'} \subset \{x \in X | x < y'\}$. If a'', b'' is another pair with the same properties, $S_{b''}$ is different from $S_{b'}$ for one has $a' < b' \leqq a'' < b''$, in which case $x'' \in S_{b''}$ and $x'' \notin S_{b'}$ or $a'' < b'' \leqq a' < b'$, in which case $x' \in S_{b'}$ and $x' \notin S_{b''}$. The pairs a', b' are thus in one-to-one correspondence with a subclass of the countable class (S). Choose then an element x' in each class a' and an element y' in each class b'. All those x' and y' form a countable set Z'.

Consider finally the countable set $Z = Z' \cup Z''$; it has all the properties required by Lemma II. Let x, y be a pair of elements of X such that $x < y$. If the open set $]x, y[$ is not empty, it contains a non-empty set S and therefore an element of Z". If the set $]x,y[$ is empty, $x \sim x' \epsilon Z'$ and $y \sim y' \epsilon Z'$. So that in any case $[x,y]$ contains an element of Z.

FOOTNOTES

1. Consider the lexicographic ordering of the plane: a point of coordinates (a',b') is better than the point (a,b) if "a' > a" or if "a' = a and b' > b". Suppose that there exists a real order-preserving function α (a,b). Take two fixed numbers $b_1 < b_2$ and with a number a associate the two numbers $\alpha_1(a) = \alpha (a,b_1)$ and $\alpha_2(a,b_2)$. To two different numbers a,a' correspond two disjoint intervals $[\alpha_1(a), \alpha_2(a)]$ and $[\alpha_1(a'), \alpha_2(a')]$. One obtains therefore a one-to-one correspondence between the set of real numbers (non-countable) and a set of non-degenerate disjoint intervals (countable).

2. For definitions relating to an equivalence relation see [1].

3. For definitions of a topology and of a continuous function see [2, § 1] and [2, § 4] respectively.

4. The closedness assumptions have already been used in a similar context by I. N. Herstein in an earlier unpublished version of [5].

BIBLIOGRAPHY

1. Bourbaki, N., Eléments de Mathématique Première partie, Livre I (Fascicule de résultats) § 5. Paris, Hermann, 1939.

2. Bourbaki, N., Eléments de Mathématique Première partie, Livre III Chap. I. Paris, Hermann, 1940.

3. Cantor, G., Beiträge zur Begründung der transfiniten Mengenlehre, §11 Mathematische Annalen Vol. 46, 1895, p. 481-512.

4. Eilenberg, S., Ordered Topological Spaces, American Journal of Mathematics, Vol. 63, Jan. 1941, p. 39-45.

5. Herstein, I. N. and Milnor, J., An Axiomatic Approach to Measurable Utility, Econometrica, Vol. 23, April 1953, p. 291-297.

6. Marschak, J., Rational Behavior, Uncertain Prospects, and Measurable Utility, Econometrica, Vol. 18, April 1950, p. 111-141.

7. von Neumann, J. and Morgenstern, O., Theory of Games and Economic Behavior, Section 3 and Appendix, Princeton University Press, 1947.

8. Wold, H., A Synthesis of Pure Demand Analysis, Part II Skandinavisk Aktuarietidkrift, Vol. 26, 1943, p. 220-263.

REFERENCES AND FURTHER READING

1.

2.

CHAPTER XII

MULTIDIMENSIONAL UTILITIES

by

Melvin Hausner

RAND CORPORATION

1. INTRODUCTION

This paper generalizes the von Neumann and Morgenstern theory of utility by omitting the Archimedean postulate. The work was done originally at The RAND Corporation in the summer of 1951 by N. Dalkey and R. M. Thrall. Refined methods were introduced by J. G. Wendel and the author in order to simplify the work and extend it to the infinite dimensional case.

Two distinct concepts enter into a formulation of utility theory: the set of prospects, which we shall call the mixture space and the ordering or utility on this set. For convenience we shall treat the mixture space first (axioms M1 - M5) and then introduce the ordering axioms (O1 - O3). The two sets of axioms, taken together, characterize a utility space. As an intermediate step, we shall consider a weak utility space, where axioms O1 - O3 are weakened. The weakened axioms are still strong enough to permit identification of "indifferent" elements and still preserve the operations of mixture and order.

The main result is that a mixture space may be embedded in a vector space; a utility space may be embedded in an ordered vector space. The last section characterizes ordered vector spaces.

2. ALGEBRAIC PRELIMINARIES

We now introduce the following notation, to be useful in what follows. Let S be any subset of a vector space V over the real numbers. We define:

$C(S)$ = the convex closure of S
= the set of elements $X \in V$ which are of the form
$X = \Sigma x_i S_i$ where $x_i > 0$, $\Sigma x_i = 1$, $S_i \in S$.

$P(S)$ = the cone generated by S

     = the set of $X \in V$ which are of the form $X = \Sigma x_i S_i$ where $x_i > 0$, $S_i \in S$.

$H(S)$ = the hyperplane generated by S

     = the set of $X \in V$ which are of the form $X = \Sigma x_i S_i$ where $\Sigma x_i = 1$, $S_i \in S$.

$V(S)$ = the vector space generated by S

     = the set of elements X of the form $X = \Sigma x_i S_i$ where $S_i \in S$.

The above sums are taken to be finite. We note that $C(S) \subseteq P(S)$, $H(S) \subseteq V(S)$.

I. The set $P(S)$ is closed under addition and scalar multiplication by positive reals. Such a set is called a cone. In the course of various embeddings to be carried out, it happens that it is frequently more natural to embed in a cone rather than in a vector space. A cone C may be characterized by the following properties (see §3, P1 – P8 for the complete set of axioms):

1. C is a commutative semigroup with cancellation under the operation +.

2. C is closed under scalar multiplication by positive reals. The usual associative and distributive laws are satisfied.

If C is a cone, it is possible to embed C in a vector space V so that addition and scalar multiplication in C may be extended to V and so that C generates V. This embedding is unique and may be accomplished by the familiar method of first embedding C in a group C' under + (cf. [3], p. 43, where a ring is embedded in a field). The group C' may be made into a vector space by defining

$$x(A-B) = xA - xB; \quad x > 0$$
$$0(A-B) = 0 \quad ;$$
$$-x(A-B) = xB - xA; \quad x > 0,\ A,\ B \in C.$$

We may then verify that C' is a vector space V and $C = P(C)$, $V = V(C)$.

II. If S is a convex subset of V $(C(S) = S)$, then $P(S)$ consists of elements of the form xA where $x > 0$ and $A \in S$. We seek a condition (given that S is convex) that this representation is unique. First, suppose the representation is not unique. Then $x_1 A_1 = x_2 A_2$ where $x_1 \neq x_2$ or $x_1 = x_2$ and $A_1 \neq A_2$. In the first case, we may assume (by dividing by $x_1 - x_2$) that $x_1 - x_2 = 1$. Then $0 = x_1 A_1 - x_2 A_2 \in H(S)$. The second case $x_1 = x_2 > 0$ is impossible. Conversely, suppose $0 \in H(S)$. Then $0 = \Sigma x_i A_i$

where $\Sigma x_i = 1$. By transposing, if necessary, we obtain $\Sigma y_i A_i = \Sigma z_i A_i$ where $y_i > 0$, $z_i > 0$ and $\Sigma y_i \neq \Sigma z_i$. This gives two different representations of the element $\Sigma y_i A_i$ in the form xA, $A \epsilon S$, since the x may be taken to be Σy_i and Σz_i. Thus, a necessary and sufficient condition that any element in $P(S)$ be represented uniquely in the form xA is that $0 \notin H(S)$.

III. We set down some definitions concerning orderings for future reference.

A relation R on a set M is said to be complete if for every pair A,B in M either ARB or BRA holds. A relation $\lesssim$ on M is said to be a weak order if it is reflexive, transitive and complete. A relation $\leqq$ on M is said to be a chain order if it is antisymmetric, transitive, and complete. If $\leqq$ is a chain order and we define $A < B$ to mean $A \leqq B$ but $A \neq B$ then $<$ is easily seen to be asymmetric, transitive and trichotomous (i.e. exactly one of $A < B$, $A = B$, or $B < A$ holds). Conversely, if $<$ is asymmetric, transitive, and trichotomous and $A \leqq B$ is defined to mean $A < B$ or $A = B$, then $\leqq$ gives a chain order. If either of the symbols $<$ or $\leqq$ has been introduced we will consider the other to be defined as above. We use $>$ and $\geqq$ to denote the transposes of $<$ and $\leqq$, i.e. $B > A$ means $A < B$ and $B \geqq A$ means $A \leqq B$.

3. MIXTURE SPACES

A mixture space is a set $M = \{A, B, \ldots\}$ which satisfies the following axioms:

M1. For any $A, B \epsilon M$ and for any real p, $0 \leqq p \leqq 1$, the p mixture of A and B, denoted by ApB, is a uniquely defined element of M.

M2. $ApB = B(1-p)A$

M3. $Ap(BrC) = (A\dfrac{p}{p+r-pr}B)(p+r-pr)C, \quad [(1-p)(1-r) \neq 1]$

M4. $ApA = A$

M5. If $ApC = BpC$ for some $p > 0$, then $A = B$.

Taking $r = 0$ and $B = C$ in M3, we have with the help of M4

$$ApB = Ap(B0B) = (A1B)pB.$$

By the cancellation law (M5) we obtain

M6. $A1B = A$.

If V is a vector space, we may define $ApB = pA + (1-p)B$. It is then easily shown that V is a mixture space. We shall show that this is the most general mixture space: any mixture space is isomorphic to a convex subset of a vector space.

The embedding of M will be accomplished by first embedding M in a cone P and then, as indicated in §2, embedding P in a vector space V. We shall be concerned only with the embedding in a cone. For convenience, we set down the axioms for a cone which were suggested in §2. A cone P is a set $\{A, B, \ldots\}$ satisfying the following axioms:

P1. There is an operation $+$ in P such that $A + B$ is a uniquely determined element of P, where $A, B \in P$. Scalar multiplication by positive real numbers x is defined so that xA is a uniquely defined element of P.

P2. $A + B = B + A$

P3. $A + (B+C) = (A+B) + C$

P4. If $A + B = A + C$ then $B = C$

P5. $x(A+B) = xA + xB, \ x > 0$

P6. $(x+y)A = xA + yA$

P7. $x(yA) = (xy)A$

P8. $1 \cdot A = A$

Given the mixture space M, we define the set P to be the space of all ordered couples (x, A) where $x > 0$, $A \in M$, and we formally write $(x, A) = xA$. Thus $xA = yB$ if and only if $x = y$ and $A = B$. (Later, A will be identified with $1 \cdot A$ and this definition of equality simply places M in V in such a way that $0 \notin H(M)$. An extraneous dimension is thus introduced.)

The set P being defined, we now define addition and scalar multiplication in P.

D1. $r(sA) = rs(A)$

D2. $rA + sB = (r+s)A \dfrac{r}{r+s} B.$

And we now verify that P is a cone.

P1. is trivial.

$$
\begin{aligned}
\text{P2.} \quad rA + sB &= (r+s)A \frac{r}{r+s} B & \text{(D2)} \\
&= (s+r)B \frac{s}{r+s} A & \text{(M2)} \\
&= sB + rA & \text{(D2).}
\end{aligned}
$$

$$
\begin{aligned}
\text{P3.} \quad rA + (sB+tC) &= rA + (s+t)B \frac{s}{s+t} C \\
&= (r+s+t)[A \frac{r}{r+s+t} (B \frac{s}{s+t} C)].
\end{aligned}
$$

Similarly,

$$(rA+sB) + tC = (r+s+t)\left[(A\frac{r}{r+s}B)\frac{r+s}{r+s+t}C\right].$$

With the help of M3 it may be verified that

$$A\frac{r}{r+s+t}(B\frac{s}{s+t}C) = (A\frac{r}{r+s}B)\frac{r+s}{r+s+t}C,$$

which proves P3.

P4. If $rA + sB = rA + tC$, then

$$(r+s)A\frac{r}{r+s}B = (r+t)A\frac{r}{r+t}C.$$

Hence, $s = t$ and by M5, $B = C$. Thus $sB = tC$ proving P4.

P5. $x(rA+sB) = x(r+s)(A\frac{r}{r+s}B)$

$\qquad\qquad = (xr+xs)(A\frac{xrs}{xr+xs}B)$

$\qquad\qquad = (xr)A + (xs)B$

$\qquad\qquad = x(rA) + x(sB)$

P6. $(x+y)rA = (xr+yr)A$

$\qquad\qquad = (xr+yr)(A\frac{xr}{xr+yr}A) \qquad\qquad (M4)$

$\qquad\qquad = (xr)A + (yr)A$

$\qquad\qquad = x(rA) + y(rA).$

P7. $x(y(rA)) = x(yrA) = (xyr)A = (xy)(rA)$

P8. $1 \cdot (rA) = (1 \cdot r)A = rA.$

P is thus a cone. If $A \in M$, we define $f(A) = 1 \cdot A \in P$ to obtain the following lemma.

Lemma 3.1. There is a function f mapping M into a cone P in such a manner that

1) f is 1-1 into P.
2) $f(ApB) = pf(A) + (1-p)f(B)$ for $0 < p < 1$.

Proof: Define $f(A) = 1 \cdot A$. Then 1) is a consequence of definition of equality in P and 2) is verified by the following computation:

$$f(ApB) = 1 \cdot ApB$$
$$= (p+(1-p))\, ApB$$
$$= pA + (1-p)B$$
$$= p(1 \cdot A) + (1-p)(1 \cdot B)$$
$$= pf(A) + (1-p)f(B).$$

As in § 1, the cone P may be taken to be a cone in some vector space V which is generated by P. The statement of the embedding theorem follows.

Theorem 3.2. Let M be a mixture space. Then there exists a vector space V over the real numbers and a function f mapping M into V such that

1. f is one-one into V.
2. $f(ApB) = pf(A) + (1-p)f(B)$, $0 \le p \le 1$.
3. $f(M) = C(f(M))$, i.e., $f(M)$ is convex.
4. $V = V(f(M))$.
5. $0 \notin H(f(M))$.

Proof: Let V be generated by the cone P of Lemma 1. Then 1. and 2. are true by Lemma 1. (The cases $p = 0$ and $p = 1$ are trivial by M6.) To prove that $f(M)$ is convex, observe that if $A', B' \in f(M)$, so that $A' = f(A)$, $B' = f(B)$, then $pA' + (1-p)B' = f(ApB) \in f(M)$ by 2. Hence $f(M)$ is convex. Since $f(M)$ generates P (because the elements $1 \cdot A$ in the proof of Lemma 1 generate P) and P generates V we have 4. As for 5., we need to prove that if $xf(A) = yf(B)$ for $x,y > 0$ then $x = y$ and $f(A) = f(B)$. In terms of the cone P of Lemma 1, we have $xA = yB$ so that $x = y$ and $A = B$, proving the result.

We now prove that the embedding is unique. To do this we first prove the following algebraic lemma.

Lemma 3.3. Let V and V' be vector spaces with elements $x,y,z \ldots$ and $x',y',z' \ldots$ respectively. Let C and C' be convex subsets of V and V' respectively and let $0 \notin H(C)$, $0 \notin H(C')$, $V = V(C)$, $V' = V'(C)$. Let g map C onto C' in such a way that

a. g is one-one from C onto C'.
b. $g(pA+(1-p)B) = pg(A) + (1-p)g(B)$ for $0 < p < 1$ and $A,B \in C$.

Then g may be extended in one and only one way to all of V such that

a'. g is one-one from V into V'.
b'. g is linear.

(Thus, if $X = \sum_i x_i A_i$, $A_i \in C$, then $g(X) = \sum x_i g(A_i)$, and this extension of g is uniquely defined and satisfies a'. and b'.)

Proof: Obviously there is at most one extension. Let us first extend g to $P(C)$, by defining $g(xA) = xg(A)$ where $x > 0$ and $A \in C$. (Observe that since C is convex, and $0 \notin H(C)$, xA is the most general element of $P(C)$. There is no question of whether g is properly defined, since the representation xA is unique.

First, g is one-one onto $P(C')$. g is one-one since if $xg(A) = yg(B)$ with $x,y > 0$, $A,B \in M$, we have $g(A)$, $g(B) \in C'$ and two representations of an element in $P(C')$. Hence $x = y$ and $g(A) = g(B)$, and therefore $A = B$. That g is onto $P(C')$ is clear.

Next, g is additive on $P(C)$. For we have

$$g(xA+yB) = g(x+y)[\frac{x}{x+y}A + \frac{y}{x+y}B]$$

$$= (x+y)g(A\frac{x}{x+y}B)$$

$$= (x+y)[g(A)\frac{x}{x+y}g(B)] \quad \text{(by b)}$$

$$= xg(A) + yg(B)$$

$$= g(xA) + g(yB).$$

Finally, g is homogeneous. For,

$$g(x(yA)) = g(xyA)$$

$$= xyg(A)$$

$$= xg(yA).$$

We now extend g to V. Let $R, S, T, U, \ldots$ denote elements of $P(C)$. The most general element X of V is of the form $X = R - S$. Define $g(x) = g(R) - g(S)$. g is properly defined, since if $R - S = T - U$ then $R + U = S + T$, $g(R) + g(U) = g(S) + g(T)$ (by additivity of g on $P(C)$) and hence $g(R) - g(S) = g(T) - g(U)$. We now prove a' and b'.

It is easily verified, from the additivity and homogeneity, that g is linear. To prove that it is one-one, assume $g(X) = 0$. Letting $X = R - S$, we have $g(R-S) = 0$, $g(R) = g(S)$. Hence, since g was shown to be one-one on $P(C')$, $R = S$ and $S = 0$. Finally, g clearly maps V onto V' and this proves the lemma.

Theorem 3.4 (Uniqueness). Let M be a mixture space and let V and V' be vector spaces. Suppose f maps M into V and f' maps M into V' as in Theorem 3.1. Then V and V' are isomorphic under a mapping g which sends an element $X = \Sigma x_i f(A_i)$ $(A_i \in M)$ into $g(X) = \Sigma x_i f'(A_i)$.

Proof: By Lemma 3.3 applied to the function $g = f'f^{-1}$.

The above discussion has not depended on the dimension of V. If the (essentially unique) V of Theorem 1 is (n+1)-dimensional, then we say that the mixture space M is n-dimensional. In this case, M is simply an n-dimensional convex set.

4. UTILITY SPACES

A utility space is a mixture space M with an order relation $\leqq$ imposed on its structure. In accord with §3, we assume that M is a convex subset of a vector space V with $V = V(M)$, $0 \notin H(M)$. The relation $\leqq$ is required to satisfy the following axioms:

O1. The relation $\leqq$ is a chain order on M.
O2. If $A < B$ and $0 < p < 1$, then $pA + (1-p)C < pB + (1-p)C$.

Observe that the converse of O2 holds since $<$ is a trichotomous, asymmetric ordering.

Before considering utility spaces, we shall consider weak utility spaces. These are mixture spaces with an ordering $\lesssim$ satisfying

W1. The relation $\lesssim$ is a weak order on M.
W2. If $A \lesssim B$ then $ApC \lesssim BpC$ for $0 < p < 1$.
W3. If $ApC \lesssim BpC$ for some p such that $0 < p < 1$, then $A \lesssim B$.

Definition 4.1. $A \sim B$ if and only if $A \lesssim B$ and $B \lesssim A$.

It is easily verified that this is an equivalence relation. Let [A] be the equivalence class containing A, i.e., $X \in [A]$ if and only if $X \sim A$.

Definition 4.2. $[A] \leqq [B]$ if and only if $A \lesssim B$.

It is then seen that the relation $\leqq$ on the equivalence classes is a chain order. Let M' be the set of equivalence classes. We make M' into a mixture space by defining

$$[A]p[B] = [ApB].$$

With the help of W2, it is easily verified that this definition is unique. That M' is a mixture space follows from the fact that M is one.

To prove O2, assume $0 < p \lessgtr 1$ and $[A] < [B]$. Since $A \lesssim B$ we have $pA + (1-p)C \lesssim pB + (1-p)C$. We need only prove that $pB + (1-p)C \not\lesssim pA + (1-p)C$. But assume that

$$pB + (1-p)C \lesssim pA + (1-p)C .$$

By W3, we would have $B \lesssim A$, hence $A \sim B$, $[A] = [B]$ which contradicts $[A] < [B]$. Hence O2 is verified.

We see that W2 was needed to define mixtures, W3 to define order.

Given a weak utility space M, we identify elements by the above process to obtain a utility space M'. Any information obtained on M' will then be reflected in M. For this reason we consider only utility spaces.

An ordered vector space V is one which satisfies the following axioms:

V1. There is a chain order $\geq$ on V'.
V2. If $A > B$ then $A + C > B + C$ for A, B, C, ϵ V.
V3. If $A > B$ and $x > 0$ then $xA > xB$.

An ordered vector space is thus a utility space. Axioms O1 and O2 are easily seen to hold. The purpose of this section is to embed a utility space in an ordered vector space. Since the utility space M is embedded in the vector space V as a mixture space, it suffices to extend the order relationship from M to V. We assume that $V = V(M)$ and $0 \notin H(M)$. The order relation will first be extended to $P = P(M)$ and then to $V = V(P)$.

To extend the order on M to $P = P(M)$, we define

$$xA > yB \text{ if and only if } x > y$$

or

$$x = y \text{ and } A > B \text{ for } x, y > 0; \; A, B \; \epsilon \; M.$$

We now verify V1, V2 and V3.

V1 is trivially verifiable.

V2. Assume $xA > yB$. We must prove that $xA + zC > yB + zC$. But $xA + zC = (x+z) A \dfrac{x}{x+z} C$ and $yB + zC = (y+z) B \dfrac{y}{y+z} C$. If $x > y$, we have the result, since $x + z > y + z$. If $x = y$, then $x + z = y + z$ and since $A > B$, we have $A \dfrac{x}{x+z} C > B \dfrac{y}{y+z} C$ by O2. Hence $xA + zC > yA + zC$ in any case.

V3.　Let $xA > yB$.　Then the condition $rxA > ryB$ is equivalent to the condition $xA > yB$.　This proves V3.

Finally, the order on P will be extended to V by defining

$A - B > C - D$　if and only if　$A + D > B + C$　for $A, B, C, D \epsilon$ P.

It is easily seen that the definition is unique and we omit this proof.　We now verify the axioms V1, V2 and V3.

V1 is trivially true.

V2.　Let $A - B > C - D$.　We must prove that

$$(A-B) + (E-F) > (C-D) + (E-F) \text{ for } A, B, \ldots F \epsilon P.$$

But we have $A + D > B + C$.　Hence $A + D + E + F > B + C + E + F$. By definition, we have $(A+E) - (B+F) > (C+E) - (D+F)$.　Hence, by rearranging, we have the result.

V3.　If $A - B > C - D$ and $x > 0$, we have

$$A + D > B + C,$$
$$xA + xD > xB + xC,$$
$$xA - xB > xC - xD,$$
$$x(A-B) > x(C-D).$$

Thus, the utility space M is embedded in an ordered vector space V.　As we have mentioned before, an extraneous dimension has been introduced since $0 \notin H(M)$.　The dimension of M has been defined as the dimension of H(M).　Once the above embedding has been carried out it is an easy matter to embed M in a vector space of its own dimension.　To do this we simply embed $H(M) \supset M$ in a vector space by selecting any point $A \epsilon H(M)$ and defining $f(X) = X - A$ for $X \epsilon H(M)$.　The image of H(M) is then a vector space whose dimension is H(M).　Moreover, f is one-one and f preserves convex combinations and order.　This seemingly roundabout method of introducing an extra dimension greatly simplifies the embedding procedure since all of our embeddings seem to be accomplished easily by first extending definitions to P(M) where $0 \notin H(M)$.　Lastly, it should be pointed out that the "proper" embedding should be thought of as an embedding in an affine space, since the relations of p-mixtures and order are preserved under the affine group.　We use a vector space for convenience in manipulation.

5. ORDERED VECTOR SPACES

We now proceed to characterize ordered vector spaces. The definition has been given in §4 by axioms V1, V2 and V3. It is convenient to introduce equivalent substitutes for V2 and V3 as follows:

V2' If $A > 0$, $B > 0$ then $A + B > 0$
V3' If $A > 0$, $x > 0$ then $xA > 0$.

We have

$$A > B \text{ if and only if } A - B > 0.$$

Thus the order is determined by the positive elements which we denote by V^+. V2' and V3' imply that V^+ is a cone. Since the order is a total order and is irreflexive, V^+ is a maximal cone not containing 0.

We now introduce a definition which reflects the failure of the Archimedean property. Let A, $B \in V^+$ $(A, B > 0)$. Then we say that A dominates B if $A > xB$ for all real $x > 0$. We write this as $A >> B$ or $B << A$. This is defined only for positive elements of V. The relation $<<$ is irreflexive and transitive; and $A << B$ implies $A < B$. Given A and B, if neither $A << B$ nor $B << A$ we write $A \sim B$: A is equivalent to B. This is the same as saying $A \sim B$ if and only if $xA < B < yA$ for some positive reals x and y. Again this is defined for $A, B \in V^+$. The relation $\sim$ is seen to be an equivalence relation. We denote by $[A]$ the equivalence class containing A. We may then define $[A] > [B]$ to mean $A << B$. We then have a total order on the equivalence classes, since this definition may be seen to depend only on the equivalence classes and not on their representatives. The seemingly irrelevant reversal of order is for later convenience.

Lemma 5.1. If $A >> B$ and $C > 0$ then $A + C >> B$.

Proof: If $x > 0$, then $A > xB$. Hence $A + C > xB$.

Lemma 5.2. If $A >> A_1, A_2, \ldots, A_n$ and $x_1, \ldots, x_n > 0$, then $A >> x_1 A_1 + \ldots + x_n A_n$.

Proof: If $x > 0$ we have

$$A > nx \, x_i A_i$$

Summing and dividing by n, we have

$$A > x(x_1 A_1 + \ldots x_n A_n),$$

proving the lemma.

Lemma 5.3. If $A \gg A_1, \ldots, A_n$ and $x, x_1, \ldots, x_n > 0$, then

$$xA + x_1A_1 + \ldots + x_kA_k \gg x_{k+1}A_{k+1} + \ldots + x_nA_n.$$

Proof: By Lemmas 5.1 and 5.2.

Corollary 5.4. If $\{A_t\}$ is a set of elements of V^+ no two of which are equivalent, then the A_t are linearly independent.

Proof: If there is a linear relation among the A_t, then we will obtain a relation of the form

$$xA + x_1A_1 + \ldots + x_kA_k = x_{k+1}A_{k+1} + \ldots + x_nA_n,$$

where the x's are positive, the A's belong to the given set, and $A \gg A_1, \ldots, A_n$. But this contradicts Lemma 5.3.

As usual, we define $|A| = \pm A$ according as A is non-negative or negative. The usual laws apply:

$$|A + B| \leqq |A| + |B|$$

$$|xA| = |x| |A|.$$

With this notation we may state the following important lemma:

Lemma 5.5. Let $A \sim |B|$. Then there is a unique real number x such that $xA = B$ or $|xA - B| \ll A$.

Proof: The uniqueness of x is immediate, for if $x_1 \neq x_2$ we have

$$|(x_1-x_2)A| \leqq |x_1A - y| + |x_2A - y|,$$

and if the terms on the right were zero or dominated by A we should have $A \ll A$.

To prove that such an x exists, we assume that $B > 0$ with no loss in generality. Since $A \sim B$, we have $yA < B < zA$ for some positive real numbers y and z. Let x be the supremum of the numbers y for which $yA < B$. Let $\mathcal{E} > 0$ be an arbitrary positive real number. Then we have

$$(x-\mathcal{E})A < B < (x+\mathcal{E})A,$$

$$-\mathcal{E}A < B - xA < \mathcal{E}A,$$

$$|B - xA| < \mathcal{E}A.$$

Then either $B - xA = 0$ or $|B - xA| \ll A$ by definition.

We may now easily characterize finite dimensional ordered vector space. The result is known (see p. 240, [1]) but we give it here as an illustration of the method used for the general (infinite-dimensional) case.

Theorem 5.6. Let V be a finite dimensional ordered vector space. A basis $A_1, A_2, \ldots, A_n$ may be chosen so that the ordering in V is lexicographic, i.e., so that

$$A = \sum_{i=1}^{n} x_i A_i > 0$$

if and only if the first non-vanishing x_i is positive.

Proof: Let V^+ be decomposed into equivalence classes as above. For each equivalence class t, let A_t be an arbitrary element of it. By Corollary 5.4, the set $\{A_t\}$ is finite. We choose the notation so that $A_1, \ldots, A_k$ are the representatives and $A_1 >> A_2 >> \ldots >> A_k$. Moreover, $k \leqq n = $ dimension of V.

Let $A \epsilon V$. If $A \neq 0$ then $|A|$ belongs to some equivalence class, say $|A| \sim A_{t_1}$. By Lemma 5.5, either $A = x_1 A_{t_1}$ or $|A - x_1 A_{t_1}| << A_{t_1}$. We repeat the process on $A - x_1 A_{t_1}$ if it is not zero and continue until the zero element is reached. (It must be reached in $\leqq k$ steps.) Thus A is a linear combination of the A_i's; and since A was arbitrary it follows that the A's constitute a basis for V. Thus k = n.

Now let

$$A = \sum x_i A_i .$$

By Lemma 5.3, $A > 0$ if and only if the first non-vanishing coefficient x_i is positive. This completes the proof. Observe that a basis $A_1, \ldots, A_n$ is a lexicographic basis if and only if $A_i > 0$ and $A_1 >> \ldots >> A_n$.

Theorem 5.7. Let $A_1, \ldots, A_n$ and $A'_1, \ldots, A'_n$ be basis elements in the sense of Theorem 5.6. Then $A'_i = TA_i$ where T is a lower triangular matrix with positive diagonal elements. Conversely, if T is such a matrix and $A_1, \ldots, A_n$ constitute a lexicographic basis then so do $TA_1, \ldots, TA_n$.

Proof: We have $A_1 >> \ldots >> A_n$ and $A'_1 >> \ldots >> A'_n$. Hence $A_i \sim A'_i$. Thus $A'_i = x_i A_i + $ terms dominated by A_i by Lemma 5.5. $A'_i = x_i A_i + x_{i+1} A_{i+1} + \ldots$ where $x_i > 0$. This proves the first part of the theorem. For the second part, we observe that $TA_i \sim A_i$. Hence $TA_1 >> \ldots >> TA_n$ proving the second part.

In terms of coordinates, we may state Theorem 5.6 as follows: With respect to some basis, the vector $X = (x_1, \ldots, x_n) > 0$ if and only if $x_1 > 0$ or $x_1 = 0$, $x_2 > 0, \ldots,$ or $x_1 = \ldots x_{n-1} = 0$, $x_n > 0$.

In order to consider the infinite dimensional case, we define a lexicographic ordered vector space as follows: Let T be a totally ordered set. Let V_T be the set of all real valued functions on T which vanish except on some well ordered subset of T. We define $f > 0$ if $f \neq 0$ and if $f(t_0) > 0$ where t_0 is the first t for which $f(t) \neq 0$. It is easily verified that V_T is an ordered vector space. For T finite, we get the finite-dimension ordered vector spaces. It may then be shown that the ordered set T is order-isomorphic to the ordered set of equivalence classes in V_T. If V is any ordered vector space, we let T be the set of equivalence classes with the previous definition of order. Then the result is that V is embeddable in a subspace of V_T which contains the characteristic functions of points. The proof is by transfinite induction. The details appear in [2].

BIBLIOGRAPHY

1. Birkhoff, Garrett, Lattice Theory, New York, 1948.

2. Hausner, Melvin and Wendel, J. G., Ordered Vector Spaces, Proc. Amer. Math. Soc., 3 (1952), 977-982.

3. van der Waerden, B. L., Moderne Algebra, Berlin, 1937.

CHAPTER XIII

APPLICATIONS OF
MULTIDIMENSIONAL UTILITY THEORY*

by

Robert M. Thrall

UNIVERSITY OF MICHIGAN

In the preceding chapter a set of axioms was given for a
(non-Archimedean) utility space. This chapter is a continuation
and amplification of the preceding one. In the first part the axioms are studied with special attention to the consequences of
weakening certain of them. In the second part several applications of non-Archimedean utilities are presented.

1. DISCUSSION OF THE MIXTURE SPACE AXIOMS

We recall that a mixture space is a set $M = \{A, B, \ldots\}$ of
elements called <u>prospects</u>, which satisfies the following axioms:

M1. For any $A, B \in M$ and for any real p, $0 \leqq p \leqq 1$, the p-
mixture of A and B, denoted by ApB, is a uniquely
defined element of M.

M2. $ApB = B(1 - p)A$

M3. $Ap(BrC) = (A \frac{p}{p+r-pr} B)(p+r-pr)C$

M4. $ApA = A$

M5. If $ApC = BpC$ for some $p > 0$, then $A = B$.

The closure axiom M1 is clearly essential for any mathematical development. In interpreting this axiom in the real
world we conceive of ApB as being the prospect of being given

---

*Most of the results described in this paper were obtained under
Contract Nonr: 374 (00) with the Office of Naval Research, but
some of them (especially in section 3) spring from work done at
RAND in the summer of 1951. The author wishes to acknowledge
the contribution made by Dr. Norman Dalkey of RAND Corporation during a series of informal discussions on the general subject of utility theory.

exactly one of the propects A and B, with the probability p of
getting A. Thus, automobile 1/100 candy bar could be realized
by a ticket in a 100-ticket lottery in which there was to be one
automobile prize and 99 candy bar prizes. This lottery interpretation fails if p is an irrational number. For example, if
p = 1/π then ApB cannot be interpreted as a lottery prize.
Again, although one can construct lotteries for such prospects
as A .55555 B and A .55556 B, it is questionable whether an
individual could distinguish between them in any natural setting.
Clearly, in any real-world case there is a limit to discrimination
just as there are natural limits to the accuracy of measurement
of length. Limitation of discriminatory capacity cannot be any
more serious as an objection to the use of real numbers p in
this theory than it would be in the theory of physical measurements. However, in applications of this theory one must take
care to avoid using conclusions which depend essentially on
exact discrimination.

   If in any interpretation axiom M1 is accepted then axioms
M2 and M4 are relatively uncontroversial. Axiom M3 is a
kind of associative law which will certainly be valid in any application if the judge proceeds according to actuarial principles.
However, its truth in a psychological sense is far from evident.
It would seem desirable, therefore, to test it experimentally to
see at least how the errors involved in using it in a real world
situation compare with errors that come from discriminatory
limitations.

   A recent experiment, reported in [2], seems to indicate that
evaluation of a prospect ApB depends not only on the value of p
but also on the manner of presentation. For example, consider
two punch boards each with one winning place, the first having
two holes and the second having twenty holes. The probabilities
of winning with one punch on the first board and of winning with
ten punches on the second are both one-half, but these two presentations of p = 1/2 are not considered equivalent by all subjects. This experiment indicates a definite limitation to the
range of applicability of axiom M1.

   Axiom M5 is a cancellation law and is included for logical
clarity. The point at issue here is not whether the judge is indifferent between ApC and BpC, but is rather what one means
by distinct prospects. Its role is logical rather than psychological and its acceptance entails no psychological assumptions.
Axiom M5 serves to "glue" the space together. Without M5
we could have the following possibility. Let M consist of three
prospects A, B, C where A = pencil, B = apple, C = nothing.

Now set $ApB = BpC = ApC = BpC = C$ for all p with $0 < p < 1$, and define $X1Y = Y0X = X$ for all X, Y in M. This system satisfies M1, M2, M3, M4, but not M5, and might even arise in practice for an individual who would evaluate as worthless all mixtures involving two distinct prospects. However, we can hardly expect a mathematical utility theory to explain such behavior.

In summary, so far as applications to the real world are concerned, the crucial mixture axioms are M1 and M3; in both of these the psychological content is open to question and, therefore, also to experimental study. It will possibly turn out that these axioms are better fitted for analysis of command level group judgments than for that of individual judgments.

2. THE ORDER AXIOMS

W1. The relation $\lesssim$ is a weak order on M. (Cf. Chapter XII.)
W2. If $A \lesssim B$ then $ApB \lesssim BpC$ for $0 < p < 1$.
W3. If $ApC \lesssim BpC$ for some p such that $0 < p < 1$, then
$A \lesssim B$.

If we have both $A \lesssim B$ and $B \lesssim A$ we write $A \sim B$ and say that A is <u>indifferent</u> to B. Indifference is an equivalence relation on M.

In many ways W1 is the order axiom most open to question. A mixture space has an infinite number of elements and the judge is asked to make judgments of preference or indifference between each pair of these elements, and these judgments are to be transitive. A prospect A is said to be <u>pure</u> if it is not the mixture BpC, $0 < p < 1$, of any two other prospects B and C. If the mixture space is generated by a finite set of pure prospects one has more hope concerning the possibility of imposing an order relation. [A set S of prospects is said to <u>generate</u> the entire space M if for each prospect C in M there exist probabilities $p_1, \ldots, p_r$ and elements $A_1, \ldots, A_r$ in S such that $C = A_1p_1(A_2p_2(\ldots(A_{r-1}pA_r)\cdots))$.]

From the practical point of view, if the number of judgments needed is finite but large, there is still the time difficulty. By the time the judge has reached the 1,000,000th choice, his standards of comparison are almost certainly not the same as initially. The theory calls for instantaneous and simultaneous judgments between all pairs, and applications should be limited to cases where there is some evidence that the judgments used have been based on reasonably constant standards.

In a way, axioms W2 and W3 help simplify the judgment problem; in principle, they show how to reduce greatly the number of judgments required. For instance, if M is generated by a finite number of pure prospects one can get by with a finite number of judgments. However, in spite of their obvious importance, there are some objections to these axioms.

For example, consider the prospects A = win five dollars, C = lose five dollars, B = neither win nor lose. This is a one dimensional case, and so utility theory requires a p for which B $\sim$ ApC. (This p need not be 1/2.) Consider an individual who has a negative utility for gambling and who accordingly has, say, B $\sim$ A .6 C. If W2 and W3 hold, then we must have

$$D = ApB \sim E = Ap(A .6 C)$$

whereas the individual might prefer D to E since D involves no chance of losing and still has some chance of winning. This type of behavior would follow from a lack of symmetry between "good" and "bad" prospects. Such a lack of symmetry has been apparent in some experiments run by Ward Edwards, reported in [1].

On the other hand attempts to weaken W2 and W3 lead to curious theoretical results. We discuss one of these.

Let M be a mixture space with a weak order $\lesssim$, and with the only connection between order and mixture being the requirement (Q_1) A $<$ B, and $0 < p < 1$ imply A $<$ ApB $<$ B. This axiom has the effect of giving a definite order sense to each line in which there exist at least two elements A and B with A $<$ B. However, this axiom is fulfilled in the following example. Let M be two-space and let $\lesssim$ be defined by A = $(a_1, a_2) \lesssim B = (b_1, b_2)$ if (i) $a_2 < b_2$ or, if (ii) $a_2 = b_2$ and $a_1 \leq b_1$ if a_2 is rational, or $a_1 \geq b_1$ if a_2 is irrational. Then any line of non-zero slope has its increasing direction upwards, but for horizontal lines the increasing direction is left-right or right-left, according as the distance of the line from the x-axis is rational or irrational. In particular, it can happen that A $<$ B but ApC $>$ BpC. This might well be described as an "irrational" utility!

3. NON-ARCHIMEDEAN UTILITY

The addition of the following (Archimedean) axiom:

W4. If A $<$ B $<$ C there exists p such that B $\sim$ ApC

limits utility spaces to one dimension, i.e., to the real numbers.

Although dealing with the real numbers is convenient, there are some situations in which axiom W4 does not seem to hold but for which higher dimensional utilities are satisfactory.

For example, if A = "be hanged at sundown," B = "be given 1 common pin," C = "be given 2 common pins," it is clear that $A < B < C$ (assuming that pins are of some use). It is not unreasonable to suppose that there are some individuals for whom W4 fails to hold in this case. However, a two dimensional utility will fit this case if we let the dominant component describe the probability of being hanged and the subordinate component refer to the relative probability of one pin versus two pins. In more detail, we assign to A, B, C, respectively, the coordinates $(0,0)$, $(1,0)$, $(1,1)$. Then the utility space can be considered as the triangle with vertices A, B, C. If D and E are two prospects, we have $D < E$ if E is closer to the side $\overline{BC}$, or if the directed line segment $\overline{DE}$ is parallel to and has the same sense as $\overline{BC}$; i.e. if $D = (a,b)$ and $E = (c,d)$ we have $D < E$ if $a < c$ or if $a = c$ and $b < d$.

Another example arises in appraising various alternatives in a military situation. The commanding general must give top priority to not losing the war; subject to this priority he tries to conserve manpower; and, finally, other things being equal he attempts to conserve supplies. This could be described by a three dimensional utility.

For a further example, consider a social group in which a certain action A is taboo, a second action B is neither good nor bad, and a third action C is moderately good. Thus $A < B < C$, but it is extremely unlikely that W4 holds.

On the other hand, if one is dealing with a purely economic situation in which axioms M1 - M5 and W1 - W3 hold, it is quite likely that W4 will hold also. Hence, for much of economics one can probably safely neglect non-Archimedean utilities.

4. CALCULATIONS WITH NON-ARCHIMEDEAN UTILITIES

Suppose that a commanding general is using a two dimensional utility to evaluate a military situation. If he has n basic strategies $P_1, \ldots, P_n$ and his enemy has m basic strategies $Q_1, \ldots, Q_m$, he must first evaluate the outcome if he chooses P_i and the enemy chooses Q_j. This evaluation will be an ordered pair of numbers (a_{ij}, b_{ij}) where, say, the first component is the dominant one. If we assume that the general is using game theory, his action will be to choose some mixed strategy. If he chooses the mixed strategy which assigns probability p_i to P_i, i.e., if he chooses a probability vector $\pi = (p_1, \ldots, p_n)$ then his expected outcome will be at least as good as the vector $f(\pi) = \min_j \Sigma p_\lambda(a_{\lambda j}, b_{\lambda j})$. Hence, his task is to choose a probability vector π so as to maximize $f(\pi)$. Since his order relation is lexicographic, he first finds those vectors π for which the first component $f_1(\pi) = \min_j \Sigma p_\lambda a_{\lambda j}$ of $f(\pi)$ is a maximum. According to the general theory of games these vectors form a non-empty convex subset S of the set of all probability vectors. If S is a one element set his problem is solved, but if S is larger than one element he now must search for vectors π in S which maximize the second component $f_2(\pi) = \min_j \Sigma p_\lambda b_{\lambda j}$ of $f(\lambda)$. Again the theory of games guarantees a solution. If instead of two dimensions the general had three or more dimensions, he would merely iterate this process.

This discussion illustrates the fact that non-Archimedean utilities are perfectly satisfactory for game theory. The equivalence of game theory and linear programming guarantees that non-Archimedean utilities will be satisfactory also for linear programming problems.

BIBLIOGRAPHY

1. Edwards, Ward, Probability Preferences in Gambling, American Journal of Psychology, 66 (1953), 349-364.

2. Nogee, Philip, An Experiment in Decision-making Under Uncertainty, mimeographed report of the Seminar in the Application of Mathematics to the Social Sciences, University of Michigan.

CHAPTER XIV

TOWARDS AN ECONOMIC THEORY OF ORGANIZATION AND INFORMATION*

by

Jacob Marschak

COWLES COMMISSION FOR RESEARCH IN ECONOMICS
UNIVERSITY OF CHICAGO

INTRODUCTION

The statement of Laplace [9] that the theory of probabilities is at bottom merely common sense reduced to calculus[1] and the saying of Schumpeter [18] that, to a layman, economics must appear halb unverstaendlich, halb selbstverstaendlich, have similar meanings. Both men said, in effect, that their respective disciplines formalized certain concepts and propositions of pre-scientific practice. Surely this did not lead them to think that their disciplines were useless. In fact, both disciplines have been fairly successful.

The present paper is conceived in the same spirit; and it happens to touch on both economic theory and probabilities. It can be interpreted as extending the economic theory of a rational firm into the domain of uncertainty, giving special regard to the character of a firm as a team. All criticisms leveled against economic theory can therefore be also raised against the type of work represented by this paper. In particular, in

*Research undertaken by the Cowles Commission for Research in Economics under contract Nonr - 358 (01), NR 047-006 with the Office of Naval Research. The bulk of the paper was written in December 1952. Its revision in August 1953 was part of the author's work at the Institute for Numerical Analysis under a contract between the National Bureau of Standards and the University of California, supported in part by the Air Research and Development Command, USAF.
Acknowledgments are due to Gerard Debreu, Roy Radner, and Leo Törnquist, of the Cowles Commission staff. The author owes much to earlier discussions with Alan Newell, Joseph Kruskal, and C. B. Tompkins.

187

concentrating on the typically "economic" question of the most efficient rules of action and communication for group members, I have pursued a line different from those who are interested in the description of existing modes of behavior within human groups. Yet, I do feel the two lines of research will meet some time, and that communication between the two types of workers is fruitful. When time comes for second approximations of the economic, normative approach, limitations on human rationality emphasized by descriptive workers will have to be properly formalized and introduced into the theory as a factual constraint. On the other hand, the criterion of efficiency of a team or of a foundation should be helpful in describing those human groups which have been created for a purpose: just as this same criterion of efficiency is a major guide in describing human artifacts such as machines or ships. The history of ships is no doubt fascinating and full of suggestions. But to buy or build a ship, it is also useful to know what makes a ship safe and fast. There is a history of political constitutions. There is also the question, What makes a constitution suitable for its task? There are many histories of business corporations. There is also the question, Which structures and procedures make a business organization profitable?

1. TEAMS, FOUNDATIONS, COALITIONS

1.1. Preference orderings. Human groups can be classified according to whether a group goal exists and according to the relation between the group goal and the goals of group members. A more formal and convenient phrase for "goal" is "preference ordering of states of the world;" or simply "ordering," or "interests." The relation $s\, G_i\, s'$ will be read: "from the point of view of i, the state s is at least as good as the state s'." The binary relations G_i, $i=1, 2, \cdots, n$ will denote the orderings by individuals (individual interests), and G_O the ordering from the point of view of the group (group interest). Groups will be classified according to which combinations of the following propositions are valid ($\mathbf{S}$ will denote the set of all states):

A. For every i ($i=1, \cdots, n$), there exists a complete ordering G_i on $\mathbf{S}$. [that is, every group member has a preference ordering]:[2] Rationality of members.

B. There exists a transitive ordering G_O on $\mathbf{S}$. [That is, the states can be ordered for the group, at least partially:

see footnote to A]: <u>Transitivity of group interests</u>.

C. For any s, s' in **S**, <u>if s G_i s' for all i=1, $\cdots$, n then</u>
<u>s G_0 s'</u>. [That is, if s is not worse than s' for any member of the group, it is not worse than s' for the group itself]: The so-called <u>Pareto optimality principle</u>.

D. For any s, s' in **S**, <u>s G_0 s' or s' G_0 s</u>. [That is, for no pair of states is it impossible to say which is preferable for the group, unless the two are equally desirable]: <u>Completeness of group preferences</u>. (Note that B and D imply together complete ordering.)

E. For all i=1, $\cdots$, n, s G_i s' <u>if and only if</u> s G_0 s'. [That is, all individuals have identical interests among themselves and with the group]: <u>Solidarity</u>.

If A is satisfied we call the n group members rational.
If A, B and C are satisfied the group is a <u>coalition</u>.
If A, B, C and D are satisfied we call it a <u>foundation</u>.
If A, B, C, D and E are satisfied we call it a <u>team</u>.

1.2. <u>Utility functions</u>. The same concepts can be defined (somewhat more narrowly[3]), if the individual complete ordering G_i (i=1, $\cdots$, n) is replaced by a numerical function u_i on **S**, the so-called satisfaction or utility function. The group members are called rational if for every i=1, $\cdots$, n there exists a numerical function $u_i(s)$ such that $u_i(s) \geqq u_i(s')$ if and only if s G_i s'. The corresponding group utility function $u_0(s)$, if it exists, may or may not be a numerical one. If $u_0(s)$ is numerical, then $u_0(s) = u_0(s')$ if and only if s G_0 s'. In the case of <u>coalitions</u> other than foundations, $u_0(s)$ is the vector $[u_1(s), \cdots, \underline{u_n(s)}]$ (vectors are partially ordered). In the case of <u>foundations</u>, $u_0(s)$ is numerical and is a monotone non-decreasing function of $u_1(s)$, $u_2(s)$, $\cdots$, $u_n(s)$. In the case of <u>teams</u>, $u_0(s) = u_1(s) = \cdots = u_n(s)$.

1.3. <u>Incentives; Bargaining</u>. To sum up: an individual is <u>rational</u> if his preferences are <u>consistent</u>. A group of such individuals is a coalition if, whenever a state is worsened for one individual and is unchanged for all others, it is considered as worsened for the group. A coalition is a foundation if all states can be compared from the point of view of group interest. A foundation is a team if group interest coincides with the interest of each member.

A team may be regarded as the simplest form of a group. If a group is a foundation but not a team, the group has a goal separate from the individual goals. This gives rise to the problem of individual incentives that would best serve the group goal. If a group is a coalition but not a foundation, there is no "group interest" to help in making all choices: when any state is reached where no member can be made better off without making another member worse off, further choices are determined by bargaining, and problems of "relative power" arise. If a group of rational men is not a coalition, there arises the general problem of a (generally non-constant-sum) game.

1.4. Some recent literature. In recent literature the paper of Herbert Simon [20] on the Employment Relationship, dealt with a coalition (in our sense) between an employer and a worker. The work of Bavelas [1] and his group deals with foundations: a group goal exists (some task is to be achieved in shortest time with least error, etc.) but there need not be complete solidarity; some of Bavelas' mathematical problems (to find the minimal number of messages needed to fully equalize the state of information among n members) are team problems. In von Neumann-Morgenstern's Theory of Games [16], coalitions have the same meaning as here; foundations do not seem to occur; teams occur, e.g., in the case of a pair of bridge partners. The process of bargaining within a coalition, and the process of forming and dissolving coalitions within a general game is not treated in the Theory of Games. A theory of bargaining has been presented by J. Nash, [13], [13a]. It is possible that such problems require postulates additional to that of the existence of consistent individual preferences. Such postulates were developed in models such as R. Bush's [3] and N. Rashevsky's [15].

This paper represents a part of the work on teams by the author and other members of the Cowles Commission, especially Beckmann [2] and Radner [12], [14]. This work included also some preliminary attempts to deal with the problem of foundations: ([10], Part III; Faxen [6]), but such attempts will not be made here.

2. ACTIVITIES: OBSERVATIONS, MESSAGES, ACTIONS

2.1. Events and actions. Each state s of the world which, as discussed in 1, is compared with other states of the world from the point of view of the team's interests, can be regarded as depending on two classes of variables: (1) variables that are controlled by the n members; we shall call them actions and denote them by $a_1, \cdots, a_n$; (2) variables that are not controlled by the members; we shall call them "state of environment" or "external variables", and summarize them by the letter x. Since the team's satisfaction depends on the state of the world s, and s depends on $a_1, \cdots, a_n$ and on x, we can denote the team's satisfaction by

(2.1.1) $u = u(a,x)$,

where $a = (a_1, \cdots, a_n)$. (Because of "solidarity" of team members we have omitted the subscript under u). u is also called payoff or gain. The environment x will be considered random, with a known distribution function.

2.2. <u>Activities</u>. To each individual i corresponds an action variable a_i. Moreover, to each individual i corresponds a set $\mathbf{X}_i$ of the values of the variable (possibly a group of variables) that he can observe, and the value he has actually observed can be denoted by $x_i \in \mathbf{X}_i$. For example, $x_1 = $ economic conditions, $x_2 = $ political conditions, etc.   Thus $x = (x_1, \cdots, x_n)$. We can distinguish three kinds of activities of i:

1) To make an <u>observation</u> x_i on the external world
2) To perform an <u>action</u> a_i upon the external world
3) To send to a co-member j a <u>message</u> (report) m_{ij}, i.e., a statement about the external world, of the form

$$x_i \in X_{ij} \subseteq \mathbf{X}_i;$$

that is, a report states that the observation x_i made by the reporter belongs to a subset X_{ij} of $\mathbf{X}_i$. The report can thus be identified as the set X_{ij}. Two extreme cases are: an "exact (or most detailed) report" when X_{ij} consists of a single element, $X_{ij} = \{x_i\}$; "no report" when $X_{ij} = \mathbf{X}_i$. We can write $X_{ii} = \mathbf{X}_i$.

2.3. <u>Cost of message</u>. Thus in general a message m_{ij} is a subset of $\mathbf{X}_i$. A non-negative number $c_i(m_{ij})$ will measure the <u>cost</u> of the message. We have

$$c_i(\{x_i\}) \geqslant c_i(\mathbf{X}_i) = 0,$$

while "inexact messages" (i.e., messages where X_{ij} consists of more than one, but not of all elements of $\mathbf{X}_i$) have intermediate cost. In special cases, c_i may be regarded as a non-increasing function of the measure of set X_{ij}.

2.4. Examples.

1) Let x_i = vector $(x_i^!, x_i^{!'})$, e.g., $x_i^!$ = leather price, $x_i^{!'}$ = shoe price. Then a report to j, giving values of $x_i^!$ and $x_i^{!'}$ (so that X_{ij} = a point in the $x_i^!$, $x_i^{!'}$ -plane), is more "exact" and more costly than one giving the value of $x_i^!$ only (so that X_{ij} = a line in the $x_i^!$, $x_i^{!'}$-plane) or of $x_i^{!'}$ only.

2) Let x_i = price and let the report X_{ij} state a sub-interval $\alpha \leqslant x_i \leqslant \beta$; then the report is the more exact and costly the smaller $\beta - \alpha$.

2.5. Three-phase team.

We shall consider three-phase teams only:

> Phase I : Observations made.
> Phase II : Messages sent and received.
> Phase III: Actions performed.

Actual teams may have, of course, many more phases. Messages will occur that do not fall under the definition of our Section 2.2.: e.g., reports transmitting a third member's message. In the present paper, after Phase I, the member i has information x_i. After Phase II his information is the logical product

$$\{x_i\} \cap X_{1i} \cap \cdots \cap X_{ni}.$$

2.6. Best rules.

We shall be concerned with determining the best rules of action and communication. A rule states, for a member i, the "response" he should make to a given "stimulus." In Phase II, the stimulus consists of the observation x_i, and the response consists in sending the n-tuple of messages, $(m_{i1}, \cdots, m_{in}) = m_i^!$ (a row vector). The rule for Phase II is a function R_i^I such that

$$(2.6.1) \qquad\qquad m_i^! = R_i^I(x_i),$$

involving a communication cost $c_i(m_i^!)$, say. In Phase III, the stimulus of i consists of the observation x_i and of the n-tuple of messages received by him, $(m_{1i}, \cdots, m_{ni}) = m_i$, a column vector. The response is the action a_i, and the rule for Phase III is a function R_i^{II} such that

$$(2.6.2) \qquad\qquad a_i = R_i^{II}(x_i, m_i).$$

We shall write x, m', m, a, R^I, R^{II} for the corresponding n-tuples $(x_1, \cdots, x_n)$, $(m_1^!, \cdots, m_n^!)$ etc., and denote by c(m)

the cost incurred when the matrix of messages sent is $[m_{ij}]$.
From now on, we shall call $u(a,x)$ the <u>gross gain</u> of the team.
The <u>net gain</u> of the team is

$$(2.6.3) \qquad v = u(a,x) - c(m) = v(x;\ R^I,\ R^{II};\ u,c),$$

a quantity depending on x; on the rules that determine m as a
function of x and a as a function of x and m; and on the functions u and c that measure the team satisfaction and the cost
of messages.

We have assumed that in the opinion of the organization or
team a probability measure on the set $\mathbf{X}$ of the states x of environment exists and is known to them. This distribution of x
will be denoted by $F(x)$. The expected value of the net gain is

$$(2.6.4) \qquad \int_{\mathbf{X}} v(x;\ R^I,\ R^{II};\ u,c)\ dF(x)\ =\ V(R^I,\ R^{II};\ u,c,F),$$

say. We want to find the rules $R^I = \hat{R}^I$ and $R^{II} = \hat{R}^{II}$ that will
maximize V. Clearly they will depend on the functions u,c and
F. We want to study this dependence. What properties of the
functions u,c and F make for more or for less frequent and
detailed communication between a given pair of members?
What conditions make it profitable to cut off direct communication between i and j?

2.8. <u>Maximizing expected utility.</u> In Section 1, a decision-
maker was called rational if the states of the world at his choice
were completely ordered (ranked) by his preferences. This ordering was represented by a numerical utility function. In the
present Section, the preferences must be conceived in a manner
that allows for the uncertainty of outcome of a decision. The
decision-maker is pictured as assuming a certain probability
distribution $F(x)$ of the environment. Therefore the outcome of
each decision is a probability distribution of events, a "prospect"; though in a special case the distribution may degenerate
into a sure event. The set $\mathbf{S}$ of 1.1 is to be reinterpreted as a
set of prospects. A rational decision-maker has a complete ordering of prospects. A numerical utility function can be attached
to prospects so that $u(s') \geqq u(s'')$ whenever prospect s' is preferred or equivalent to prospect s''. That is, the rational man
chooses that prospect s for which $u(s)$ is a maximum.

However, the concept of rationality which we shall use is
stronger than the one just stated. The rational decision-maker
is defined as being able to represent his preferences by a numerical utility function possessing the following property.

Denote by $(s_1, \cdots, s_m; p_1, \cdots, p_m)$ a prospect consisting of the anticipation of prospects (possibly, sure events) $s_1, \cdots, s_m$ with respective probabilities $p_1, \cdots, p_m$. Then $u(s_1, \cdots, s_m; p_1', \cdots, p_m') \geqslant u(s_1, \cdots, s_m; p_1'', \cdots, p_m'')$ if and only if

$$\sum_1^m p_i' \, u(s_i) \geqslant \sum_1^m p_i'' \, u(s_i).$$

In other words: if we regard $u(s_1), \cdots, u(s_m)$ as alternative values of a random variable $u(s)$, the choice between two prospects characterized by the probability vectors $\{p_i'\}$ and $\{p_i''\}$ respectively depends on the values of a single parameter of the two considered distributions of $u(s)$, viz, on its expectation (mean). In this sense, the rational man is defined as maximizing expected utility. This definition was used in 2.6 where we ask for the rules of action and communication that would maximize the team's expected net gain.

This definition of rational decision under uncertainty goes back to Daniel Bernoulli and has been recently much discussed, under the impact of certain behavior postulates formulated in the Theory of Games. Here we shall not discuss these, or similar, postulates in detail.[4] Instead, it will suffice to show, in heuristic fashion, a way to assign to one's prospects a utility scale possessing the required property; and to claim that a system of preferences permitting such a scale does characterize an ideally consistent decision-maker, e.g. an ideal organizer and legislator for a team.

Assume provisionally that there exists for such a decision-maker a "worst" and a "best" state of the world. Denote them to by s_0 and s_1, respectively. Assign them utility numbers $u(s_0) = 0$ and $u(s_1) = 1$, and proceed to "calibrate" on this scale the utilities of all other states. To begin with, consider a prospect promising s_1 with probability π and s_0 with probability $1 - \pi$. In the notation just proposed above, such a prospect will be denoted by $(s_1, s_0; \pi, 1 - \pi)$. The decision-maker—you, the reader, for example—will (a postulate is hidden here!) consider such a prospect better than s_0 and worse than s_1. Therefore you will assign to it a utility number between 0 and 1. The probability is itself such a number. It is therefore permissible to choose a utility function u such that $u(s_1, s_0; \pi, 1 - \pi) = \pi$, for any π between 0 and 1, including 0 and 1 themselves [since $u(s_1, s_0; 0, 1) = u(s_0) = 0$ and $u(s_1, s_0; 1, 0) = 1$].

Consider next some prospect s that is neither s_0 nor s_1 nor the promise of s_1 or s_0 with some probabilities. If the

decision-maker is indifferent between s and s_1, or, alternatively, between s and s_0, then, of course, $u(s) = 0$ or 1, respectively. There remains the case when he considers s better
than s_0 but worse than s_1. In this case, by scanning all possible prospects of the type $(s_1, s_0; \pi, 1 - \pi)$, with π ranging
continuously from 0 to 1, one will find (a postulate is hidden
here!) one such prospect that the decision-maker will be indifferent between it and the prospect s. That is, there will be a π
such that $u(s) = u(s_1, s_0; \pi, 1 - \pi)$. And since, on the utility
scale chosen above, $u(s_1, s_0; \pi, 1 - \pi) = \pi$, we shall have $u(s) = \pi$.
Thus we have assigned utility numbers to all prospects.

To show that this utility scale possesses the required property, compute the utility of the prospect $s = (t_1, t_2, \cdots, t_m;$
$p_1, p_2, \cdots, p_m)$, where $t_1, \cdots, t_m$ are prospects (possibly
sure events) and $p_1, \cdots, p_m$ their probabilities. Let the utility
of each t_i be measured on our scale; that is, $u(t_i) = \pi_i$ if the decision-maker is indifferent between t_i and $(t_1, t_0; \pi_i, 1 - \pi_i)$.
Then the decision-maker is indifferent between the prospect
$(t_1, \cdots, t_m; p_1, \cdots, p_m)$ and the prospect $[(s_1, s_0; \pi_1, 1 - \pi_1),$
$(s_1, s_0; \pi_2, 1 - \pi_2), \cdots, (s_1, s_0; \pi_m, 1 - \pi_m); p_1, \cdots, p_m],$
(actually a postulate is hidden here). But the latter prospect is
nothing but the promise of s_1 with probability $p_1\pi_1 + p_2\pi_2 + \cdots$

$p_m\pi_m = \sum_1^m p_i u(t_i)$; and of s_0 with probability $1 - \sum_1^m p_i u(t_i)$. Now,

on our scale, the utility of such a prospect is simply equal to
the probability of s_1. Hence

$$u(t_1, \cdots, t_m; p_1, \cdots, p_m) = \sum_1^m p_i u(t_i);$$

the expression on the right is the "expected utility" of the prospect $(t_1, \cdots, t_m; p_1, \cdots, p_m)$. Hence, if two prospects
$(t_1, \cdots, t_m; p_1', \cdots, p_m')$ and $(t_1, \cdots, t_m; p_1'', \cdots, p_m'')$ are
compared, the preferred one will have the higher expected
utility.

The provisional assumption that there exist a best and a
worst states can be dropped. We can assign utilities 1 and 0
to any two states, s_1 and s_0 of which the former is preferred
to the latter; and assign, as before, utility numbers $\pi (0 \leqq \pi \leqq 1)$
to all prospects which are not better than s_1 and not worse than
s_0. To assign a utility number to a prospect (say s_2) that is
better than s_1, we first form a number $\pi (0 < \pi < 1)$ such that
the decision-maker is indifferent between s_1 and $(s_2, s_0; \pi, 1 - \pi)$;
and let, accordingly, $u(s_2)$ satisfy the condition

$\pi.u(s_2) + (1 - \pi) u(s_0) = u(s_1)$, and hence $\pi.u(s_2) = 1$, $u(s_2) = \frac{1}{\pi} > 1$.

Similarly, if s_2 is worse than s_0, we find a number π such that the decision-maker is indifferent between s_0 and $(s_1, s_2; \pi, 1 - \pi)$, and define $u(s_2)$ by $u(s_0) = \pi.u(s_1) + (1 - \pi).u(s_2)$; and hence $u(s_2) = - \pi/(1 - \pi) < 0$. It is easy to see that this utility scale, now extended beyond the interval $[s_0, s_1]$, will still possess the required property. Of course, the numbers in the scale will change linearly as s_0, s_1—the prospects chosen to have zero-utility and unit-utility—are changed; but the required property is preserved.

The postulates tacitly used in this observation of utility-scaling can be roughly listed as follows:

1. Numerical function $u(s)$ exists, such that $u(s_1) \geqslant u(s_2)$ if and only if s_1 is preferred or equivalent to s_2.
2. If $u(s_1) > u(s_2)$ then, for any s_3 and any probability p, $u(s_1, s_3; p, 1 - p) \geqq u(s_2, s_3; p, 1 - p)$.
3. If $u(s_1) > u(s_2) > u(s_3)$ then there exists a probability p such that $u(s_2) = u(s_1, s_3; p, 1 - p)$.

2.9. Unknown and subjective probabilities. A natural objection against formulations like ours is to say that in reality the probability distribution F of external conditions is not known. In this case the problem becomes one of statistical inference, invoking principles like "known a priori distribution on the space of F's," "minimax," etc. For the case of a "one-person team" (when activities consist only of observations and actions, no messages being sent) one might refer to works like Dvoretsky-Kiefer-Wolfowitz' second article on Inventories [5].

The assumption of a known a priori probability distribution is particularly germane to our problem, whether in the simple case of three-phase-teams or in more complicated cases. In a three-phase-team, there is no opportunity to acquire or improve the knowledge of the distribution F in the course of the team's operations. In this case, and if F is not known from appropriate statistical manipulation of data collected in the past, we shall still say that a rational decision-maker, if he makes at all choices among actions, has to make consistent assumptions about the probabilities of outcomes of the actions just as he has a consistent scale of the utilities of those outcomes. A postulational basis for the simultaneous existence of subjective utilities and probabilities, extending in a plausible way the postulates of 2.8, was proposed by Frank Ramsey, and more recently by L. J. Savage.[5]

If the operations of a team form a sequence of more than three phases, it is still useful to obtain the benefit of subjective probabilities. The rational decision-maker will start with some subjective probabilities. Even if they are mere hunches roughly summarizing his previous experience they will help him to lay down a plan as to how best to respond to any given sequence of future observations by an appropriate sequence of actions and communications. His actions, in this case, may but need not include data manipulation to provide progressively improved estimates of the distribution F of observables.

2.10. <u>Orders</u>. In 2.2 all messages were defined as statements (reports) about the external world. Reports are different in verbal content (and therefore differ in cost) from "orders" or "task assignments." It seems, however, that by introducing orders no essential change will be introduced in our problem, at least at the present stage of analysis.

For example, suppose the relevant features of the world are characterized by two variables, x_1 and x_2. Let team member 1 observe x_1 and team member 2 observe x_2, and let the respective observed values be x_1^0 and x_2^0. Consider first the following rules: R^I consists of R_1^I only, viz.: 1 tells 2 the observed value x_1^0; R^O consists of R_2^{II} only, viz.: 2 chooses $a_2 = a_2^0$ that will minimize $u(a_2, x_1^0, x_2^0)$. In this case, member 1 is a mere "reporter." The payoff function $u(a_2, x_1, x_2)$ — a function of <u>three</u> variables—is fully known to member 2, but need not be known to member 1.

Now suppose, instead, that it is the member 1 who knows the function $u(a_2, x_1, x_2)$, and let the rule $R^I = R_1^I$ be as follows: 1 shall communicate to 2, not the observed value x_1^0, but the "task," i.e., the function of <u>two</u> variables

$$u_0(a_2, x_2) = u(a_2, x_1^0, x_2).$$

Member 2 then proceeds to accomplish the task. That is, the rule $R^{II} = R_2^{II}$ is: member 2 (who had observed $x_2 = x_2^0$) shall choose $a_2 = a_2^0$ so as to maximize $u_0(a_2, x_2^0)$. In this case, member 1 is the "boss": he determines, in the light of his knowledge of $x_1 = x_1^0$, the special task that member 2, the "subordinate," has to fulfill—i.e., the specialized payoff function u_0 that 2 has to maximize. In military terminology, 1 is in charge of strategy, while 2 is in charge of tactics. The observable x_1 may consist of information about the overall plans of the enemy (plus the information received by the commander during his training), while x_2 may be a local situation. The distinction between reports and orders will not be pursued further in this paper.[6]

2.11. Non-additive costs. The definition of net gain in (2.6.3) is quite appropriate when the amount to be maximized is the expected net money gain. In more general cases, one cannot represent the maximand as the difference between (expected) gain and (expected) cost and will use some more general function to describe net gain. However, (2.6.3) will help us fix the ideas.

2.12. A remark on the general multi-phase case.[7] The three-phase case can be generalized by constructing, for every phase $t = 1, \cdots, T$, the following matrix with $n+1$ rows and columns (regarding a_i as a set of values):

a_{ij}^t means: "what i tells j" (a subset of $\mathbf{X}_i$ or $\mathbf{a}_j$)

a_{io}^t means: "what i does to the outside world" (an element of $\mathbf{a}_i$)

a_{oi}^t means: "what i observes in the outside world" (an element of $\mathbf{X}_i$)

a_{ii}^t, a_{oo}^t are empty.

Then a_i^t = i-th column = i's recently acquired information,

$\vec{a}_i^t$ = sequence $(a_i^t, \vec{a}_i^{t-1})$ = i's state of information,

$a_{i\prime}^t$ = i-th row = i's messages and actions.

In a stationary team there exists a set of rules $R = (R_1, \cdots, R_n)$, independent of time, such that

$$a_{i\prime}^t = R(\vec{a}_i^{t-1}), \quad i = 1, \cdots, n.$$

The team's gross gain for the period ending at T depends on the sequence of external events, $\vec{a}_o^T$; and on the sequence of actions taken, $\vec{a}_{o\prime}^T$; but since the latter depend on $\vec{a}_o^T$ and on the rule R, the gross gain is $u(\vec{a}_o^T, R)$, say. The cost of communications will also depend on $\vec{a}_o^T$, R. Hence the net gain is $v(\vec{a}_o^T, R)$, say. The distribution of external states a_o^t depends, in general, on the sequence of previous states as well as on the sequence of previous actions ("controlled stochastic process"). Hence the distribution of the sequence $\vec{a}_o^T$ depends on the initial state a_o^0 and on the rule R. Write this distribution as $F(\vec{a}_o^T; a_o^0, R)$. Then the expected net gain (integrated over the space of all sequences $\vec{a}_o^T$) is

$$\int v(\vec{a}_0^T, R) \, dF(\vec{a}_0^T; a_0^0, R) = V(R; a_0; v, F),$$

say. The rule $R=\hat{R}$ that maximizes this expression will depend on a_0, v and F. As in the three-phase case, the problem is to find how certain classes of rules (certain networks and procedures) correspond to certain classes of tasks—or, more generally, to certain classes of net gain functions—and to certain classes of distribution of external conditions.

2.13. Procedures and Networks. In the problem defined so far, one seeks to determine what each member has to do or to communicate in response to observations he makes and to messages he receives. Which are the members from whom he can receive and to whom he can send messages is a given not an unknown of this problem. The unknown of the problem is, in other words, the best procedure (the rule R), given the network of communication. The other givens are the cost c of sending a message; the gross payoff function u depending on certain action variables and observables; and the probability distribution F of the observables.

In a more complete team problem (it may be called the problem of the team's constitution), the network is not given. In addition to the cost c of sending a message over an existing network (cost of using the network) there is the cost $C = C(N)$ of constructing a network N. More precisely, if the team is a three-phase-team, $C(N)$ is the cost of maintaining and amortizing communication facilities per period of time needed to go through its three phases. The cost C depends on the nature of the network N—involving, for example, one-way communications (letters), two-way communications (telephone), many-way communications (conferences) between certain members. C does not depend on whether certain communication lines are or are not being used, i.e., on whether a message is or is not actually sent.

Given, then, the cost c of sending a message; given the function $C(N)$ determining for each network the cost of maintaining and operating it; and given the functions u and F, the constitutional problem seeks to find simultaneously the best pair (N,R), i.e., the network and the procedural rule such that the expected net payoff be a maximum. The procedural rule R consists, in three-phase teams, of the communication rule R^I and the action rule R^{II}. The unknowns of the complete team problem are: N, R^I and R^{II}.

Note that the concept of network does not confine itself to the physical communication plant. The description of a given network (also called "organization chart") states all the permanent "positions" within the team, thus including all long-tern employment contracts, all regularly occurring conferences (but not emergency conferences), periodical reports (but not ad hoc reports), etc. The number of team members is thus itself a characteristic of the team, and the optimal size of a team for a given task—i.e., for a given function u(a, x)—is a part of the constitutional problem.

The distinction between network and procedure is analogous to the economists' distinction between long-run decisions (such as building a plant) and short-run decisions (such as buying a certain amount of fuel). Although important intermediate cases exist, the distinction is useful at the present stage of analysis.

One way to study the complete team problem is to start with "pure network problems" and "pure procedural problems." In pure procedural problems, the network is given. Hence the function C(N) (costs of maintaining a network) is not involved, but the cost c of sending a message is. The unknowns of the pure procedural problem are (in three-phase teams): the communication rule R^I and the action rule R^{II}.

In pure network problems, on the other hand, the network N is not given, and the cost c of sending a message is assumed negligible. Therefore, any communication line if it exists can be assumed to be used, so that R^I is uniquely defined for each N. The unknowns of the pure network problem are (in three-phase teams): the action rule R^{II} and the network N.

Section 3 of the present paper can be said to deal with a pure network problem, although in a very rudimentary form. A somewhat more detailed analysis of pure network problems and of complete team problems has been attempted elsewhere: see [12], [14]. Section 4 starts with a pure procedural and ends with a constitutional problem of a very simple nature.

3. BUYING INFORMATION

3.1. The value of an inquiry. Some important aspects of the team problem are brought out in the following simple case. A person's profit (utility) is u(a,x) where a is his action and x is the state of environment (an element of the set **X**). The person knows the distribution F(x). Assuming that he tries to maximize expected profit, how much should he be willing to pay for exact information on x ?

Compare the maximum expected profit U under two alternatives: when the person has not inquired, and when he has inquired about the actual value of x. If he has not inquired, he will choose an action which is independent of x and which will maximize the expectation of the profit. This expectation will therefore be

$$U = U_0 = \max_a Eu(a,x).$$

If, on the other hand, the person has inquired about the actual value of x he will be able to choose an action that will maximize the actual profit. The action chosen will depend on x. The actual profit will be $\max_a u(a,x)$. The expectation of profit will be

$$U = U_1 = E \max_a u(a,x).$$

The difference $U_1 - U_0$ can be called w, the value of inquiry:

(3.1.1) $\qquad w = E \max_a u(a,x) - \max_a Eu(a,x) \geqslant 0,$

for U_1 can never be smaller than U_0.[8]

The statement that an inquiry can never have negative value ("no damage in knowledge!") is easily confirmed as follows. Consider first the case when inquiry has been made. Then to each observed value of x will correspond a best value $\hat{a}$ of the action variable a, viz., the value of a that maximizes $u(a,x)$ for the observed value of x. The relation between x and $\hat{a}$ we can write as $\hat{a} = \hat{\alpha}(x)$. We call the function $\hat{\alpha}$ the best rule of action. Since in applying this rule of action one obtains the highest value of $u(a,x)$ consistent with the observed value of x, the result of applying this rule of action for every x is to obtain a higher expected value of $u(a,x)$ than in applying any other rule of action. We can thus write

$$U_1 = \max_\alpha Eu(\alpha(x),x) = Eu(\hat{\alpha}(x),x),$$

to indicate that the expected utility has been maximized with respect to the function α. Note that in the equations just written the symbol a does not appear; the utility u was expressed as depending on x and on the rule of action, α.

Now consider the case when inquiry has not been made. This time the unknown function $\alpha(x)$ degenerates into a single unknown constant, since expected utility has now to be maximized in ignorance of x. We can write

U_0 = max $E u(\alpha(x),x)$ where $\alpha(x)$ = unknown constant.

Thus U_1 and U_0 are both obtained by maximizing the same quantity over a set of functions, but in the case of U_0 this set is restricted by the condition that $\alpha(x)$ be a constant. It is clear that if one is restricted in the choice of the rule of action one can never obtain a better result than if one is not so restricted. That is, $U_1 \geq U_0$.

3.2. Example I: "guessing the color." The player knows that an urn contains a proportion $p \geq 1/2$ of black balls, the other balls being red. A ball is drawn from the urn. It is not shown to the player but may be shown to his agent. The player has to state the color of the ball. He wins a dollar if his statement is correct, loses a dollar if it is wrong. How much should he be willing to pay the agent for informing him about the actual drawing?

Solution: If the player would not employ an agent his best action would be to bet on black. This would yield him an expected gain $U_0 = p\cdot1 + (1 - p)(-1) = 2p - 1$ dollars. If, on the other hand, he employs an agent, his expected gain is $U_1 = 1$. Hence the player should be willing to pay the agent any amount up to $w = U_1 - U_0 = 2 - 2p$. We call w "the value of inquiry".

3.3. Example II: "a monopolist." A monopolist sets the price a of his product and produces just enough for the demand. At price a the demand is $hx - ka$ where x is a random variable depending on the public's taste, and k is a positive coefficient. The mean μ and the variance σ^2 of x are both known to the monopolist. For greater convenience, and without loss of generality, the coefficients h and k can be made equal to 2 and 1, respectively, by appropriate choice of units. Then the profit is equal to $a(2x - a)$ minus the cost of production. Assume this cost to be independent of the amount produced. How much can the monopolist pay a market research agency for keeping him informed of current public tastes, i.e., of the actual value of x? (We shall assume that, for the monopolist, utility and profit are identical, i.e., he maximizes expected profit.)

Solution: Since cost is independent of his decision, the monopolist can disregard it. He will maximize the expectation of the quantity $u = a(2x - a)$. If he is ignorant of the actual value of x he chooses the price a so as to maximize $Eu = E a(2x - a) = a(2\mu - a)$; the chosen price will be $a = \mu$, resulting in an expected profit (disregarding constant cost) $U_0 = \mu^2$. If, on the other hand, the monopolist is informed of the actual value of x, he will choose every time the price a so as to maximize $u = a(2x - a)$; i.e., his best rule of action will be: $a = x$. This yields an expected profit (disregarding cost) $U_1 = E x^2 = (\mu^2 + \sigma^2)$. Hence the value of inquiry is $w = U_1 - U_0 = \sigma^2$. Thus the services of the market research agency are the more valuable the stronger the variability of tastes; (although, if the demand were not a linear function of price, the approximate measure of variability would turn out to be not σ^2 but some other parameter of the distribution of x). I shall not subscribe to a newspaper if the news does not vary much from day to day!

3.4. Example III: "a speculator." Suppose a speculator cannot buy or sell more than one unit of a commodity. Let x be the difference between tomorrow's and today's price. The speculator knows that x is distributed uniformly between $\mu - \rho$ and $\mu + \rho$. How much is it worth for him to foresee exactly the price change, x?

Solution: Suppose first that he is ignorant of x. If the mean, μ (known to him!) is positive his best action is to buy one unit; if μ is negative, the best action is to sell one unit. The expected gain is $U_0 = |\mu|$. If, on the other hand, he is informed of the actual value of x his best rule of action is: to buy one unit if x is positive, to sell one unit if x is negative. This yields him a gain $|x|$. To compute the expected gain $U_1 = E|x|$ distinguish two cases: 1) if $|\mu| \gtreqless \rho$, x has always the same sign and $U_1 = E|x| = |\mu| = U_0$; 2) if $|\mu| \lesseqgtr \rho$, we have

$$U_1 = E|x| = \frac{1}{2\rho}\left(\int_0^{\mu+\rho} x\, dx + \int_{\mu-\rho}^0 - x\, dx\right)$$

$$= \frac{1}{2\rho}\left(\frac{(\mu+\rho)^2}{2} + \frac{(\mu-\rho)^2}{2}\right) = \frac{\mu^2 + \rho^2}{2\rho}.$$

Therefore the value of inquiry is

$$(3.4) \qquad w = U_1 - U_0 = \begin{cases} 0 & \text{if } |\mu| \gtreqless \rho \\ \\ (|\mu| - \rho)^2/2\rho & \text{if } |\mu| \lesseqgtr \rho. \end{cases}$$

Thus, inquiry is the less valuable the stronger is the known bias $|\mu|$ of the distribution of the price difference x; and the smaller is the range 2ρ of its variation. (See Figure 1.) This is as would be expected on intuitive grounds.

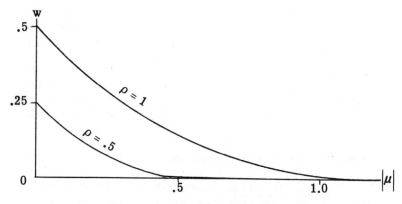

Fig. 1. The "speculator's case".

Value (w) of inquiry when x is distributed uniformly with mean μ and range 2ρ.

3.4.1. It may be noted that the "speculator's case" as defined has a more general application than it might appear. Instead of interpreting the extreme values of a as "buy or sell one unit" one might regard them as "do or don't." In fact, any two-valued set of decisions, so frequently occurring in practice, would fit the example, provided u is linear in a; and, only for the sake of simplifying the computations, x, or some transform of it, is assumed to be uniformly distributed. For example a = +1 may mean "attack," a = -1 "don't attack," and x = difference between our forces and those of the enemy. In all these interpretations, since u = ax, positive x makes a = 1 advisable, and negative x makes a = -1 advisable. Clearly, with u linear in a, the choice of action that will maximize the expected value of ax is not affected if the pair (-1, +1) is replaced by (0, 1) or by any other pair of numbers of which the first is smaller than the second.

3.5. Value of inquiry and "amount of information." Let us now summarize our examples using our general notation.

In the "monopolist's case", u = a(2x - a) and F(x) has known mean μ and variance σ^2. One obtains

$$U_0 = \max_a E\, u = \mu^2; \quad (\text{best } a = \mu);$$
$$U_1 = E \max_a u = (\mu^2 + \sigma^2); \quad (\text{best rule of action: } a = x);$$
$$w = \sigma^2.$$

In the "speculator's case", u = ax; $-1 \leqslant a \leqslant 1$; F(x) is uniform, the lowest and highest values of x being, respectively, $\mu - \rho$ and $\mu + \rho$. The quantities U_0, U_1, w were evaluated in 3.4 above.

The case of "guessing the color" is a variant of the speculator's case; u = ax; a and x have each only one pair of values (-1 and 1).

Thus, the value of inquiry, w, depends on both the distribution F(x) and the payoff function u(a,x). The amount of information as defined by Shannon [19] (or its negative, the "entropy" or "uncertainty" or "randomness") depends on F(x) only, as does the amount of information defined by R. A. Fisher [7]. As a result, the value of an inquiry, for a given payoff function, need not coincide with, or be related in any simple way to, the amount of uncertainty in Shannon's sense. For example, in 3.2, the value of inquiry—permitting now p to be smaller than 1/2 and writing q = 1-p—is w = 1 - |p - q|, while Shannon's uncertainty in the case of binomial distribution is proportionate to (or to the logarithm of) $p^p q^q$. Note that both expressions have a maximum when p = 1/2 (maximum uncertainty) and a minimum when p = 1 or 0 (certainty). If x is uniformly distributed with mean μ and range 2ρ, Shannon's entropy depends on ρ only; while the "value of inquiry" in the case of such a distribution and assuming the payoff to depend linearly on a bounded action variable a, depends also on the mean, μ, as in (3.4) above. Finally, in our example of 3.3, the value of inquiry is proportional to the variance σ_x^2, for any distribution, while entropy is related to variance in a simple way in the case of normal distribution but not in general.

The concepts of value of inquiry and of amount of information are thus different. They serve different purposes.

4. ONE OBSERVER, ONE ACTOR: NETWORK, PROCEDURE, CONSTITUTION

4.1. The problem of "buying information" as a network problem. In 2.13, we distinguished between "pure network problems," "pure procedural problems," and complete or "constitutional" problems. In Section 3 we have dealt with a simple (perhaps the simplest possible) pure network problem. The decision always to obtain information or never to obtain it was supposed to be taken once for all. Such decision defines a network. If the decision is never to receive information, the network chosen is that of a team consisting of a single man, an "actor," who takes no observations, but always acts in a certain way, that is the best on the average: a "traditional" or "routine" system. If the decision is always to receive information, the network chosen can be interpreted in two ways:

1) as a team consisting of a single man ("observer-actor") who is provided with more or less costly physical facilities for observations, or uses a non-negligible part of his time for observations;

2) as a two-man team—an actor and an observer—with more or less costly physical facilities for observation and communication; in this case, the cost of using the communication line, once such a line is established (or once a fixed, non-negligible part of the team's time is set aside for communication), is negligible, so that the observed value of x is always communicated by the observer to the actor, regardless of the observed value of x (e.g., regardless of whether there is or there is no "emergency").

4.2. A procedural problem. Let us, now, consider as given the following network: One member of the team (the "observer") makes observations on the external world. There is a one-way communication line between him and the other member (the "actor"). After having made the observation the observer may either communicate or not communicate it to the actor. In the former case, a cost, c dollars, is charged to the team, and the actor chooses his action on the basis of the observation communicated to him. In the latter case no communication cost is charged, but the actor has to choose his action without knowledge of the actual state of the external world. Of course, the probability distribution of the states of the world is assumed to be known in each case.

The problem is: 1) to find the rule of communication for the observer, i.e., to determine conditions (observed states of the world) under which he shall or shall not report to the actor; and 2) to find the rule of action for the actor, i.e., to determine which actions he shall perform upon receiving certain communications or upon receiving none.

Denote as before by $\mathbf{X}$ the set of all states of the world x. Let $X \subseteq \mathbf{X}$ be the subset of $\mathbf{X}$ such that if the observed state belongs to X, the observer shall send no report. Thus, not to send a report is tantamount to telling the actor that x is in X. The rule of communication can be written as follows (with X yet to find):

$$(4.2.1) \quad \begin{aligned} R(x) &= \mathbf{X} \ \text{ if } \ x \, \epsilon \, X \quad \text{(no report sent);} \\ &= \{x\} \ \text{ if } \ x \, \epsilon \, \mathbf{X} - X \quad \text{(report sent).} \end{aligned}$$

The function R corresponds to R^I of Section 2.6. Its value R(x) is the information made available to the actor. The rule of action can be written as follows:

$$(4.2.2) \quad \left\{ \begin{aligned} &\text{Action } a^O \ \text{ if } \ R(x) = \mathbf{X}, \ x \, \epsilon \, X \\ &\text{Action } \alpha(x) \ \text{ if } \ R(x) = \{x\}, x \notin X. \end{aligned} \right.$$

The action a^O and the function α are yet to find. a^O is the action that maximizes the conditional expectation of gross payoff, given that x belongs to $\mathbf{X}$:

$$(4.2.3) \quad \max_a \int_X u(a,x) \, dF(x) = \int_X u(a^O,x) \, dF(x).$$

Thus a^O does not depend on x. It depends on the set $\mathbf{X}$ that the team chooses in advance of observation. We can write $a^O = a^O(\mathbf{X})$. On the other hand, $\alpha(x)$ is the action that maximizes u(a,x) for given x:

$$(4.2.4) \quad \max_a u(a,x) = u[\alpha(x),x], \ x \, \epsilon \, \mathbf{X} - X.$$

The function α together with the constant a^O correspond to R^{II} of Section 2.6. Clearly, it is advantageous for the team to have the report withheld whenever the observed x is such that $u[a^O(\mathbf{X}),x]$ is larger than $u[\alpha(x),x] - c$. That is, the net expected gain is maximized if $\mathbf{X}$, a^O and α satisfy the following condition:

$$(4.2.5) \quad \mathbf{X} = \{ x \,|\, u[a^O(\mathbf{X}),x] > u[\alpha(x),x] - c \}.$$

[This intuitive result can be easily obtained formally by expressing the net expected gain through combining (4.2.3) and (4.2.4)].

4.3. Example: the procedural aspect of the "speculator's problem". As in Section 3.4, let u = ax, $-1 \leqslant a \leqslant 1$. Then u takes its maximum when a is either -1 or +1. a = 1 may mean "buying one unit" and a = -1 "selling one unit." The observable x may mean the predicted price change, and u the profit. Therefore a negative x makes a = -1 advisable; a positive x makes a = +1 advisable. [As remarked in 3.4.1 above, a = 1 may also mean "attack," a = -1 may mean "don't attack," and x may mean "difference between our forces and those of the enemy."]

To simplify computations, x is assumed to have uniform probability distribution.

The pure network aspect of the team problem given by the described nature of a, x and u was discussed in 3.4 above. We shall now deal with the procedural aspect of the same problem and, later (in 4.5) present the solution of the complete problem of "best constitution" when a, x and u are as described.

4.4. In our example, the observer finds the actual value of x and may or may not communicate it (at cost c) to the actor who, in either case, has to decide whether to buy or sell one unit. What are the best rules for communication and action, given the (uniform) probability distribution of x? To simplify the problem we shall first assume the mean $\mu = 0$, so that $-\rho \leqq x \leqq \rho$.

The communication rule can belong to one of two classes:

$\mathbf{r}_+$: call only if the desirable action $= 1$ ($=$ "buy")
$\mathbf{r}_-$: call only if the desirable action $= -1$ ($=$ "sell").

Let us first look for the best rule in $\mathbf{r}^+$. Then, if the actor is called, he will choose $a = 1$; if he is not called, he will choose $a = -1$. In the notation of Section 4.2,

$$a = \alpha(x) = 1, \quad x \notin X$$
$$a = a^0 = -1, \quad x \in X.$$

Since $u = ax$, condition (4.2.5) defines the best set X as follows: X (the set of observations that are not communicated) shall consist of all x such that

$$-x > x - c, \quad \text{i.e.,} \quad x < c/2.$$

Hence the best communication rule belonging to the class $\mathbf{r}^+$ is: to call whenever $x \geqq c/2$. The corresponding best action rule is: buy if called, sell if not called.

We find by a similar reasoning that the best communication rule belonging to the class $\mathbf{r}^-$ is: to call whenever $x \leqq -c/2$. The corresponding best action rule is: sell if called, buy if not called.

Using now the known distribution of x, we have to compute the net expected gains (V^+ and V^-, say) obtained under these two competing rules, and choose the rule yielding the higher net expected gain. In our case, we have

$$V^+ = \frac{1}{2\rho}\left[\int_{-\rho}^{c/2} - x dx + \int_{c/2}^{\rho} (x - c)dx\right], \quad \frac{c}{2} \leq \rho$$

$$= 0 \qquad\qquad\qquad\qquad , \quad \frac{c}{2} \geq \rho .$$

$$V^- = \frac{1}{2\rho}\left[\int_{-\rho}^{-c/2} (-x - c)dx + \int_{-2/2}^{\rho} x dx\right], \quad \frac{c}{2} \leq \rho$$

$$= 0 \qquad\qquad\qquad\qquad , \quad \frac{c}{2} \geq \rho .$$

Hence

$$V^+ = V^- = (\rho - \frac{c}{2})^2 / 2\rho , \quad c \leq 2\rho$$

$$= 0 \qquad\qquad , \quad c \geq 2\rho .$$

Thus in our case both rules are equally good and can be summed up as follows: if the cost of communication exceeds or is equal to the range 2ρ of the observable, the observer shall never communicate, and the actor shall take any action he pleases (since the expected gain = 0 in any case); if the cost of communication is less than 2ρ, then either (1) the observer shall call whenever $x > c/2$, and the actor shall buy whenever called; or (2) the observer shall call whenever $x < -c/2$, and the actor shall sell whenever called. We shall call these rules (1) and (2).

4.5. If we had not assumed uniform distribution of x to be symmetrical (midpoint $\mu = 0$) the two rules would not turn out to be equivalent. In this, more general, case the solution is as follows: If $c/2 \geq \rho - |\mu|$, never call; buy (sell) if $\mu > 0 \; (< 0)$, always yielding the expected gain $|\mu|$. If $c/2 \leq (\rho - |\mu|)$, then apply rule (1), or rule (2) above depending on whether μ is negative or positive (See Figure 2.) This agrees with common sense. If $\mu < 0$, then a large positive $x(\geq c/2)$ is less likely to occur than a numerically large negative $x(\leq -c/2)$; and it is, of course, preferable to pay for signalling rarely rather than frequently.

If, as suggested in 3.4.1, a = +1 means "do" (e.g., "attack") and a = -1 means "don't," then rule (1) becomes: "call to encourage doing whenever the situation is very favorable relative to cost of communication $(x > c/2)$"; rule (2) becomes: "call to warn against doing, whenever the situation is very unfavorable relative to the cost of communication $(x < -c/2)$". Roughly, if favorable situations are less likely to occur $(\mu < 0)$, apply rule (1); otherwise, apply rule (2).

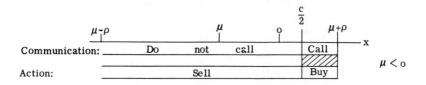

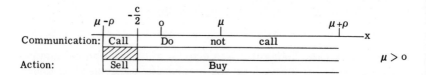

Fig. 2. The "speculator's case" with one observer.

Rules of action and communication ("call" region shaded) when x is distributed uniformly with range 2ρ and with mean μ, negative (above) or positive (below).

If $\mu \neq 0$ and the best appropriate rule is applied, a reasoning similar [but more complicated: see [12], pp. 15-17] to that in 4.4 yields the following net expected gain:

$$(4.5.1) \quad V = |\mu| + (\rho - |\mu| - \frac{c}{2})^2/2\rho \quad \text{if } \frac{c}{2} \leq \rho - |\mu|;$$

$$= |\mu| \qquad \qquad \text{otherwise.}$$

4.6. <u>The "constitutional" problem.</u> Let the cost of having an observer (per time period needed for one decision) be C. We have now the choice between two networks: one without, the other with observer. In each network the best appropriate rules will be applied. We have thus to choose between two "constitutions": I) not to have an observer, and let the actor use the best action; II) to have an observer, and to let him apply the best rule of communication while letting the actor apply the best rule of action.

Under Constitution I, the best action is: a = -1 if $\mu < 0$, a = 1 if $\mu > 0$. This results in a net expected gain Eax = aEx = $a\mu$ =

$$V_I = |\mu|.$$

Under Constitution II, the expected gain obtained under the best rules of communication and action was shown in (4.5.1), where the cost c of sending a message but not the cost C of maintaining an observer (per period of time needed for each decision) was taken into account. The expected gain, correcting for this latter cost, is therefore

$$V_{II} = -C + |\mu| + (\rho - |\mu| - \tfrac{c}{2})^2/2\rho \text{ if } \tfrac{c}{2} \leq \rho - |\mu| ;$$

$$= -C + |\mu| \qquad\qquad\qquad \text{otherwise.}$$

Therefore the difference $V_{II} - V_I$ is positive, and hence Constitution II is preferable to I if the parameters $\rho, |\mu|$, c and C obey the conditions

$$(\rho - |\mu| - \tfrac{c}{2})^2 \geq 2C\rho , \quad \rho - |\mu| - \tfrac{c}{2} \geq 0 ;$$

hence (taking the positive square root because of the second inequality and dividing by ρ):

$$\frac{|\mu|}{\rho} + \frac{c}{2\rho} + \sqrt{\frac{2C}{\rho}} \leq 1 .$$

That is, if best rules of action and communication are used, the team shall have an observer only if, relative to the variability (measured by ρ) of external events x, 1) the costs c and C are small and 2) the expectation μ of x is not too far from zero (i.e., if favorable events are not much more, and not much less, likely to occur than unfavorable ones). (See Figure 3.)

5. OPTIMAL INEXACT INFORMATION

5.1. In Sections 3 and 4 the observer could send either an exact report or none at all. In Section 2, however, the problem was defined more generally. Information can be given with varying degrees of precision.

The organizer of the team can determine in advance a partitioning $\mathbf{p}$ of the set $\mathbf{X}$ of states of nature into disjoint subsets (possibly infinite in number) which we shall denote by

$$X_p^{(1)}, X_p^{(2)}, \cdots .$$

The observer finds that x belongs to $X_p^{(m)}$, say. He communicates to the actor the index m. This index will thus depend on x, the actual state of nature; and on $\mathbf{p}$, the partitioning chosen in

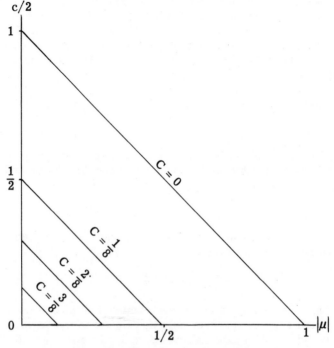

Fig. 3. The "speculator's case."

Region (triangular) where use of observer is advisable.

(With $\rho = 1$ and $C = 0, \frac{1}{8}, \frac{2}{8}, \frac{3}{8}$.)

advance. The actor chooses then an action a that will maximize the conditional expectation

$$E\left\{u(a,x)\,|\,x \,\epsilon\, X_p^{(m)}\right\} = \frac{\displaystyle\int_{X_p^{(m)}} u(a,x)\,dF(x)}{\displaystyle\int_{X_p^{(m)}} dF(x)},$$

the denominator being the probability that x falls into the subset $X_p^{(m)}$. Hence to the partition $\mathbf{p}$ and to the given functions u and F will correspond an expected payoff

$$U = U(\mathbf{p}; u,F) = \sum_m \max_a \int_{X_p^{(m)}} u(a,x)dF(x) .$$

The quantities U_1 and U_0 defined in 3.1 were extreme cases.
$U = U_1$ if every $X_p^{(m)}$ consists of a single element of $\mathbf{X}$
("exact information"). $U = U_0$ ("no information") if $X_p^{(1)} = \mathbf{X}$;

therefore $U_0 = \max_a \int_{\mathbf{X}} u(a,x)dF(x)$. We can thus define the

value of an inquiry corresponding to a particular partition $\mathbf{p}$ as

$$w(\mathbf{p}) = U(\mathbf{p}) - U_0 .$$

The actor will be informed into which subset $X_p^{(m)}$ x falls, only
if such communication costs less than $w(\mathbf{p})$.

5.2. Code. A given partition $\mathbf{p}$ determines a "code," according to which an observed state x will induce a signal
m = m(x). The function m(x) may be called a "code." The code
studied in Section 4 was a two-valued one: either "call" or "no
call" depending on whether x falls into the one or the other of
the two intervals into which $\mathbf{X}$ was partitioned. (Fig. 2.) A call
as well as the absence of a call conveyed to the actor a certain
information. We have seen that in order to implement the code
two kinds of cost had to be borne: a constant cost C of maintaining the network and a (random) variable cost of using it.
The variable cost had two values, c and zero, depending on
which of the two signals ("call," "no call") was used. In a more
general case, the variable cost may have more values: at most
as many as there are subsets $X_p^{(m)}$.
With the cost thus defined the "constitutional" problem of
Section 4 can be extended as follows: how many observers shall
there be in the team, and what codes shall they use? We shall
not touch in this paper on a still more general extension that
would introduce two or more actors.
Two types of optimal partitions $\mathbf{p}$ of the set $\mathbf{X}$ present
special interest: 1) an optimal system of intervals for each of a
given number of observables; 2) an optimal set of observables.

5.3. Optimal system of intervals. If x is a real number, and
$\mathbf{X}$ an interval, $\mathbf{X}$ may be partitioned into sub-intervals. These
may or may not be of equal length. If they are, their number n
measures the precision of information. For example, if $n = 10^k$,
k integer, variations of precision are expressed by the number
k of decimal digits. We have then a sequence of partitions:

$\mathbf{p}_k$, $k = 0, 1, \cdots$. On the lines of (3.1.1) the gross expected utility will increase, or at least not decrease, with increasing precision of information; while the costs of both maintaining and using the network will presumably also increase or at least not decrease. The problem is to find the optimal value of k.

5.3.1. If x is a real vector of, say d dimensions, $x = (x_1, \cdots, x_d)$, the same principle applies: about each—say the i-th—of the d components, an inquiry of precision k_i can be made. The expected gross payoff as well as the cost will depend on the vector $(k_1, \cdots, k_d)$; and the vector maximizing expected net payoff will be chosen.

5.3.2. As pointed out by L. Törnqvist the optimal code will, in general, consist, for each real variable, of intervals of unequal rather than equal length. (The unequal "brackets" of published income statistics provide a well known example.) Thus the maximization of net expected payoff will be performed, not with respect to a precision measure k but rather with respect to the code function m(x), as defined in 5.2.

5.4. Optimal set of observables. Another concept of precision of an inquiry concerning a d-dimensional state of nature $(x_1, \cdots, x_d)$ is determined by the components—not necessarily real numbers—about which information is sought, this information being exact. For example, if x_1 represents future weather and x_2 represents future prices, a farmer may wish to inquire about none or one or both of these, before making a decision on what to plant. Presumably both the gross expected payoff and the cost of maintaining and using the network will increase (or at least not decrease) if, to a given set of observables, an additional observable is added.

5.4.1. If some of the components $(x_1, \cdots, x_d)$ are real numbers, the principles of 5.4 (choosing the variables about which information is sought) can be combined with those of 5.3 (choosing the best system of intervals for each of these variables). If all components are real numbers, 5.3.1 embraces both principles: $k_i = 0$ means that no information is given about the i-th component.

5.5. An example of buying precision. Consider again the "monopolist's case" of 3.3:

(5.5.1) $$u = a(2x - a).$$

We have seen that $U_0 = \mu^2$, $U_1 = U_0 + \sigma^2$. To simplify our illustration assume in addition that x is distributed uniformly over the interval $0 \leqq x \leqq \rho$. Then $\mu = \rho/2$, $\sigma^2 = \rho^2/12$, $U_0 = \rho^2/4$, $U_1 = \rho^2/3$. Let us investigate the "buying of precision," in the sense of 5.3, but without confining ourselves to the case when n, the number of sub-intervals, is 10^k (or 2^k, etc.), where k = the number of decimal (or binary, etc.) digits used. The observer informs the actor about the interval into which x falls. That is, the observer gives the integer m, such that

$$(5.5.2) \qquad 1 \leqq m \leqq n \quad \text{and} \quad \frac{m-1}{n}\rho \leqq x \leqq \frac{m}{n}\rho .$$

Thus m depends on n and x; m is the smallest integer not exceeded by $\frac{nx}{\rho}$. Upon learning m, the actor chooses an action in the midpoint of the interval: $a = a(m,n) = \rho(m - \frac{1}{2})/n$, since, under our assumptions, this maximizes the conditional expectation

$$E\left\{u(a,x) \,|\, m-1 \,<\, nx/\rho \leqq m\right\}$$

which then takes the value

$$U(m,n) = [a(m,n)]^2 = (m - \frac{1}{2})^2 \cdot \rho^2/n^2 .$$

Hence, the (non-conditional) expectation of payoff that the actor has if he chooses a degree n of precision is

$$U(n) = \sum_{m=1}^{n} U(m,n)/n = \frac{\rho^2}{n^3} \left[\frac{n(n+1)(2n+1)}{6} - \frac{n(n+1)}{2} + \frac{n}{4} \right]$$

$$= \rho^2 \left(\frac{1}{3} - \frac{1}{12n^2}\right) .$$

This agrees with the two extreme cases computed above:

$$U(1) = U_0 = \rho^2/4 \text{ (case of "no inquiry")};$$

$$U(\infty) = U_1 = \rho^2/3 \text{ (case of "exact inquiry")}.$$

If the "value of precision"

$$w(n) = U(n) - U(1) = \rho^2(1 - \frac{1}{n^2})/12$$

falls short of the cost of inquiry, inquiry will not be made with that precision.

We might develop our example further by assuming that both the cost and the precision depend on the size of a sample.

5.6. <u>An extension to several observables.</u> Let

$$(5.6.1) \qquad u = a(2 \cdot \sum_{i=1}^{d} \gamma_i x_i - a),$$

an extension of (5.5.1), with x_i being distributed uniformly and independently over the interval $0 < x_i \leq \rho_i$. Thus γ_i (a positive number) signifies the importance of and ρ_i the uncertainty about the variable x_i. The actor chooses, for each i, the precision n_i: i.e., he asks about the value of m_i that satisfies

$$(5.6.2) \qquad \frac{m_i - 1}{n_1} < x_i \leq \frac{m_i}{n_i} \rho_i, \quad i = 1, \cdots, \quad .$$

In particular, if $n_i = 1$, no inquiry is made about x_i. Thus we have the situation described in the last sentence of 5.4.1. By a reasoning extending that of 5.5, one can show that the precision n_i for the variable x_i becomes more valuable as its uncertainty ρ_i and/or its importance γ_i increase.

5.7. <u>The role of statistical dependence.</u> It can be further conjectured that, the larger the statistical dependence between x_1 and x_2, the smaller is the advantage of learning about both over learning about only one of them. In the example that follows, we drop the assumption of independent distribution of the x's; and we consider only the case—5.4—where each variable can be learned either exactly or not at all. Let, as in (5.6.1) (but with γ's all equal)

$$u = a(2x_1 + 2x_2 - a),$$

and assume x_i to be two-valued, with the following probability distribution:

$$
(5.7.1) \qquad
\begin{array}{c}
 \\
\end{array}
\begin{array}{cc}
 x_2 & \\
\end{array}
$$

	x_2	
x_1	1	0
1	p_{11}	p_{12}
0	p_{21}	p_{22}

If the determinant $p_{11} p_{22} - p_{21} p_{12}$ is denoted by d, and the marginal probabilities by $p_1 = p_{11} + p_{12} = 1 - q_1$, $p_2 = p_{11} + p_{21} = 1 - q_2$, then the above matrix of probabilities is equal to

$$(5.7.2) \qquad \begin{bmatrix} p_1\, p_2 + d & p_1\, q_2 - d \\ p_2\, q_1 - d & q_1\, 2_2 + d \end{bmatrix}.$$

$p_i q_i$ measures the "uncertainty" about x_j; (it has its maximum for $p_i = 1/2$, minimum for $p_i = 1$ or 0). d^2 measures the statistical dependence between x_1 and x_2.[9]

Denote the maximum expected payoff by

$\qquad U_{00}$ if no inquiry is made

$\qquad U_{11}$ if inquiry is made on x_1 and x_2

$\qquad U_{10}$ if inquiry is made on x_1 only

$\qquad U_{01}$ if inquiry is made on x_2 only.

Then $U_{00} = \max\limits_a Eu = [E(x_1 + x_2)]^2 = (p_1 + p_2)^2$

$(5.7.3)$
$$U_{11} = E \max\limits_a u = E(x_1 + x_2)^2 = U_{00} + p_1 q_1 + p_2 q_2 + 2d .$$

To compute U_{10}, write

$$\max\limits_a a\left[-a + 2E(x_1 + x_2 | x_1 = 1)\right] = \left[E(x_1 + x_2 | x_1 = 1)\right]^2 = u_1 ;$$

$$\max\limits_a a\left[-a + 2E(x_1 + x_2 | x_1 = 0)\right] = \left[E(x_1 + x_2 | x_1 = 0)\right]^2 = u_0 ,$$

say. Then $U_{10} = u_1 p_1 + u_0 q_1$ and therefore

$$(5.7.4) \qquad\qquad U_{11} = U_{10} + p_2 q_2 - \frac{d^2}{p_1 q_1}.$$

We see from (5.7.3) that the value of inquiring about both variables, compared with no inquiry at all, is the larger the larger the uncertainty $p_i q_i$ about each variable. We see from (5.7.4) that the advantage of inquiring about both variables, compared with inquiring about one only is the larger the larger those uncertainties and the smaller the statistical dependence (d^2) between the two variables. I am not going to subscribe to a second newspaper if it mainly repeats what the first paper says, or if it always says the opposite! [As to the role of the algebraic value of d in (5.7.3), and, hence, of positive vs. negative correlation, this has probably to do with the concave nature of the assumed payoff function u with respect to a. But this is only a conjecture.]

6. CONCLUDING REMARK

The results obtained in our various examples seem to agree with common sense, but, I think, only with common sense revealed by hindsight, except possibly for those "exact minds who feel by a sort of instinct" who appeared in the quotation from Laplace in Footnote 1 of this paper. I may remind the reader that the problems solved here surely belong to the simplest team problems that one can imagine. As the networks and the payoff functions become more complex, as statistical dependence between observables is introduced, as non-additive costs are admitted, as the simple three-phase models are abandoned in favor of models permitting feedbacks, etc., unarmed common sense will become more and more powerless, and precise logical analysis more and more necessary. Even though such analysis will always have to use simplified models while reality includes many "things that cannot be submitted to calculus, it gives the surest hints that can guide us in our judgment · · · and teaches us to avoid illusions that ofttimes confuse us."

FOOTNOTES

1. Laplace adds: "it makes us appreciate with exactitude that which exact minds feel by a sort of instinct without being able ofttimes to give a reason for it. . . . Even in the things that cannot be submitted to calculus, it gives the surest hints that can guide us in our judgment . . . and teaches us to avoid the illusions that ofttimes confuse us."

2. Note: an ordering G_i on $\mathbf{S}$ is said to be complete if it has the following two properties: (a) if s, s', s" are in $\mathbf{S}$ then s G_i s' and s' G_i s" imply s G_i s" (transitivity); (b) if s and s' are in $\mathbf{S}$ then s G_i s' or s' G_i s (completeness). If (a) but not (b) is satisfied, the ordering G_i is said to be partial.

3. See G. Debreu [4].

4. See [14], [10].

5. See [17], [10].

6. In an earlier paper a different definition of orders was given. An order was defined as a message restricting the actions of the subordinate to a certain subset of possible actions. The present definition resulted from discussions with Roy Radner and Herbert Simon.

7. See L. Hurwicz [8].

8. This is easily shown formally for the case when x takes discrete values x_i with probabilities p_i $(i = 1, 2, \cdots)$. By definition

$$\max_a u(a, x_i) \geqq u(a, x_i) \qquad \text{for all a,i.}$$

Multiplying by p_i (all non-negative) and summing over i:

$$\sum_i p_i \max_a u(a, x_i) \geqslant \sum_i p_i u(a, x_i) \qquad \text{for all a}$$

$$E \max_a u(a, x) \geqslant E u(a, x) \qquad \text{for all a.}$$

The last relation holds also when a on the right side takes the value that maximizes $Eu(a,x)$. This proves (3.1.1). Briefly, the average of maxima cannot be smaller than the maximum average.

9. A suggestion by R. Radner.

BIBLIOGRAPHY

1. Bavelas, A., Communication Patterns in Task-Oriented Groups, Policy Sciences, ed. by H. D. Lasswell and D. Lerner.

2. Beckmann, M., On Marschak's Model of an Arbitrage Firm, Abstract in Econometrica, April 1953, p. 347 (see also [21] below).

3. Bush, R., Hays and McEachern, A. W., A Mathematical Model for Two-Person Interactions, December 5, 1951. Laboratory of Social Relations, Harvard University (mimeographed).

4. Debreu, G., Representation of a Preference Ordering by a Numerical Function, Chapter XI, Supra.

5. Dvoretzky, A., Kiefer, J., and Wolfowitz, J., The Inventory Problem: II. Case of Unknown Distributions of Demand, Econometrica, July 1952.

6. Faxen, K., Incentive Functions and the Arbitrage Firm, Cowles Commission Discussion Paper Economics 2059, November 24, 1952 (hectographed). See also abstract in Econometrica, April 1953, p. 346.

7. Fisher, R. A., The Logic of Inductive Inference, Journal of the Royal Statistical Society, 1935. (Reprinted in R. A. Fisher's Contributions to Mathematical Statistics, New York, 1950.)

8. Hurwicz, L., Theory of Economic Organization, Econometrica, July 1951, p. 54. Abstract of paper.

9. Laplace, A philosophical essay on the theory of probabilities. Translation by Truscott and Emory. 1902. p. 196.

10. Marschak, J., Probability in the Social Sciences. In Mathematical Thinking in the Social Sciences, ed. by Paul F. Lazarsfeld, The Free Press, 1954.

11. Marschak, J., Organized Decision-Making, Colloques Internationaux du Centre National de la Recherche Scientifique, Vol. 40, Econometrie, Colloque du Mai 1952, pp. 201-211. Paris, 1953.

12. Marschak, J., and Radner, R., Structural and Operational Communication Problems in Teams, I. Cowles Commission Discussion Papers, Economics 2076. See also abstract in Econometrica, July 1953, p. 485.

13. Nash, J., The Bargaining Problem. Econometrica, April 1950.

13a. Nash, J., Two-Person Cooperative Games, Econometrica, January 1953.

14. Marschak, J., and Radner, R., The Firm as a Team. Cowles Commission Discussion Paper Economics 2093 (hectographed).

15. Rashevsky, N., Mathematical Biology of Social Behavior, p. 33.

16. von Neumann, J., and Morgenstern, O., Theory of Games and Economic Behavior, 1944.

Added in Proof

17. Savage, L. J., Foundations of Statistics, John Wiley & Sons (in press).

18. Schumpeter, J., Hauptinhalt und Wesen der theoretischen Nationaloekonomie, 1908.

19. Shannon, C., and Weaver, W., The Mathematical Theory of Communication, 1949.

20. Simon, H., A Formal Theory of Employment Relationship, Econometrica, 1951, 293-305.

21. Kiefer, J., and Orey, P., On the Arbitrage Problem, Cowles Commission Discussion Paper, Economics 2068, February 1953.

CHAPTER XV

THE LOGICAL STRUCTURE OF THE UTILITY CONCEPT

by

Herbert G. Bohnert

RAND CORPORATION

No concept can be regarded as clear unless the form of statement in which that concept is used to assert a simple, singular proposition is completely determined. Since the form of a singular sentence should not depend on the particular individual names appearing in it, it cannot be regarded as determined unless it is possible, when the individual constants in a sample singular sentence are replaced by variables, to specify the class over which each variable is to range. In other words, a determination of the singular sentence form of a concept involves determination of the nature of the entities to which the concept is to be ascribed.

This requirement may be left aside as long as a concept figures primarily in theoretical discussions. Equations can be studied formally as soon as the quantities involved are characterized with respect to their values; and order postulates can be laid down without inquiring into the nature of the entities being ordered. However, once the problem of empirical measurement is raised, the form of sentence in which the results of measurement are to be expressed must be determined.

Although it may be obvious that both traditional and current treatments of the utility concept are not entirely satisfactory in this respect, I should like to review their limitations more explicitly before going on to suggest a different approach.

In classical analyses, utility is treated as a real-valued function defined over points in n-space. The form of singular sentences for the concept might then appear to be something like: "The utility of x for entities 1, 2, ..., n, in the amounts $y_1, y_2, ..., y_n$, is equal to u utiles." In other words utility appears here as a quantitative relation between an individual and $\underline{n}$ magnitudes, or, equivalently, as a non-quantitative relation ("being the utility function of") between an individual and a function of $\underline{n}$ magnitudes. Now this sort of formulation raises various questions.

First, the magnitudes over which the quantity is defined are (usually) "timeless". The individual involved, however, is time-extended. But a magnitude cannot be unambiguously ascribed to a system extended in space or time without some further constructions or conventions being made. Is static utility to be based upon an empirical assumption that a dynamic utility stays relatively constant during certain periods? Or is it to be a statistical construction from such a dynamic quantity (e.g., a time-average)? If an underlying dynamic utility is assumed, is it to be taken as continuously characterizing the $(n+1)$-tuple (the individual and the $\overline{n}$ quantities) during sleep, for example, or only at times of decis$\overline{\text{i}}$on? And what about these quantities? Are they to be dated themselves, as stocks and flows in the typical analyses would be? And if so, are their "dates" to be identical with that on which the utility is ascribed to the individual? Until such a static concept is unambiguously related to time-dependent concepts we cannot be said to have a concept at all but only a partial set of specifications for one.

Time indeterminacy is only one aspect of the more general question. Another aspect is seen in the fact that the number of dimensions, n, is left undetermined in economic discussions. Yet the dimensionality of the space over which any empirical magnitude is defined is a fixed formal property of that magnitude. Indeed, the interpretation of the magnitude on each dimension must be fixed and unchanging if the concept is to have a fixed, clear meaning.

One reaction to this problem is to suppose that in principle utility is to be defined over a space of a very great number of dimensions, most of which are ignored as uncritical in any given problem. But is there any complete set of commodities or environmental variables over which this ultimate utility can be conceived as being defined? It seems doubtful. In any case, until such a set is determined, the form of the singular sentence for a utility so conceived is indeterminate. Thus all statements concerning measurement must be regarded as ellipses for very elaborate assertions whose form is unknown.

A further problem in connection with the conception of utility as defined over a (commodity) space, is that it makes difficult the intelligible measurement of money or any other single variable. The very conception of such a space is based on the supposition that the utility at any point is not just the sum of separate utilities for separate commodities.

Another reaction to the problem is put forward in what I shall call the portability doctrine. According to this view, utility should not be regarded as defined independently of any problem or experimental situation. Rather, the detailed interpretations and logical decisions concerning its form are to be made in the context of a given problem. The concept is to be treated as a sort of portable partial framework, carried from problem to problem, to be filled out in structure and exact significance according to the demands of the specific problem. This would render it unlike any concept in the physical sciences, although its supporters often compare the development of the utility concept to that of "temperature" and other physical magnitudes [4]. (Quantities such as temperature might be said to vary in meaning from axiom-system to axiom-system—e.g., from statistical mechanics to thermodynamics—or from one mode of measurement to another, but hardly from problem to problem.) In any case, measurements could be carried out only for this specifically interpreted "utility", not for utility in general. So the results would have no direct consequence for the general theory of utility.

A third approach to the problem may be derived from the traditional "satisfaction" interpretation of utility. In the classical analyses of consumer behavior, utility appears to be informally interpreted as a satisfaction caused by receiving the specified amounts of the commodities. The form of singular sentence for such a satisfaction concept might be: "The satisfaction caused in x at time t by receiving commodities 1, 2, . . . , n, at the rates y_1, y_2, . . . , y_n (measured at time t) equals s degrees.'♦ This has the same sort of difficulties as the previously considered forms. If s is just the amount of satisfaction due to these commodities, is total satisfaction due to other commodities besides? And is s to be added or otherwise combined with other satisfactions to arrive at a total satisfaction? These and other questions are obviated, however, if we take satisfaction as a state variable of the individual concerned in the same way that temperature is a state variable of a system or point within a system. No matter what temperature causally depends on in various circumstances, the form of its singular sentence is: "The temperature of system x (or point x) at time t is equal to T degrees." It is not: "The temperature of x at time t due to . . . . equals T degrees" (where the dots are replaced by any explicitly given list of physical magnitudes). If we choose to use a state variable, "pleasure" would be a better word than "satisfaction" since the latter term carries a suggested reference to external cause. The type-sentence for pleasure would then be: "The pleasure of x at time t equals p degrees." We would then have the empirical problem of determining what pleasure depends on, rather than the pseudo-logical one of deciding what entities utility is to be ascribed to. However difficult such a task might appear, it would seem a more honest and healthy relocation of the problem. Science is better equipped to unravel intricate causal connections with the help of clear concepts than to interpret measurements of ill-defined quantities.

So much for the traditional treatment. Turning now to the von Neumann-Morgenstern approach we see that their concept of utility is defined over the class of all probability combinations of events in a class of mutually exclusive events, conceived as capable of taking place in the immediate future of a given individual x at a time t. Provisionally, this seems clear enough from the standpoint of singular sentence structure. Its form seems to be something like the following: "The utility of E for x at time t equals u utiles." This contains no dots nor indeterminate number n. All we have to ascertain is the nature of the entities over which the variable E is to range. Are probability combinations of events also events? Before looking into this question let us consider only the original set of alternative events. The word "event" is used in two distinct ways which it is essential to distinguish. For this purpose I shall make use of Rudolf Carnap's term "proposition" [1] for the sort of entity designated by a complete sentence. More suggestive synonyms might be "situation" or "state-of-affairs". That a certain coin, a, was tossed at a certain moment, t_1, is a proposition, true or false. The class of tosses with that coin, on the other hand, is not a proposition. The class determines a frequency, but not a truth value. It may be regarded as a propositional function of time in the sense that it is designated by an expression ("coin a is tossed at t") which determines a proposition, true or false, for each specification of the time variable. Those probabilists who adhere to a relative frequency interpretation of probability use the term "event" in the sense of propositional function. Von Neumann and Morgenstern explicitly adopt the relative frequency view. Yet the events in the basic class are conceived as related to a "standardized moment. . . in the immediate future". This suggests that preference is basically conceived as holding between propositions rather than propositional functions. This is borne out by the fact that the limitation is applied in order to avoid "the problems of preferences between events in different periods in the future". It is, of course, possible to rank propositional functions at each moment according to preferences among the propositions obtained by specifying that moment.

However, this question becomes more serious when we consider what is involved in expressing a preference between two probability combinations of the members of the basic set. Suppose one combination consists of basic element A with probability p and basic element B with probability 1 - p. If the probability involved is relative frequency probability, A and B can obviously not be propositions. Now suppose they are propositional functions. The probability of A must be the relative frequency of A with respect to some other propositional function C (reference class). (For simplicity I ignore the problem of relative frequency limits in infinite classes.) Presumably, then, it is this event C that is being offered as an alternative to the events in the basic set rather than a probability combination conceived in some more abstract sense. This seems borne out by the fact that in discussion of actual cases, where a person is presented with a probability combination involving event A he is informed that something like a roulette wheel will be spun if he chooses the combination and that $A(t_1)$ will be made true for a specified t_1 if the ball rests in a certain region of the wheel. For the subject to make a meaningful choice he must believe that the experimenter has the power and intention to fulfill his part of the bargain. That is, for a person to have a probability combination pA + (1 - p)B as a genuine alternative to his basic set of mutually exclusive events (propositional functions) there must be possible for him the alternative of another event C exclusive from each of the others. For instance, C may be the event of accepting an offer made by a certain person, accompanied by a certain promise. Further, C must be capable of occurring at the standard future time; it must be such than an occurrence of C is always followed by occurrence of A or by occurrence of B, and finally, C must be such that the relative frequency of joint occurrences of A and C with respect to occurrences of C is p. This requirement, while possibly making clear the logical status of probability combinations of events as events themselves (propositional functions of time), seems to limit the application of the Neumann-Morgenstern approach to such matters as consumer tastes. Alternatives arising in real life are seldom controllable by the outcome of a pre-set random device; this makes it misleading, if not meaningless, to consider choices between probability combinations of them.

The reason von Neumann and Morgenstern give for adopting the relative frequency approach is that it yields a magnitude rather than an ordering. However this does not appear to be exclusively a feature of the relative frequency approach since the work of Carnap [2], (also see [3]).

Although Carnap's work has not yet provided a very general theory of logical probability, the development of more general theories along the same lines seems inevitable, and it may be well to investigate its implications for the utility concept.

First a few words about the concept of logical probability. Logical probability is a straightforward generalization of the basic concept of logical implication. If a sentence e logically implies a sentence h, this means that in virtue alone of the formal meanings of the sentences any possible world in which e is true must be such that h also is true. In other words, the range of possible worlds in which e would be true is a subset of the range of possible world in which h would be true. The concept of "possible world" can be made precise for the purposes of the logic of a given axiom system in terms of certain strongest sentences (state-descriptions) formulable in the terms of the system. It seems then a natural and inevitable step to develop a theory covering the relation that holds between sentences whose ranges overlap, but without the simple containment corresponding to logical implication. Here we would have something weaker than logical implication which we might call support or confirmation or logical probability. If a reasonable measure of range is found, this theory can become quantitative. Carnap has found such a measure for languages (axiom systems) involving a denumerable number of individual terms and a finite number of predicates of any degree. If $m(h)$ is such a measure of range for the sentence h and $h \cdot e$ is the conjunction of the sentences h and e, then we can take $\dfrac{m(h \cdot e)}{m(e)}$ as the logical probability of the hypothesis h on the evidence e. As might be expected this quantity takes the value 1 when e logically implies h. This ratio bears an obvious resemblance to relative frequency but here there is no question of the "favorable event" h having a frequency. Being a sentence, it can only be true or false. The multiplicity needed for arriving at a meaningful ratio comes from the ensemble of possible world states. I use the term "ensemble" here deliberately to suggest to those familiar with the use of this term in statistical mechanics that it may be logical probability rather than relative frequency probability which is used implicitly in statistical mechanics.

Using the concept of logical probabiltiy, it seems possible to sketch out the form of a utility concept which takes propositions as its principal arguments rather than either indeterminate numbers of commodities or events in the relative frequentist's sense, and which is potentially wider in its field of application than the latter. Since logical probability is in no sense a subjective probability, the concept first defined will be normative, a rational utility suitable for the definition of rational preference and rational decision. After this, the possibility of using a similar schema for a non-normative empirical utility will be discussed.

Although it is not essential to this approach, I shall couch my discussion in hedonistic terms for three reasons. First, because pleasure is a state variable having a clear logical form, it can serve as a model of form for alternative formulations. Secondly it seems of interest to see that the difficulties noted earlier in connection with the attempt to base utility on satisfaction can be avoided by use of probabilistic considerations. Thirdly, this procedure may suggest the possibility that some similar sort of psychological interpretation may offer ways of arriving at empirical utility estimates in addition to observing actual decisional behavior, though without making the choice-potential approach more difficult or less valuable.

Let $P(x,t)$ be the pleasure or "hedonic tone" of x at time t. For any x this determines a time series which we may picture oscillating irregularly about a normal position from birth to death. Let

$$H(x,t,s) = \int_t^{t+s} P(x,\tau)d\tau.$$

$H(x,t,s)$ may be called the prospective happiness of x during s beginning at t. Of course, hedonist x at time t will not know the value of $H(x,t,s)$ for any positive s, but he may be able to form estimates of it and he will hope that it is as large as possible.

With logical probability we can form a concept corresponding to mathematical expectation of a magnitude z which we may call the estimate of z with respect to given evidence e. Let $E(z,w,e)$ be the estimate of magnitude z for the argument w on the basis of the proposition e. (I shall use "e" as a variable over propositions rather than over sentences, in contradistinction to Carnap. With the development of modal logic this becomes a perfectly feasible alteration conducive to simplicity of discussion without affecting the fundamental idea.)

Let $e(x,t)$ be a proposition representing the total experience x has accumulated by time t (the concept being defined makes the fiction that x has total recall). We may now lay down the following definition.

The proximate rational utility of proposition p for x at t with respect to time-span s equals u utiles if and only if p is logically compatible with the total experience of x at t and the estimate of his prospective happiness during s beginning at t on the basis of p together with his total experience at t equals u.

Using the symbols already defined, together with the sign $\Diamond$ from modal logic for logical possibility (see p. 175, [1]) this can be written out:

$$U(p,x,t,s) = u =_{df} \Diamond(p \cdot e(\dot{x},t)) \cdot (E(H,x,t,s,p \cdot e(x,t)) = u)$$

where the dot denotes conjunction of propositions.

Absolute utility could be defined with respect to total prospective happiness:

$$U(p,x,t) =_{df} U(p,x,t,\infty).$$

Proximate utility seems a more useful concept, however, since absolute utility might vary too slightly between propositions to be of help in practical decisions.

The above formulation does not purport to be a definition of utility but rather a sketch of one possible form of such definition, which would confer a clear logical structure on the utility concept. The essential point is the employment of propositions as the entities to which utility is attributed. This permits utility to be attributed to a situation consisting just of receipt of d dollars by x_1 at t_1 without raising questions of complementarity or the need to specify a total world future of which this was a part; for the definition requires that complementarities, possible world futures, and the like, in so far as x can determine them on the basis of $e(x,t)$, are taken into account in the estimation.

Propositions can be as simple or complex as we please and hence provide an extremely flexible base for theory or measurement (once they become well-defined through specification of the details of the language system employed). Indeed, the effects are about what could be hoped for from the portability doctrine with the difference that we would have here, at least potentially, a single, completely interpreted concept. Furthermore, instead of being restricted to sets of mutually exclusive acts or strategies we could attach a utility to any propositions not contradicted by our experience. We could then decide our preferences among them according to this utility regardless of whether they are within our control or whether they are mutually exclusive. For example, p and p·q are not mutually exclusive but it might be rational to prefer p to p·q if q is unpleasant, simply because p does not entail p·q. It would seem essential to rational conduct to be able to evaluate situations directly without regard to whether they are possible consequences of our actions. And it seems not inconsistent with normal experience to feel preferences even among past events or among general laws as long as our own experience does not directly contradict them. On the other hand it should be noted that the suggested definition confers equal utility for x on all propositions known by x to be true. I am not sure how this corresponds to common feeling on the matter but it could not affect any actual decision behavior.

Using symbols already introduced, rational preference (x rationally prefers proposition p to proposition q at time t) could thus be defined as follows:

$$P(x,p,q,t) =_{df} \Diamond(p \cdot e(x,t)) \cdot \Diamond(q \cdot e(x,t)) \cdot (U(p,x,t) > U(q,x,t))$$

In fact the measure of this preference could be taken to be the difference of the utilities.

A definition of rational decision among courses of action could be based on the above definition if one could define some such concept as "p is a possible course of action for x at t" where "possible" is meant in the ordinary, not the purely logical, sense. It should be noted that Carnap's formulation of Bernoulli's rule of rational decision, which rests upon an undefined concept of utility, has been made the basis for the present definition-schema for utility itself.

The fact that rational utility is here sketched as defined directly, with rational preference as a derivative concept, does not mean that measurements of <u>empirical</u> utility might not rest heavily on observed preferences. Nevertheless, I would be inclined to define empirical utility in basically the same way. Instead of using strict logical probability based on a Carnap measure function though, I would suppose that the individual's subjective probability could be represented by a measure function varying in certain ways from the norm; and instead of taking his total experience, I would take that part of it which he actually brings to bear in making his choice. Using such a definition, in fact, one might be able to reason backward (under certain controlled conditions) from observed choices to partial determination of a man's information, his proximate objectives, or the peculiarities of his subjective probability measure. On the other hand, one would not be limited to observation of overt choices.

BIBLIOGRAPHY

1. Carnap, Rudolf, Meaning and Necessity: A Study in Semantics and Modal Logic, Chicago, 1947.

2. Carnap, Rudolf, Logical Foundations of Probability, Chicago, 1950.

3. Helmer, O. and Oppenheim, P., A Syntactical Definition of Probability and of Degree of Confirmation, Journal of Symbolic Logic, X (1945), 25-60.

4. von Neumann, J. and Morgenstern, O., Theory of Games and Economic Behavior, Princeton, 1944.

CHAPTER XVI

TENDENCIES TOWARD GROUP COMPARABILITY IN COMPETITIVE BARGAINING*

by

Paul J. Hoffman, Leon Festinger, Douglas H. Lawrence

STANFORD UNIVERSITY, UNIVERSITY OF MINNESOTA
STANFORD UNIVERSITY

Introduction

The present study is concerned with some of the socio-psychological factors that determine behavior in a situation where some ability is being revealed or measured. In such a situation, in order to evaluate their ability, persons frequently tend to compare their own performance with the performance of others whom they accept as comparable to themselves. As a consequence, the individual's behavior is determined more by his performance relative to those others than by the absolute level of his performance. If the situation in which the particular ability is measured is a bargaining situation where coalitions can form, it is possible to predict both the type and strength of the coalitions that form, and the relative stability of these when the composition of the group and the importance of the task for the participants is varied.

A motivational analysis of this type has implications, not only for social psychological theory but also for the theory of games [2]. This is seen most clearly when "rational" bargaining behavior in the typical game situation is analyzed under the assumption that the only motivation present is a tendency on the part of each player to maximize the total number of points he obtains. Imagine a game involving three players where a fixed amount of money, points, or some commodity is to be divided

---

*This study was conducted under contract N onr 225 (01) between the Office of Naval Research and Stanford University, and in cooperation with the Laboratory for Research in Social Relations of the University of Minnesota. The theoretical formulations on which the study is based were developed by Dr. Leon Festinger, and he will extend them in a forthcoming article.

among them. The rules of the game are such that no one individual can obtain the total amount by his own efforts. If any two of them agree to cooperate they can share the amount on any basis satisfactory to the two of them.

Procedure. In addition the following conditions are assumed: (1) that all individuals are equally and singly motivated to obtain as large a share of the points as possible, and (2) that they are all equal in bargaining skill. Two things should be noted about this game. First of all, while it is mandatory for two of the three players to form a coalition in order to obtain points, a given player has no rational basis for selecting between the other two members in attempting to form the initial partnership. Hence, in the long run, each of the three possible coalitions in this group will be formed equally often. The second point to note is that there is no logical termination to the bargaining process. Each player can break up any coalition formed in opposition to him by offering one player more points than he is getting from his present coalition. Hence an endless process of bargaining would develop and be maintained.

This result, however, is contrary to everyday experience. It is to be expected that coalitions will form between particular pairs of players more frequently than between others and that these will be of a relatively stable and permanent nature. The difference between the "rational" prediction illustrated above and common psychological expectation centers about the nature and variety of the motivations operating in the bargaining situation.

When the sole motivation present is the desire to obtain a maximum number of points and when the players have equal bargaining skill, all coalitions between members are equivalent and equally likely to occur. Predictable and stable coalitions can form, however, when there is a variety of motives operating and their strengths are unequally distributed among the players. Then even though two players make identical offers to a third in terms of the absolute number of points involved, these offers are not equivalent in value for that player in terms of the other satisfactions they can provide. This results in the possibility that a particular individual may find himself in an advantageous position relative to the others. His offers may carry both the potentiality of points and the potentiality of other satisfactions. To the extent that a second individual requires both of these types of satisfaction, there is a high probability that he will accept offers from the first player. Moreover, the player left out of such a coalition will be relatively impotent in his attempts to break it up as long as the desire for points is subordinate to the other motivations of the coalition members. From this point of view, it is obvious that coalitions may in fact become predictable and stable.

The hypotheses underlying the present experiment are first, that these additional motivations in a bargaining situation arise in part from each individual's concern about his comparability to other members of the group on the ability that is shown in the bargaining. This results in pressures to achieve uniformity in the group. In our culture, at least, there are also motivations to strive to be better than others which operate simultaneously with the pressures toward uniformity. The contrast between these types of motivation and the motivation to obtain a maximum share of the points is seen most clearly in situations where the points involved are ratings, prestige objects or other symbolic representations of relative status. The individual's concern about them arises not because of their absolute or intrinsic value, but because in this activity they are indicative of his status relative to others. In a competitive society, such concern about the status significance indicated by the symbols tends to operate even where money or other commodities of direct utilitarian value are involved.

The influence of the concern about relative status on the formation of coalitions can be shown by referring to the previously described game. Assume that one of the individuals obtains an early initial advantage of a number of points while the others at this stage have few or none. These points function as symbols indicating to the others that this person is superior to the other two in that activity. The result is an increase in the motivation of the other two individuals of the group to draw close to him. Consequently they will be strongly motivated to form a coalition against him insofar as this aids in overcoming his lead. Furthermore, they will resist any attempt on his part to disrupt this coalition even though by accepting his offers either one of them might gain more points than he is able to obtain by remaining in the coalition. This happens because a conflict has developed between their desire to acquire the maximum number of points possible, and their desire to reduce the discrepancy between themselves and others. The refusal of offers from a person with the large initial advantage in points indicates that the conflict has been resolved in favor of the desire to reduce the discrepancy.

This analysis is based on the hypothesis that a major

motivation of each individual is to compare himself with and to draw close to or surpass the others in the group. The reference individuals with whom each compares himself, however, are not selected indiscriminately. The amateur golfer does not compare himself with the professional, nor is the occasional bridge player concerned with his status relative to the expert. The conditions determining which individuals are selected as a reference group are not clearly defined as yet, but in general an individual is concerned about his status relative to others whom he considers of approximately equal ability. He tends to exclude from his comparisons individuals who appear definitely superior or inferior to him in this activity. This is identical to the process of "rejection" when pressures toward uniformity arise concerning opinions. There the individual does not evaluate his opinions by comparison with others who are too divergent. Similarly, individuals do not evaluate their abilities by comparison with those who are too divergent [1].

Conditions in which all members of a group regard themselves as comparable are known as "peer" conditions. Conditions in which one or more individuals are regarded by the others as non-comparable, i.e., as definitely superior or inferior, are known as "non-peer" conditions. In terms of the previous analysis, it is expected that in peer conditions predictable and stable coalitions will form in opposition to the individual who has an initial advantage. In non-peer conditions, however, this tendency will be reduced because the other members of the group are motivated to surpass each other and are less concerned with the status of the non-comparable individual. Even though the tendency to compete with the non-comparable individual is reduced, it does not disappear because the condition of non-comparability is relative and continuous, rather than all or none.

There is a second important determinant of decisions involving the formation of coalitions. It is obvious that the desire to achieve and maintain relative status will vary depending upon whether or not the individual regards his status on that task as important. The golfer or bridge player will be concerned about status differentials which develop in the play of these games but not on a wide variety of others. Similarly, performance on an activity which requires the use of intellectual abilities will result in a motivation to achieve status in direct proportion to the degree to which this type of activity is considered important by the individuals involved. Increasing the importance of a task in effect increases the individual's concern about any status differences that may develop with the result that he becomes even more motivated to equal or surpass the others. Consequently, he becomes even less willing to cooperate with anyone having an initial advantage. Thus under conditions of high task importance the coalitions become highly stable. In contrast, conditions of low task importance may result in a situation in which incidental motivations are as strong as the concern about relative status. In this case the stability of the coalitions is reduced.

In summary, it is postulated that an important motivation in a bargaining situation is the individual's concern about his status in the activity relative to other members of the group and his desire to equal or surpass them. The accumulation of points is significant for him because these represent the degree of comparability among the participating individuals. Consequently, predictable and stable coalitions in opposition to an individual having an initial advantage will occur more frequently when that individual is a peer member of the group than when he is a non-peer member. Similarly, increases in the value placed on the points as a result of making the task important to the individual increases his concern over comparability and indirectly his tendency to form stable coalitions in opposition to an individual who obtains an initial advantage. These predictions are tested by the following experiment.

SUBJECTS AND PROCEDURE

Twenty-eight groups of subjects participated in the original experiment which was performed at Stanford University. The entire experiment was then replicated with twenty-eight groups at the City College of San Francisco. Subjects were undergraduates, drawn from the introductory psychology courses. The two groups were alike with respect to age, but the Stanford subjects were of a higher socio-economic level and probably of higher average intelligence because of the differences in entrance requirements at the two schools. Stanford subjects also appeared to be somewhat more mature and less naive than the San Francisco students, most of whom had had no previous experience as subjects in psychological experiments. Only male students were used.

The twenty-eight groups in each replication were randomly but equally distributed between the four experimental conditions: (1) high task importance and peer relations, (2) high task importance and non-peer relations, (3) low task importance and peer relations, and (4) low task importance and non-peer relations. Of the three individuals in each group, two were subjects and the third was a paid-participant trained beforehand in the role he was to play. Two paid-participants were selected from Stanford for use in the Stanford experiment, and three from San Francisco City College for participation with those groups. These were male seniors who were unknown to the subjects. When the two subjects and the paid-participant arrived for the experiment, a check was made to see that the two subjects had no more than a passing acquaintance with each other and that neither knew the paid-participant. In cases where this was not true, the group was discarded. The three group members were seated around a table with the positions clearly labeled as A, B, and C. The paid-participant invariably was seated at A.

Each group was informed that the purpose of the experiment was to collect standardization and validation data on a new type intelligence test consisting of three parts. Subjects were told that the first part of the test was similar to the usual type of paper and pencil intelligence test, the second measured the ability to interact with others, and the third was designed to measure insight into one's own behavior and the behavior of others. In actuality the first was a paper and pencil intelligence test included to lend credibility to the situation, the second was the bargaining situation or test proper, and the third was a questionnaire to provide independent evidence that the experimental manipulations had changed the individuals' attitudes and perceptions. The low versus high task importance and the peer versus non-peer conditions were established in the following ways:

1. Task importance. The importance of the task to the subjects was manipulated in two ways: (1) by the instructions given them concerning the validity of the test purported to be measuring intelligence, and (2) by the content of the paper and pencil test. In the high importance groups, the instructions given them just prior to beginning the experiment were as follows:

> We have asked you to come here today to take a new
> intelligence test which has recently been devised and
> which has shown itself to be highly superior to the usual
> kind of intelligence test. We have scheduled three of you
> together because, although some parts of the test are

taken individually, other parts of the test require interaction among three persons. The test is separated into
a number of parts and we will explain each part to you
when we come to it.

Let me explain to you why we are asking you to take
this test. Recent research in psychology has produced
new knowledge about intelligence and intelligent behavior
in people which has enabled psychologists to construct
this new test. It has been tried out with many different
kinds of people and in every case has been shown to be
greatly superior and more valid in measuring the intelligence of individuals than the older type test. Needless to
say, when such an important development occurs it is
extremely valuable to accumulate as much data using the
test as possible. As the test has not yet been used with
people on the West Coast, we are especially interested in
the data we will collect here.

After we measure your I.Q. with this test we will compare it with other records we can get on you and with
scores you have made on the older kinds of tests. There
will be some of you for whom we do not have sufficient
records. If that turns out to be the case we may have to
ask you to take some other tests sometime within the
next month. The results so far with this new test indicate
that now, for perhaps the first time, we can really measure how intelligent a person is with an extremely high degree of accuracy. We shall of course be glad to inform
each of you about your I.Q. after we have scored the test.

This emphasis on the validity of the test was underscored by
the content of the items given the high importance groups during
the pencil and paper part of the experiment. The printed booklet
given these groups contained 24 synonym-antonym items and 20
verbal analogy items drawn from the Terman Concept Mastery
test, a section from the paragraph comprehension section of the
Ohio State Psychological Examination, and 10 items from the
Minnesota Paper Form Board. A ten minute time limit was imposed on this test.

The instructions for the low importance groups were designed
to belittle the validity of the test. After the same introductory
paragraph as used for the high importance group, the instructions were as follows:

Let me explain some things to you about why we are
asking you to take this test. The psychologist who

published the test claimed that it was useful in measuring intelligence. Other people, trying the test out, have disputed this claim and have shown by their results that it has nothing to do with intelligence. In fact their results seem to show that it has nothing to do with anything. We have decided in the department here to do some very careful research to settle once and for all whether or not the test is any good. We have already given the test to large numbers of people, and, comparing their scores on this test with scores on other tests, with grades, and with many other measures, we are quite convinced that the present test which you will take is pretty meaningless. Nevertheless we want more data so that when we publish our results there will be absolutely no question about it.

This lack of validity was underscored by the content of the printed booklet given the low importance groups during the pencil and paper part of the test. The improvised items were of the following types: (a) general information of an extremely low difficulty level, (b) items requiring value judgments on moralistic questions, (c) items requiring judgments of occupation from facial expression, (d) items requiring judgments of emotion from facial expression, and (e) jokes to be rated in terms of their humor.

2. Peer versus non-peer. The peer condition, in which each subject was to regard the other subject and the paid-participant as comparable to himself in intellectual ability, was established in part by instructions and in part by the behavior of the paid-participant. These instructions were given just after the completion of the pencil and paper test and just prior to the bargaining situation. For the peer condition they were as follows:

Before we start the next part of the test, I would like you to know some of the reasons for scheduling you particular three persons together in the same group. This next part of the test requires that in each of our groups the three persons should be approximately equal in intelligence and mental ability insofar as this can be roughly determined in advance. We consequently have taken the liberty of looking up your grades, your various achievement and aptitude test results, and as much else as we could get about you. We are reasonably certain that you three are very close together in intelligence as measured by those tests.

In this next part of the test you will see why it is necessary to have the three of you matched so closely in intelligence. The next part requires that each of you deal
with the other members in the group and consequently it
is necessary that all three of you be as equal in intelligence as we could manage.

The paid-participant emphasized his equality with the others
by pacing himself during the pencil and paper test at the same
rate as the two subjects in the group.

In the non-peer groups, where the two subjects were to regard the paid-participant as definitely superior to themselves
in intellectual ability and therefore as non-comparable, the instructions were as follows:

> Before we actually start taking the second part of the
> test, I would like you to know some of the reasons for
> scheduling you particular three persons together in the
> same group. We wanted to be sure that in each of our
> groups that take this test, there was at least one person
> of very superior intelligence. Now one of you here has
> taken an intensive battery of tests earlier in the quarter,
> and we asked specifically that he sign up for this hour.
> The person in this group who took this intensive battery
> of tests earlier is the one of extremely superior intelli-
> gence.

> In this part of the test, part "B", you will see the rea-
> son we were so careful to be sure that there was at least
> one person in the group of extremely high intelligence.
> The next part of the test involves dealing with others in
> the group and in the way the test is standardized, it is
> necessary that such discrepancies in intelligence among
> you exist.

As neither of the two subjects in the group had taken an in-
tensive battery of tests, it was assumed that each would conclude
that either the other subject or the paid-participant must be the
one of extremely superior intelligence. This speculation was
then directed at the paid-participant as the result of his subsequent behavior. During the paper and pencil test, he worked
through the booklet easily and quickly, turning it in well before
the expiration of the time limit.

Following these instructions, the next part of the test was the
bargaining situation. Each of the three members of a group was
given a set of triangular pieces cut out of masonite, the sets

differing from each other only in color. By assembling these pieces correctly it was possible for each member of the group to form an individual square requiring six of the seven pieces provided him. The seventh piece was a large right-angled isosceles triangle. Any combination of two players could form a "group" square by combining their large triangles. This group square had a larger area than did the individual square.

The bargaining was governed by a set of rules read to the subjects in advance of the trials. These rules emphasized that the objective of the players was to earn points, since these points were to be added to the scores on the paper and pencil test to determine the I.Q. There were to be a series of five trials, each of four minute duration, and on each of which it was possible to earn as many as eight points. These could be earned in one of two ways. If a person assembled his individual square and no other squares were formed on that trial, the square was worth eight points. If two persons combined pieces to form a group square, this square was also worth eight points, provided that the two partners agreed on how they would divide these eight points between themselves. It was permissible for either of the two persons in an agreement of this sort to break it at any time during the trial and to enter into a new agreement with the third person in the group. In the event that more than one square was formed in a given trial, only the largest square would win. In case two squares of the same size were formed, no one would get any points. There was one exception to these rules. If any person succeeded in forming the individual square on the first trial, he automatically won that trial and in addition received a bonus of twelve points which he could divide among the three players in any way he wished.

These rules achieved the following results. On the first trial while the situation was still somewhat unstructured for the subjects, each of them attempted to form an individual square because of the bonus of twelve points offered. The problem was so difficult, however, that only the paid-participant was able to do it. He always decided to keep the points for himself, thereby obtaining an initial lead of 20 points over the other two members. Because of his manipulation of the pieces, it was always clear to the other two subjects by the end of the first trial how they should go about constructing their individual squares. But since the assembly of an individual square by either of the remaining group members would result in a tie, with no points awarded, this solution became functionally useless for the remaining four trials. The only possibility remaining was for two

players to form a group square from the large isosceles triangles. The paid-participant emphasized this point at the beginning of the second trial by first forming such a square with
individual B and then with C as though he were just exploring
the possibilities in the situation. As this group square was obviously larger than the individual square, it would always win
the points when formed.

The bargaining behavior of the paid-participant during the
second through the fifth trial was predetermined. At the beginning of the trial he offered to make the group square with B
and to give him four of the eight points. From this point on his
behavior was governed by the following rules:

1. If B said "yes", A rested until something else happened.
   If B said "no" A waited for a moment until some agreement between B and C had been reached.
2. If B and C did not reach an agreement, A offered B five
   points. If the offer was refused, he offered six. If this
   was refused, he offered seven. After any acceptance, he
   rested until something else occurred. If the offer of seven
   was refused, he began directing offers to C in the same
   sequence.
3. If the person left out made A an offer, A accepted it if it
   gave him more points. He did not take the initiative as
   long as he was in a coalition.
4. If the BC coalition formed on an even split, A proceeded
   as in 2.
5. If the BC coalition formed on an uneven split, A made an
   offer of four to that player who was getting the least. If
   the answer was "yes", he rested. If "no", he proceeded
   as in 2 continuing to direct his offers to the same person
   until an offer was accepted or until an offer of seven
   points was refused. In this latter case he began directing
   his offers to the other coalition member.

The purpose of these rules was in part to make the bargaining behavior of the paid-participant appear natural, but at the
same time to ensure that when forced he would always offer up
to seven points. In this way the strength of the coalitions
against him could be measured. As each offer was made, it
was recorded sequentially by the experimenter in such a manner as to indicate the size of the offer, by whom it was made,
toward whom it was directed, and whether it was accepted,
ignored, or rejected. In the Stanford experiment, the subjects
were given a warning 30 seconds before the end of each trial.

This was eliminated in the San Francisco replication since its effect was to materially reduce the amount of bidding within the period prior to the warning.

RESULTS

The results of this experiment are described under three headings. First the data from the questionnaire are analyzed to determine the extent to which differences in task importance and in peer relations were actually established between the various groups. Following this, the results bearing on the choice behavior during the last four trials of bargaining are presented under two headings. The first of these covers terminal coalitions, i.e., the agreements which existed at the end of a trial and thereby determined the distribution of points. The second presents the results pertaining to temporary coalitions, i.e., those tentative agreements existing prior to the formation of the terminal coalition.

The Success of the Experimental Manipulations

One item of the questionnaire given as the final part of the test had each subject rate his own I.Q. and that of the paid-participant on the assumption that discrepancies in these ratings would be indicative of the extent to which a given subject regarded A, the paid-participant, as comparable to himself. The mean discrepancies in I.Q. ratings (rating of paid-participant minus self-rating) are evaluated in the analysis of Table 1. The subjects' rating of A in the peer conditions averages 3.27 I.Q. points more than the subject's rating of himself, but in the non-peer condition it averages 13.00 points more. This difference is significant (P < .001). Discrepancies are not significantly different for comparisons involving task importance, schools, or interactions. The assertion can therefore be made with a high degree of certainty that perceived differences in comparability were in fact established between the peer and the non-peer conditions, such differences being based upon assessment of intellectual status.

A second item in the questionnaire had the subject evaluate the bargaining situation as to the degree of validity they believed it to have as a measure of intelligence. It is possible to infer from these ratings the degree to which subjects considered their performance in the bargaining situation as important, and thus the extent to which they were thereby motivated. The

Table 1

Analysis of Discrepancies Between Subject's Rating
of Paid-participant and Rating of Self on I.Q.

Source	d.f.	Variance Est.	P
Importance	1	11.16	
Peer vs. Non-Peer	1	5,304.02	$< .001$
Schools	1	75.45	
Interactions	4	211.66	
Error	48	92.70	

obtained ratings on this item are evaluated in the analysis of
Table 2. Subjects assigned to conditions of high task importance
tend to rate the bargaining procedure as a more valid measure
of intelligence than do subjects assigned to conditions of low
importance $(P < .001)$. In addition the difference attributable
to the replications of the experiment is significant $(P < .01)$,
with the San Francisco subjects rating the bargaining situation
as more valid than do subjects of the Stanford experiment.
Since the San Francisco subjects represented a somewhat less
select group in terms of college aptitude, it is reasonable to
expect that they would be more concerned over their intellectual
status and would consequently ascribe a higher importance to
the task.

Table 2

Rated Validity of Bargaining Situation
as a Measure of Intelligence

Source	d.f.	Variance Est.	P
Importance	1	46.29	$< .001$
Peer vs. Non-Peer	1	0.57	
Schools	1	7.00	$< .01$
Interactions	4	0.14	
Error	104	0.76	

The Formation of Coalitions

Assuming that the groups were differentiated with respect to
the importance of the task and the degree of comparability between members of the group, the major question is the influence
of these variables on the formation of coalitions. A relatively
direct measure of the extent to which coalitions were formed in

opposition to the paid-participant is the discrepancy between the number of points he was able to obtain on each trial and the number he would be expected to obtain if the coalitions were formed on the basis of chance. On a chance basis the paid-participant, hereafter referred to as A, would be expected to receive on the average a third of the eight points available for division, or 2.67 points per trial, as would each of the two subjects, B and C. In the event that A receives significantly less than the average of the other members of the group, he is being discriminated against by them as far as their willingness to form coalitions with him is concerned.

The average number of points per trial earned by A in the last four trials under the various conditions of the experiment is shown in Table 3, along with the statistical analysis of the sums on which the averages are based.

Table 3a

Average Points Per Trial Earned by A

Impor.	School	Peer	Non-Peer	Avg.
High	S.F.	1.29	1.75	1.52
	Stan.	1.57	2.39	1.98
	(Avg.)	(1.43)	(2.07)	(1.75)
Low	S.F.	1.32	2.54	1.93
	Stan.	2.50	4.36	3.43
	(Avg.)	(1.91)	(3.45)	(2.68)
(S. F. Avg.)		1.30	2.15	1.72
(Stan. Avg.)		2.04	3.37	2.71
(Avg.)		(1.67)	(2.76)	(2.21)

Table 3b

Analysis of Average Points Per Trial for A

Source	d.f.	Variance	P
Importance	1	200.65	$< .02$
Peer vs. Non-Peer	1	274.57	$< .01$
Schools	1	208.28	$< .01$
Interactions	4	39.25	
Error	48	24.89	

It is apparent from Table 3 that A is generally unable to obtain a chance number of points under the various conditions. The one exception is the condition of low importance and non-peer relations at Stanford, in which A receives significantly more points than would be expected. Under each of the two replications of the experiment the pattern of results is essentially the same. A obtains more points under low importance than when task importance is high (P < .02), and more under the non-peer conditions than under peer conditions (P < .01). These differences are in the direction predicted by the theoretical assumptions underlying the experiment. It should be noted that in each experimental condition A receives fewer points in the San Francisco replication than at Stanford (P < .01). This consistent discrepancy becomes more meaningful when it is recalled that the questionnaire data gave evidence of higher importance being ascribed to the task in the San Francisco groups than at Stanford. The experiment might therefore be interpreted as including three different levels of task importance instead of two. This interpretation would reconcile the differences between the two replications.

The failure of A to secure the number of points expected by chance is due to two factors: (1) he was unable to form a fair share (2/3) of terminal coalitions even though he was willing to offer as many as seven points, and (2) even in those coalitions of which he was a member he was unable to obtain a fair division (4 out of 8) of the points. The influence of the first factor is demonstrated in Table 4 where the average number of terminal coalitions including A during the four trials is tabulated. The pattern of results is the same as that involving point totals for A.

Table 4a

Average Percent of Terminal Coalitions Having A as a Member

Impor.	School	Peer	Non-Peer	Avg.
High	S.F.	36	46	41
	Stan.	57	64	60
	(Avg.)	(46)	(55)	(50)
Low	S.F.	43	64	54
	Stan.	61	86	74
	(Avg.)	(52)	(75)	(64)
(S. F. Avg.)		40	55	48
(Stan. Avg.)		59	75	67
(Avg.)		(50)	(65)	(58)

Table 4b

Analysis of Average Number of Coalitions
Having A as a Member

Source	d.f.	Variance	P
Importance	1	4.57	< .05
Peer Cond.	1	5.78	< .05
Schools	1	5.78	< .05
Interactions	4	0.18	
Error	48	1.01	

For all conditions combined, A is able to form fewer terminal coalitions than would be expected on the basis of chance $(P < .01)$, and therefore fewer than the average of the two subjects. Differences for each of the experimental conditions are significant at the five per cent level and are in the expected direction.

The influence of the second factor is shown in Table 5 where the average number of points per coalition obtained by A when A is in a coalition is tabulated. This analysis shows whether or not A is able to obtain a fair share of the points when he is one of the partners in a coalition. It is apparent from the table that the differences between means are once more in the anticipated directions.

Table 5

Average Points Per Coalition Earned by A

Motiv.	School	Peer	Non-peer	Avg.
High	S. F.	3.60 *	3.58 **	3.59
	Stan.	3.19	3.77	3.48
	Avg.	(3.36)	(3.68)	(3.53)
Low	S. F.	3.12 *	4.00	3.63
	Stan.	4.15 **	5.16	4.69
	Avg.	(3.68)	(4.57)	(4.18)
S. F.	Avg.	3.36	3.81	3.61
Stan.	Avg.	3.63	4.46	4.06
		(3.51)	(4.15)	(3.86)

*mean based on 5 groups.
**mean based on 6 groups.

Those groups in which A never succeeded in entering a coalition had to be omitted from the analysis.

The differences between the peer and non-peer conditions and between the high and low importance conditions are only significant at the 10% level of confidence.[1]

The results of these three analyses are consistent in indicating that coalitions tend to form in opposition to the player who obtains an initial advantage. The strength of this tendency is greatest when the task is of high importance to the members of the group and when they perceive each other as peers or equals. As a result of this tendency, the paid participant is unable to form his fair share of terminal coalitions and must pay more than a fair share of the points in order to form such coalitions.

One additional analysis of the terminal coalition data was made to check on the validity of a deduction which was made from the theoretical formulation of this experiment. We would expect that in the peer situation B and C would be competing primarily with A and not with each other. We should then find that terminal coalitions between B and C took the form of an even division of the points. Conversely, under non-peer conditions, B and C would be competing primarily with each other, since A would be regarded as non-comparable by both of them. As a result, terminal coalitions involving B and C would tend to take the form of an uneven division of the points. An analysis of the types of terminal coalitions involving B and C supports this deduction. Under peer conditions 63% of such coalitions involved an equal split, but under non-peer conditions only 34% of them did so, a difference significant beyond the .05 level. Thus, comparability of A to the other members in the group, induced by the peer conditions, makes a coalition involving an even split a desirable and stable outcome for the two subjects. Conversely, when A is incomparable, the competition between B and C makes the desirable outcome, for either one, an agreement which gives him more than the opposing subject.

Another indication of the opposition to A is shown by an analysis of the temporary coalitions, that is, those coalitions tentatively agreed to during the bargaining process. One measure of these is the number of excess points A must pay in order to break up an existing coalition between B and C. A discrepancy score was computed for all temporary coalitions in which A was not a member. This score is the difference between what the coalition subject was receiving in the coalition and what he accepted from A in breaking up the coalition. If the subject refused all offers from A then the discrepancy was calculated as if the subject had accepted an offer of 9 points, one more than the total number available. The average of these for each experimental condition is shown in Table 6.

Table 6a

Average Discrepancy Paid to Break B-C Coalition

Impor.	School	Peer	Non-Peer	Total
High	S. F.	2.2	2.0	2.1
	Stan.	3.4	2.2	2.8
	(Avg.)	(2.8)	(2.1)	(2.5)
Low	S. F.	2.4	1.8	2.1
	Stan.	1.6	1.2	1.4
	(Avg.)	(2.0)	(1.5)	(1.8)
(S. F. Avg.)		2.3	1.9	2.1
(Stan. Avg.)		2.5	1.7	2.1
(Avg.)		(2.4)	(1.8)	(2.1)

Table 6b

Analysis of Discrepancy Paid to Break B-C Coalition

Source	d.f.	Variance	Est. P
Impor.	1	841.1	$<.05$
Peer Cond.	1	841.1	$<.05$
Schools	1	1.4	
Impor. Schools	1	970.9	$<.05$
Inter.	3	14.1	
Error	48	164.1	

The results follow the expected pattern. A must offer more points when the task is of high importance than when it is of low importance, and must offer more under peer conditions than under non-peer. The significant interaction between Importance and Schools is due to the fact that in the San Francisco data there are no differences between the High and Low Importance conditions while in the Stanford data these differences are large.

DISCUSSION

The theory which forms the basis for this experiment hypothesizes that competition arises because individuals, in situations where they are evaluating some ability, are strongly motivated by a concern about their comparability to other members of the group with respect to the ability which they are evaluating. This concern over comparability leads to attempts to assess the abilities of others in relation to themselves. But an individual is not concerned over the comparability of all individuals. Rather, he tends to exclude those who are perceived as definitely superior or inferior to himself in this activity and to concentrate on those who are perceived as being within the same general range of ability.

To the extent that concern over comparability is present, discrepancies in points or other symbols come to have relative rather than absolute value. They tend to be interpreted primarily as indicators of the individual's status with respect to the other members rather than as something of direct utilitarian value. This is especially true when the points gained represent intellectual, athletic, or social ability, but it is also probably true to a large extent when they represent money or commodities. As a result, whenever the task is made more important to an individual, the value of these points increases. This, in turn, adds to his concern over comparability to others and also to his motivation to surpass them on the task.

It follows from these assumptions that in a bargaining situation where all group members regard one another as comparable, stable coalitions will form in opposition to any member of the group who gains an advantage. The point advantage held by this member of the group is interpreted by the other group members as a loss in status to them, and they are consequently motivated to overcome it. Coalitions between them satisfy the motivations of both to retain comparability with each other while at the same time reducing the discrepancy between them and the individual with the initial advantage. The individual with the advantage in points cannot offer the same type of satisfaction. He will be compelled to offer excessive points commensurate with the score differential which exists in order to form a coalition. On the other hand, if this advantage is held by an individual regarded by the other two as non-comparable, coalitions in opposition to him will have less tendency to form, for his point advantage represents a smaller loss of status. Non-peer conditions would therefore be expected to be more favorable for a person with an initial advantage than would peer conditions.

It similarly would be predicted that the formation of stable coalitions will be even more prominent as the importance of the task is increased. This follows from the assumption that any increase in the importance of the symbols involved strengthens the motivation to achieve comparability in the group. Thus, conditions of high task importance will be less favorable to the person with an initial advantage than will conditions of low importance.

The results of the experiment strongly support this general formulation of the motivations involved in bargaining behavior. This is shown clearly in the evidence that a group member receiving an initial advantage in points is generally discriminated against throughout the remaining trials. It is reflected in the inability of the paid-participant to enter into the expected number of terminal coalitions, in the relatively high price he is required to pay in order to enter such coalitions, and in discriminatory bargaining in opposition to him as shown in the within-trials analyses.

The evidence indicates that the strength of this opposition is a direct function of task importance and of the degree of comparability between the group members. Such an interpretation is strengthened by evidence from the questionnaire that the conditions of the experiment were successfully manipulated.

Differences between the two conditions of importance in the experiment are reliable and consistent in the analyses involving terminal coalitions, and in the intra-trial analysis of the excess of points required to break up a coalition between the two subjects. In each of these cases the bargaining was shown to be more favorable to the paid-participant under conditions of low importance than when importance was high.

The effects of the peer and non-peer conditions are similarly in substantial accord with the predictions. Under peer conditions the paid-participant is less able to obtain points, less successful in entering into terminal coalitions, and he is required to pay a higher price in order to do so than under non-peer conditions. This influence of peer relations is shown also by the excess of points which A is forced to pay in order to break up an existing coalition.

It appears then that a large initial advantage in points results in an intensification of competition against the paid-participant when that individual is regarded as comparable in ability. If the individual involved is regarded as non-comparable, the competition persists among the remaining group members, but the discrepant individual gains additional advantage by becoming the medium by which changes in status can be accomplished between the others. Support for this latter statement comes from two sources: (1) examination of the relative

frequencies of occurrence of even and uneven point distributions
in terminal coalitions involving B and C show that these tend to
be formed with equal division of the points under peer conditions, but that under non-peer conditions such coalitions involve
mainly inequitable distributions, and (2) an examination of the
low importance, non-peer condition indicates that the paid-
participant was able to obtain a significantly larger number of
points than the average of the two subjects. (Table 3)

Insofar as the findings in this experiment have generality,
they have implications for two fields of inquiry, that of game
theory and that of motivational theory, especially as each applies to social situations. Game theory specifies that the
choices between alternative strategies or courses of action
should be chosen in such a way as to maximize utility.

The present study suggests that the nature of the utility function for individuals is not necessarily invariant, but is subject
to modification from the effects of situational variables which
may differ greatly from one context to the next. Consequently,
these results indicate that motivational factors such as those
suggested in the present experiment need to be included in
formulations relating utility to external or behavioral reference
points.

The findings are more directly relevant to theories of social
motivation and perception, especially as these pertain to behavior in groups. The suggestion is that an important determinant of behavior in group situations where all members are en-
gaged in a common activity is the concern of each member about
his status relative to others on that activity. This is especially
true in activities where there is no clear cut criterion available
for individuals evaluating the adequacy of their performance.
Consequently when a discrepancy between their own standing
and that of others is perceived, individuals are motivated to reduce that discrepancy. This motivation will manifest itself in a
variety of ways, one of which is to form coalitions in opposition
to any other member having a higher status on this task.

Assuming that this formulation has generality, it gives rise
to two important theoretical problems. The results of this experiment have shown that the strength of the motivational factors involved depends in part upon the importance of the task to
the individuals involved and in part on the degree of comparability between the group members. Consequently, it becomes
necessary to formulate the conditions that determine whether
or not a given task will be accepted as important by a given individual, and the factors controlling his acceptance or rejection

of other individuals as a standard against which to evaluate his own performance. These factors undoubtedly include cultural and social variables as well as those unique to the past history of the given individual.

SUMMARY

The present experiment on competitive bargaining behavior in a group situation utilized 56 groups, each composed of two subjects and a paid-participant. The experimental variables were: (1) the importance of the task for the individuals involved, and (2) the degree of comparability between group members (peer versus non-peer conditions). Subjects were assigned to one of four experimental conditions as follows: (1) high task importance, peer relations, (2) high task importance, non-peer relations, (3) low task importance, peer relations, and (4) low task importance, non-peer relations.

The experiment was designed so that the three group members were competing among themselves for points, but the formation of a coalition between two of them was necessary in order for points to be earned. The procedures used ensured that the paid-participant always obtained a large initial advantage. The rules governing the formation of coalitions specified that any agreements could be broken by either member of the coalition if he desired to enter a coalition with the third member. This made possible a continuous sequence of bargaining between the three members until the conclusion of the trial.

The results of the experiment were as follows:

1. The group member receiving a large initial advantage in points received significantly fewer opportunities to form coalitions than did the other group members, and was required to pay a relatively higher price in order to do so.

2. The reduction in opportunity to form coalitions and the commensurate increase in price demanded of the person receiving a large initial advantage in points were more pronounced under conditions of high task importance than under conditions of low importance.

3. The reduction in opportunity to form coalitions and the corresponding increase in price demanded of the person receiving a large initial advantage in points were more evident under peer conditions than under non-peer conditions.

4. The results summarized in the three preceding paragraphs were reflected not only in the formation of terminal coalitions and the distribution of points therein, but also in the pattern of bargaining which occurred within trials.

FOOTNOTE

1. An analysis of co-variance on average points per trial earned by A adjusted for differences in number of coalitions of which A was a member yields the same conclusions.

BIBLIOGRAPHY

1. Festinger, L., Informal Social Communication. Psychological Review, 1950, 57, 5, 271-282.

2. Von Neumann, J. and Morgenstern, O., Theory of Games and Economic Behavior. Princeton: Princeton University Press, 1944. (2nd Edition, 1947).

CHAPTER XVII

ON DECISION-MAKING UNDER UNCERTAINTY*

by

C. H. Coombs and David Beardslee

UNIVERSITY OF MICHIGAN

I. INTRODUCTION

This paper presents a model which is a framework for a great variety of experiments in the area of decision-making under uncertainty. It is intended that this model will relate and organize experiments that have already been carried out and also suggest many more. The behavior with which the model is concerned is the preferential decisions of an individual among a set of "offers". Each of the offers consists of a "prize" (what he stands to win), a "stake" (what he stands to lose) and a probability of winning.

Willingness to gamble, or utility for risk, will be regarded as a suppressed variable primarily relevant for explaining differences between individuals' decisions not explained by differences in their utilities or probabilities. The three variables, prize, stake, and probability of winning, are each regarded as psychological variables, not necessarily linearly or even monotonically related to, their "real" properties, e.g., "dollar" values or "objective" probabilities. The three variables, then, with which the model is concerned, are utility for prize ($U(P)$), utility for stake ($U(S)$), and psychological probability (ψ).

The problem of the measurement of utilities and psychological probabilities is currently of great concern to psychologists [4],

---

*This paper was initiated under a Ford Foundation Grant (Decision Processes) to the University of Michigan for the Summer Seminar, and completed under Office of Naval Research Contract Nonr-374 (00), NR-041-011. We have benefited from the criticisms and suggestions of many people in the course of constructing and testing this theory. It will not be possible to mention all of them, but we wish to express our appreciation particularly to N. C. Dalkey, Ward Edwards, Leon Festinger, and R. M. Thrall.

[5], [9], mathematicians [8], [11], philosophers [1], and economists [10], [12]. Measurement of such variables on an interval scale requires the existence of a common unit of measurement and a common arbitrary origin, and further requires estimates of these. While models have been constructed for such purposes, as yet they have not been adequately tested and sustained experimentally. The method [3] of the experiments reported here does not require such assumptions, as it leads to an ordered metric scale [2] in which the stimuli are ordered and order relations on the distances between some pairs of stimuli are known. This method permits constructing such scales for a particular individual. This is a desirable feature, as it may be anticipated that utilities and psychological probabilities are peculiar to individuals.

In the section that follows, the component variables of the theory will be briefly discussed; then there will be a section classifying the different kinds of decision-making under uncertainty, giving, in effect, the different "dimensions" of the problem. A descriptive theory of decision-making under uncertainty is then presented in detail and followed by some experimental results.

II. THE COMPONENTS

A. <u>Utility</u>. Throughout this paper the term "utility" will be regarded as synonymous with "preferability." Degree of utility will be taken to be degree of preferability. If an individual says he prefers A to B, for whatever reason, this will be interpreted as meaning he has a higher utility for A than for B at that moment. If there is inconsistency of his judgment under replication the majority judgment may be taken as indicative of relative utility. If an individual says that A and B are "harder to choose between" (as stakes or prizes) than are B and C, this will be said to imply that the <u>difference</u> in utility (as stakes or prizes, respectively) of A and $\overline{B}$ (the <u>distance</u> between them on a utility scale) is less than that between $\overline{B}$ and C. Formally,

(1) $\qquad A >_P B$ if and only if $U(P_A) > U(P_B)$

(2) $\qquad A >_S B$ if and only if $U(S_A) < U(S_B)$

(3) $\qquad (AB) \gtreqless_S (CD)$ if and only if $\overline{AB} \lesseqgtr_S \overline{CD}$

where:

concerning their additivity to questions concerning the effect of information, attitudes, and beliefs on the psychological probabilities. As in the case of utility, the theory constructed in this paper is not concerned with the source of psychological probabilities and factors affecting them but rather with measuring them as they exist at a given time for an individual and the role they play in decision-making under uncertainty.

C. Utility for Risk. While liking to gamble or willingness to take a risk may also be a parameter of decision-making under uncertainty it is a suppressed variable in this theory. The model conceived here can only be constructed for each individual separately. This is because there are no assumptions which permit comparing utilities or psychological probabilities between individuals. Utility for risk would play an important role in comparisons between individuals in decision-making under uncertainty.

D. The Measurement of Utility and Psychological Probability. The theory and experiments discussed in this paper are concerned with the nature of the interrelated roles that psychological probability and utility for stakes and prizes play in the decision-making of an individual. Clearly, utilities for objects and psychological probabilities may be expected to be personal to an individual and are not assumed here to be given as any prescribed function of their real world characteristics. Hence, their measurement must be derived from the judgments of an individual and the measures obtained are unique to him.

The paradigm of these experiments involves the independent measurement of utilities and psychological probabilities and then independent observations on their "product space." The method used to observe and derive measures of the utilities and the psychological probabilities is an adaptation of the Unfolding Technique to the study of stimulus scales. This methodology is described in some detail elsewhere [3] so only certain characteristics of the measures will be discussed here.

The methodology begins with the hypotheses that a certain set of objects (prizes, stakes, statements of probability or events, etc.) is an ordered set and that, in addition, pairs of objects are elements of a partially ordered set. The latter set gives a "distance function." If the judgments of the individual satisfy certain conditions, the above hypotheses are sustained and the scale is recovered as an ordered metric [2]. Such a scale has the objects simply ordered and, in addition, some of the "distances" between

pairs of objects are known to be greater or less than other distances. Such a scale lacks the convenience and power of measurement with numbers, as for example on an interval scale.
However, it also lacks some of the assumptions required for
measurement with an interval scale and also is vulnerable. By
vulnerable is meant that the procedure for analyzing data does
not necessarily yield a unidimensional scale, and thus it permits a test of the existence of such a scale. Hence, if unidimensional scales of utility or psychological probability are
obtained, they are not consequences of the model alone.

III. CLASSES OF DECISION-MAKING UNDER UNCERTAINTY

The general area of decision-making under uncertainty includes a wide variety of kinds of "environmental" conditions. It
will be desirable to recognize explicitly some of these "dimensions" on which decision-making under uncertainty may vary.
The following dichotomous classes are an initial attempt to
identify these dimensions and the theory presented in this paper
will be characterized in these different respects.

A. Wager vs. Pay-to-Play. In a wager the individual's stake
is forfeited in the event that he fails to win. In the case of pay-
to-play the individual pays a fee which he loses regardless of
the outcome of the play. A bet on a football game with another
person is a wager, whereas buying into a pool on a game is pay-
to-play. Buying a lottery ticket essentially characterizes pay-
to-play.
The theory presented here is explicitly for wager and not for
pay-to-play. A possible modification of the theory to embrace
pay-to-play would be to hypothesize that the utility of the price
to play reduces the utility of the prize by a corresponding
amount and the individual is playing a wager with "price to play"
as stake and a prize worth that much less.

B. Play Once vs. Repetitive Play. In the first case the game
is only going to be played once, whereas in the second the game
is going to be played a number of times. Conceivably, an individual's choice between playing a silver dollar slot machine or
a nickel slot machine might be conditioned by whether the game
is to be played only once or repetitively. An hypothesis might
be that an individual would be willing to take a greater risk in
"play once" than in "repetitive play."

In repetitive play there are a number of subclasses of environmental situations: the successive offers may be the same or different, the length of the series may be known or unknown to the subject, the length of the series may be determined by the subject or the experimenter and before or in the course of the play. There are, in addition to these subclasses of repetitive play, subclasses pertaining to feedback, which may be immediate or delayed. Knowledge of success or failure may be immediate or delayed, and if immediate there may be either immediate or delayed payoff. Knowledge of success or failure is information which may affect psychological probabilities; payoff changes assets which may affect preferences between offers (i.e., the locus of the indifference curves).

The experiments reported here are all under the play once rule.

C. Method of Choice vs. Method of Single Stimuli. In the Method of Single Stimuli an offer is available which an individual may accept or reject. In the Method of Choice two or more alternative offers are available and the individual expresses a preference. The information contained in the data is different under these two conditions. In the Method of Single Stimuli the information is an absolute judgment as to whether the offer is on one side or another of an indifference surface in the product space. This surface thus partitions the space into a "play" and "no play" region. In the Method of Choice the information is a relative judgment as to which of the offers is "better", in some sense, to the individual.

The Method of Choice may be further characterized as to whether the choice is compulsory or voluntary. If the choice is voluntary no preference will be expressed when all offers lie in the "no play" region; hence, there is some absolute information in such judgments, as well as relative. If the choice is compulsory a preference is always expressed and the entire product space may be studied, but there is no information in the data from which "play" and "no play" regions may be constructed.

The theory presented here is constructed explicitly for Method of Choice and the experiments all involve compulsory preference judgments.

IV. A DESCRIPTIVE THEORY

A. A General Psychological Hypothesis—The Maximization of Expected Utility. The continua described permit a simple descriptive theory of decision-making under uncertainty. It is assumed that the psychological continua underlying these variables have ratio scale properties but in the experimental procedure used these scales are only recovered up to an ordered metric. The basic hypothesis is that in deciding between uncertain outcomes or events the individual chooses that offer or alternative which maximizes his expected utility. Note that this theory deals with maximization of "expected utility," not with "utility of objective expected value." "Expected utility" is determined by some combination of $U(P)$, $U(S)$, and ψ, and is to be distinguished from utility of expected outcome, U [objective probability x objective prize].

This hypothesis is precisely analogous to the assumption frequently made in economics, save that the quantity maximized here is one involving $U(P)$, $U(S)$ and ψ, all of which are psychological magnitudes. To decide which one offer involves a higher ψ, a larger $U(P)$, and less $U(S)$ than any other offer, the simplest hypothesis is that the individual will prefer the offer that is maximal in some sense. When the individual must choose between two offers, one of which involves a larger prize than the other but with a lower ψ of obtaining it, he must in some way decide "how much" utility to give up for a given increase in ψ, or how much larger stake he will give to obtain a chance on a larger prize, and so on.

This theory is offered as an hypothesis about the "rates of exchange" in such decisions. The hypothesis is that the individual always chooses that one of the available alternatives for which E is largest, where:

(4) $$E = \psi_W^X \, U(P)^y - \psi_L^Z \, U(S)^W \, , \text{ and }$$

E = expected utility;

ψ_W = psychological probability of winning the prize, $0 \leq \psi_W \leq 1$;

$U(P)$ = utility of the prize;

ψ_L = psychological probability of losing the stake, $0 \leq \psi_L \leq 1$;

$U(S)$ = utility of the stake;

the exponents x, y, z, w are parameters defining
for the individual the "relative weight" or "relative
importance" of ψ_W, U(P), ψ_L, and U(S), and are
all ≥ 0.

It is to be remembered that E, U(P), and U(S) are all psychological magnitudes, rather than stimulus parameters.
Equation (4) describes a general theory with more parameters than desirable. In the discussion and experiments which
follow, only the case in which $\psi_L = 1 - \psi_W$ will be treated, although the general theory as stated in equation (4) allows for
situations in which the probability of losing the stake is not
equal to $1 - \psi_W$. A further restriction in the discussion and
experiments which follow is the assumption that x = y = z = w = 1
unless otherwise noted. One illustration of a case in which x
might not be equal to 1 might be "wishful thinking," that is, an
overestimation of the ψ of winning. "Utility for risk" may be
interpreted through these parameters. Such considerations will
not, however, be pursued in any detail here, and, unless specifically noted, the discussion which follows will concern only
the theory modified by the simplifying assumptions just mentioned.

Although the working hypothesis that utility of a given object
as stake is the negative of the utility of that same object as a
negative prize appears here, this assumption is not necessary
to the validity of the general theory. It is not assumed, on the
other hand, that the utility of an object as positive prize is the
negative of the utility for winning a debt of that object as a negative prize. Symbolically, the working hypothesis is

(5)   If $U(P_A) \cdot U(S_A) < 0$, then $|U(P_A)| = |U(S_A)|$

(and it is not assumed that $|U(P_A)| = |U(S_A)|$ when
$U(P_A) \cdot U(S_A) > 0$.)

This theory as expressed in equation (4) involves the following assumptions of a psychological nature. First, the scales of
utility and psychological probability are assumed to exist and
satisfy the axioms for the real numbers, but these scales will
be recovered only at the level of an ordered metric. Second,
the hypothesis implies that the variables are independent, that
they do not interact when combined in an alternative. By this
is meant that a measure on any one of the variables U(P), U(S),
and ψ is independent of any measure on each of the other two
variables with which it is associated in an offer. For example,
an object A constituting a prize is assumed to have a measure,

$U(P_A)$, which is independent of the probability of winning it and independent of the stake involved. It is this assumption which is implicit in the determination of the ψ, $U(P)$, and $U(S)$ scales as independent variables. The measures of $U(P)$ and of $U(S)$ are obtained in a situation in which ψ is implicitly constant; the measures of psychological probability are obtained without mention of $U(P)$ or $U(S)$. However, the parameters x, y, z, and w allow the individual to make his own "idiosyncratic weightings" of ψ, $U(P)$, and $U(S)$ in arriving at an expected utility. The effect of these parameters is, of course, to carry through an exponential transformation on the axes as measured.

Thirdly, in the general case, it would be assumed that the values x, y, z, and w were constant for this individual over at least the set of alternatives under study. Lastly, the theory assumes that the individual does combine ψ, $U(P)$, and $U(S)$ into an E (the psychological value of an offer, or the utility of an outcome), and chooses on a basis of maximizing E. If the E of one offer equals the E of a second offer, the individual is said to be "indifferent" between the two offers; that is, he will not care which offer he chooses. Behaviorally, indifference will appear as a frequency of choice not significantly different from 50% in repeated choices between alternatives 1 and 2. (This is discussed in greater detail in [8], page 374.)

If it were possible to obtain measures of the three variables ψ, $U(P)$, and $U(S)$, and the parameters x, y, z, and w which were elements of ratio scales, the hypothesis would be simple to test. Since one cannot obtain even interval scale values for psychological magnitudes without strong assumptions, it is necessary to see what properties of the model can be made the subject of hypotheses testable at the level of an ordered metric on the variables.

One way of visualizing the relations between ψ, $U(P)$, and $U(S)$ is to regard them as orthogonal axes of a Euclidean space. Each alternative can then be represented by a point (ψ, $U(P)$, $U(S)$) in this space. The equation for E then defines for any value of E a three dimensional surface. (If ψ_L is not assumed to equal $1 - \psi_W$, it is of course necessary to deal with a four dimensional model.) These surfaces over which E is constant will be called "indifference surfaces," since by definition the individual does not care which of two alternatives is chosen if their E are equal.

The relation between ψ, $U(P)$, and $U(S)$ will be clarified by examining successively the relation between each pair of them with the third held constant. First, the relation between ψ and U(P) will be examined with U(S) held constant.

B. <u>Stake Constant.</u> Holding stake, U(S), constant is equivalent, geometrically, to passing a plane through the three dimensional space perpendicular to the stake axis. These planes, in which U(S) = K, will be called "stake planes." In these,

$$E = \psi U(P) - (1 - \psi)K$$

1. Zero Stake. If U(S) = 0, then $E = \psi U(P)$. Geometrically, this is a plane which passes through the origin and is the locus of all offers in which the individual puts up something which has no utility, positive or negative, for him. This zero stake plane cuts the indifference surfaces in a family of truncated hyperbolas which describe those combinations of ψ and $U(P)$ which make up offers between which the individual is indifferent. The indifference curves sketched in Figure 1 summarize the fact that for positive prizes the individual is indifferent between a small prize with a high ψ of winning and a larger prize with a smaller ψ of winning. For negative prizes (U(P) < 0), he will be indifferent between a small negative prize with a high ψ and a large negative prize with low ψ. For a prize U(P) = 0, the indifference curve will be vertical, since if the individual never wins or loses anything, the odds do not matter. This vertical indifference curve will be called the "null line."

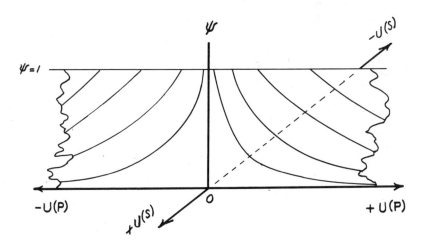

Fig. 1.

The theory implies that indifference curves other than the null line will be <u>convex</u>. This means that the slope of a given curve increases monotonically with increasing distance from $U(P) = 0$. The slope of an indifference curve indicates at that point the "rate of exchange" between psychological probability and utility for prize. An indifference surface or curve may be identified (labelled) by the value E associated with all points on it. When $\psi = 1$, $E = U(P)$. (See Figure 2.)

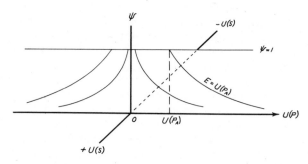

Fig. 2.

Note that in this case the general form of indifference curves is <u>not</u> dependent on the assumption for the parameters that $x = y = \overline{1}$. For when $E = \psi^x U(P)^y$, $x \geq 0$, $y \geq 0$, the indifference curve will certainly be convex.

2. <u>Positive Stake</u>. If $U(S) = K$, $K > 0$, then

$$E = \psi U(P) - (1 - \psi)K.$$

In addition to a family of truncated hyperbolas, there will exist a vertical indifference curve (null line) located at $U(P) = E = -K$, and the indifference curves in the plane $U(S) = K$ will have the form shown in Figure 3.

This vertical indifference curve occurs when the prize to be acquired has a negative utility equal to the utility of the stake to be lost. In this case, the individual obviously will not care whether he wins or loses, since whichever happens he has to give up the same amount of utility. Consequently, he will not care what ψ he is offered.

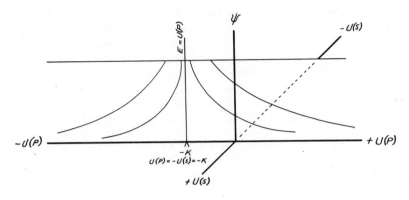

Fig. 3.

3. Negative Stake. When $U(S) = K$, $K < 0$, by the assumption of equality of negative prize and positive stake or of positive prize and negative stake (equation (5)) the situation is a translation of that for positive stake. The null line will be at

$$U(P) = E = -K.$$

4. Some General Properties of Stake Planes. By hypothesis, an individual's preference among any offers will depend upon their psychological expected values, E, i.e., upon the relations of the indifference surfaces (here, curves) in which those offers lie. Offer 1 $(\psi_1, U(P_1))$ will be preferred to offer 2 $(\psi_2, U(P_2))$ if and only if the indifference curve through $(\psi_1, U(P_1))$ lies "to the right of" or "above" the indifference curve through $(\psi_2, U(P_2))$. This is the information assumed to be contained in the data when the Method of Choice is used to observe behavior.

In general, when $\psi = 1$, $E = U(P)$. The indifference curve which contains the offer $\psi = 1$, $U(P) = 0$ is the locus of all offers for which $E = 0$, i.e., all offers in which the individual's expected outcome is zero. This curve divides the plane into a "positive expected outcome" and a "negative expected outcome" portion.

That portion of the plane for which $E > 0$ is presumably the locus of all offers which the individual will wish to take when the alternative is not to play, since refusing to play is accepting the alternative $(\psi = 0, U(P) = 0, U(S) = 0)$. In the general case, the $E = 0$ surface partitions the space into those offers the individual will take, and those he will refuse if he is permitted to do so.

The portion of the space (or plane) for which $E > 0$ we term the "play region" and its complement the "no play region." These are the two regions which are distinguished when the Method of Single Stimuli is used to observe behavior. The $E = 0$ surface is called the boundary-of-play surface.

The vertical indifference curves mentioned previously in connection with the stake planes are the intersections of the stake planes with a vertical surface through the origin called the "null surface." The null surface contains all points for which $U(P)^y \psi = U(S)^w \psi$. If $y = w$ the null surface becomes a null plane as indicated in Figure 4. This plane intersects a horizontal plane in a line for which $U(P) \psi = U(S) \psi$.

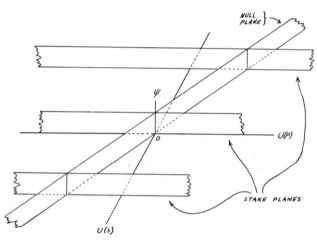

Fig. 4.

The indifference curves through points on a line parallel to the null plane, ψ constant, have the same slope. This can be seen by noting that if we take a given indifference curve through $(\psi_1, U(P_1), U(S_1))$ and consider the curve through

$$(\psi_1, \ U(P_1) - C, \ U(S_1) + C).$$

Let the parameters of these two curves (cf. equation (4)) be E and E' respectively, then we have:

$$E' = \psi_1(U(P_1) + C) - (1 - \psi_1)(U(S_1) + C)$$

or

$$E' = \psi_1 U(P_1) - (1 - \psi_1) U(S_1) - C .$$

Hence, $E' = E - C$, and the rate of exchange of ψ and $U(P)$ is unchanged. Since it is the relation of ψ and $U(P)$ which defines the shape of the curves in stake planes, the indifference curves related by $U(P)' = U(P) - C$, $U(S)' = U(S) + C$ are all of the same shape. It is clear that if $U(S)$ is increased, the slope of the indifference curve through a given ψ and $U(P)$ becomes less.

If x and z are not both equal to 1, the shapes of the indifference curves will change and certain indifference curves will now possess points of inflection. An example of an inflected indifference curve is shown in Figure 5. What psychological applications such a situation might have have not been studied. Bizarre as such an indifference function may seem, it is worth noting that the existence of an inflected indifference curve is potentially determinable at the level of ordered metric data. It is at least conceivable that some cases of "apparently irrational behavior" might be explicable on some such hypothesis as x or $z \neq 1$. It would still be the case that one offer will be preferred to a second offer if the indifference curve containing the first lies to the right of the indifference curve containing the second.

C. <u>Prize Constant</u>. By holding prize, $U(P)$, constant, planes perpendicular to the $U(P)$ axis are obtained. Indifference curves in these "prize planes" will be truncated hyperbolas similar to those in stake planes, save that the preference is assumed to be for <u>smaller</u> stakes and for higher probabilities. The effect of this is to "invert" the generalized hyperbolas in the sense of Figures 6, 7, 8.

1. <u>Zero Prize</u>. ($U(P) = 0$). In the case that $U(S) > 0$, the individual cannot win anything, and he will prefer to put up smaller stakes, and will prefer smaller probabilities of losing his stake. Since $\psi_L = 1 - \psi_W$, he will prefer therefore larger $\psi_W = \psi$. If $U(S) < 0$, implying that getting rid of his stake has positive utility for him, he will prefer larger negative stakes to smaller negative stakes, and of course larger probabilities of losing the stake. The relations are shown in Figure 6. Since in this plane $E = (1 - \psi)^z U(S)^W$ the preference is for the offer whose indifference curve is to the right of the curves for other alternatives in the set.

2. <u>Positive Prize</u>. When $U(P) = K$, $K > 0$, and hence $E = \underline{\psi K - (1 - \psi) U(S)}$, we have an inverse of the situation for a positive stake place. When $-U(S) = U(P)$ the probability of winning is irrelevant and there exists a vertical indifference curve

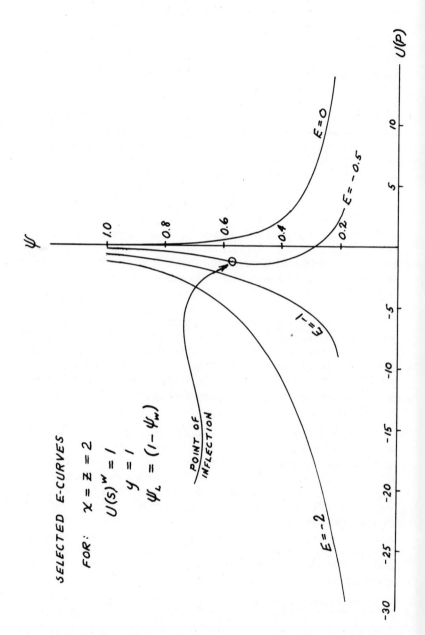

Fig. 5.

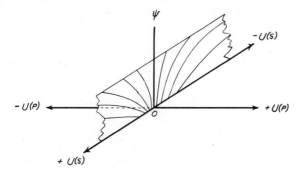

Fig. 6.

(null curve), as in Figure 7, which is the intersection of the prize plane with the null plane previously defined. As with the zero prize plane, one offer is preferred to a second offer if the indifference curve through the first lies to the right of the indifference curve through the second.

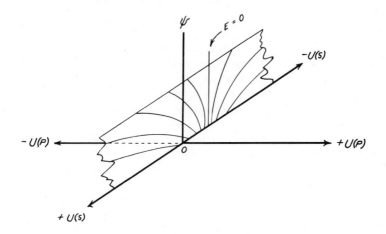

Fig. 7.

3. Negative Prize. (U(S) < 0). This situation is a translation of that for positive prize, with the null line and the indifference curves displaced to the left of the origin, as indicated

in Figure 8. The null line is located at U(P) = -U(S) = E. Preference relations remain as before.

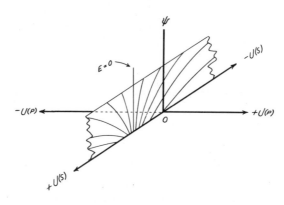

Fig. 8.

D. <u>Probability Constant.</u> Setting ψ = K yields a plane normal to the ψ-axis, with ψ constant throughout, which will be referred to as a <u>probability plane.</u> For ψ = 1 (the certainty plane), the player is indifferent as between stakes—he's going to win anyway. His preference is strictly for a larger prize; hence, the indifference curves are straight lines, parallel to the U(S) axis. For ψ = 0 (the certain-loss plane), the player is indifferent as between prizes; he can't possibly win. His preference is for the smallest possible stake; hence, the indifference curves are straight lines, parallel to the U(P) axis. The two situations are represented by Figure 9.

It is assumed that the transition from the certain-win plane to the certain-loss plane is continuous. The nature of this transition is described as follows. (We are indebted to Charles H. Hubbell for this development.)

The player is indifferent as between all situations having the same expectation of gain:

$$E = \psi U(P) - (1 - \psi) U(S)$$

Solving for prize and stake:

$$U(P) = \frac{1-\psi}{\psi} U(S) + \frac{E}{\psi}$$

$$U(S) = \frac{\psi}{1-\psi} U(P) + \frac{E}{1-\psi}$$

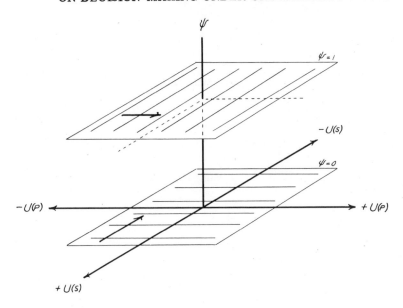

Fig. 9.

For fixed ψ (i.e., for a given probability plane), these are straight lines. In particular, the line through the origin (E = 0) constitutes a boundary between willingness to play (E > 0) and reluctance to play (E < 0). All indifference lines in the same ψ plane are parallel to this, having the same slope. Regardless of the value of ψ, the boundary-of-play line passes through the point (U(P) = 0, U(S) = 0).

If ψ is allowed to vary, this boundary-of-play line rotates, as shown in Figure 10, where (+) and (-), for each boundary-of-play line, indicate "play" and "no play" regions. This rotating line moves from $\psi = 1$ to $\psi = 0$, as it rotates. In so doing, it sweeps out the indifference surface for E = 0. At $\psi = 1$, it is coincident with the projection of the U(S) axis, and at $\psi = 0$, with the U(P) axis. This is shaped something like a circular staircase, as in Figures 11 and 12. For E = 0, it is the boundary-of-play surface.

If E $\neq$ 0, then (U(P) = E, U(S) = -E) is the axis of rotation. All such axes lie in the null plane, all points of which satisfy the expectation equation:

$$E = \psi U(P) - (1 - \psi) U(S)$$

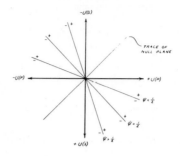

Fig. 10.

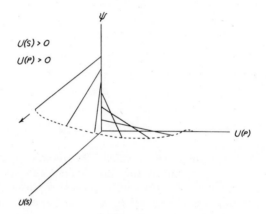

Fig. 11.

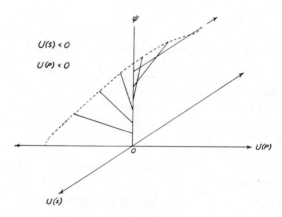

Fig. 12.

as was indicated above.

The generation of each indifference surface is exactly similar to that for the boundary-of-play surface, with U(P) = E,
U(S) = -E as the axis of rotation. Hence, all indifference surfaces are similar. Since each is completely described by the
regular motion of a straight line (the <u>generator</u>), they are
known, mathematically, as <u>ruled surfaces.</u>

These surfaces actually have two sets of rulings. The other
ruling, for the boundary-of-play surface, has as its axis of rotation, a line in the probability plane $\psi = 1/2$, normal to the
null plane. The generating line is at all times perpendicular to
the axis, and rotates in such a way that it always passes through
the U(P) axis and through the projection of the U(S) axis on the
certainty-plane. Its intercepts on those lines are equal, and of
like sign. For U(P) = U(S) = 0, the generator coincides with
the ψ axis. (See Figure 13.)

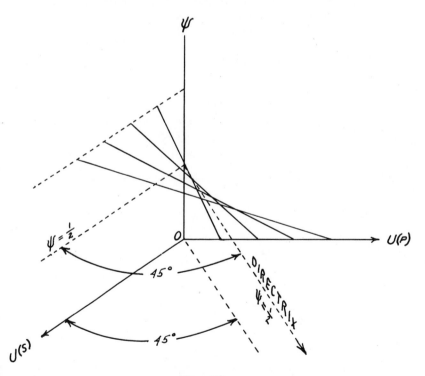

Fig. 13.

V. SOME EXPERIMENTAL DATA

A. An Illustrative Pilot Study. A pilot experiment was conducted during the summer of 1952 (This experiment was conducted by David Beardslee and Stefan Vail. The subject was one of the secretaries for the project.) to see if some of the things predicted by the model happened, and to serve as an illustration of the method. For stimuli for the U(P) scale, five objects were selected which were pictured in the advertising pages of a newspaper. These were to be the "prizes" in an imaginary lottery. These stimuli were as follows:

a - a rattan chair,
b - an electric broiler,
c - a typewriter,
d - a radio,
e - a portable phonograph.

The pictures, of course, provided the subject with a concrete stimulus which was perhaps more susceptible to constant valuation than the names of the objects are. These stimuli were presented by the Method of Similarities [3] and the subject's U(P) scale obtained. The obtained I scales are given in Table 1.

Table 1.

Stimulus at Head of I Scale	Chair	Broiler	Typewriter	Radio	Phonograph
	a	b	c	d	e
Reduction of Paired Comparison Judgments to a Rank Order I Scale	a	b	c	d	e
	b	c	e	c	c
	c	d	d	e	d
	d	e	b	b	b
	e	a	a	a	a

It is to be noted that these five I scales do not satisfy the same simple order. Three are consistent with the ordering of the stimuli a b c d e from low to high in utility, and two are consistent with the ordering a b d c e.

At the end of the experiment, however, the subject was asked to place the stimuli in rank order and the obtained rank order

was a b c d e. Also, the data of a later experiment in which
these stimuli served as components of uncertain offers are compatible with the hypothesis that the proper rank order is a b c
d e.

The data also contained the metric information that

$$\overline{ab} > \overline{be}$$

$$\overline{cd} > \overline{de}$$

that is, that the difference in utility U(P) between stimuli a and
b was greater than the difference in U(P) between b and e; and
the difference in U(P) between c and d was greater than the
difference between d and e.

Time did not permit the determination in this pilot experiment of a scale on some probability stimuli, so explicit objective probabilities were used in constructing offers, and it was
assumed that ψ = objective probability. The probabilities used
were .10, .30, .40, .60, and .70. This ψ scale in combination
with the U(P) scale above defines 25 offers in the product
space, of which eight were selected for study. Two additional
offers were made up by combining "both a and b" as prizes
with two of the probabilities.

These 10 points are shown in Figure 14, which represents a
stake plane. It must be kept in mind that only the order of
stimuli on the two axes and certain metric information is actually known; although the illustration is drawn as though the
points had known numerical values, such is not the case. The
stimuli F and I in the space have been located ordinally on the
U(P) axis from metric information contained in the data. They
were not located on the U(P) scale empirically as they might
have been.

The offers were presented to the subject for judgment by the
Method of Triads. The responses of the subject are given in
Table 2. This tabulation was arrived at as follows. The subject
was presented with every possible triad, of which there were
$\binom{10}{3}$ = 120, and instructed to judge in each triad which "chance"
she would most prefer to take and which least. The game was
free, the subject had no stake, i.e., U(S) = 0.

For example, E, H, and I constituted one such triad. In this
triad the subject said she preferred E the most and I the least.
This was tabulated as three paired comparison judgments,
E ≻ H, E ≻ I, and H ≻ I (where the symbol ≻ signifies preferred to). Each of these pairs occurred in eight triads, n-2,
and hence each such paired comparison was made eight times.

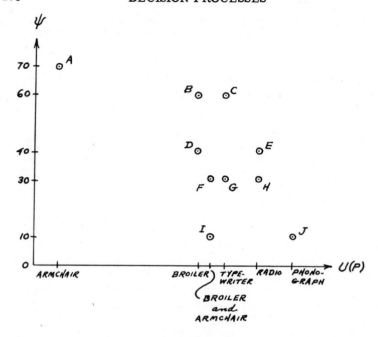

Fig. 14.

Table 2.

A, B 8*	8 B, C	5 C, E 3	D, H 8	F, H 8
A, C 8	8 B, D	8 C, F	7 D, I 1	7 F, I 1
A, D 8	B, E 8	7 C, G 1	D, J 8	F, J 8
A, E 8	8 B, F	8 C, H	8 E, F	G, H 8
2 A, F 6	1 B, G 7	8 C, I	7 E, G 1	8 G, I
A, G 8	B, H 8	7 C, J 1	8 E, H	8 G, J
A, H 8	8 B, I	D, E 8	8 E, I	8, H, I
2 A, I 6	2 B, J 6	3 D, F 5	8 E, J	8, K, J
A, J 8	8 C, D	D, C 8	F, G 8	I, J 8

*To be read "no judgments of A preferred to B, eight judgments of B preferred to A."

The tabulation of these eight judgments for each pair is contained in Table 2. It should be noted that there are <u>two</u>

judgments made on a triad which are here decomposed into three which are consequently transitive. Thus, on the average, there are only 2/3 of a degree of freedom associated with each paired comparison judgment. But the eight times each judgment was made accumulates these degrees of freedom so they may be regarded as having five and one-third degrees of freedom per paired comparison, assuming the successive presentations of triads are experimentally independent.

Table 2 reveals that an offer to the right or above another offer in the product space is preferred. There were eighteen comparisons of such pairs. On three of these pairs the judgments were inconsistent: 7 C, G 1; 7 E, G 1; and 7 F, I 1. According to the theory these should all have been 8 and 0. The other 15 pairs were all consistent, 8 to 0, and as predicted.

Another experiment was then run on the same subject using just five stimuli and the Method of Paired Comparisons but repeated under conditions of a stake (imaginary) of $1, $10, $15, and a negative utility for stake (a studio couch which the subject wanted to get rid of but which would cost money to have hauled away).

The stimuli used are indicated in Figure 15. At each stake the subject made 10 paired comparisons. In each instance the 10 paired comparisons were transitive so the data are given below as a rank order in Table 3.

Table 3.

Stake	I Scale				
$15	A	B	C	D	E
10	B	A	C	D	E
1	C	D	E	B	A
Studio Couch	D	E	C	B	A

These I scales define certain "pieces" of indifference curves which are shown in Figures 16 - 19. These figures represent only order relations and some metric information. Innumerable transformations on the axes are permissible, so the shapes indicated for the indifference curves represent confidence in the theory rather than experimental demonstration of it.

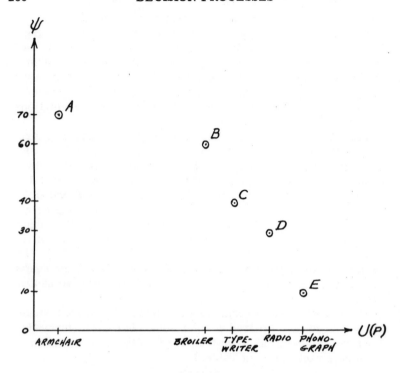

Fig. 15.

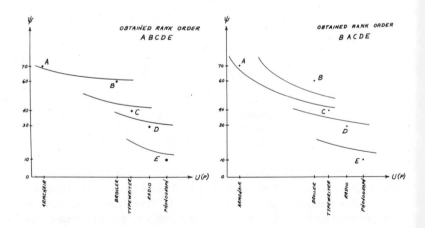

Fig. 16. U(S) = U(S_{$15})   Fig. 17. U(S) = U(S_{$10})

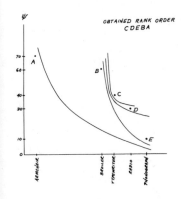

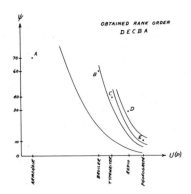

Fig. 18. U(S) = U(S$_{\$1}$)

Fig. 19. U(S$_{\text{studio couch,}}$
not wanted)

B. Experimental Tests of the Shape of Indifference Curves.
In a more extensive study, Coombs and Milholland have obtained the metrics of the ψ and U(P) axes independently, and
were able to show that there existed at least one convex indifference curve for one of their subjects [4]. In another study [6],
Fliege found additional evidence of the existence of convex indifference curves.

C. Mosteller and Nogee's Experiment. Mosteller and Nogee
have reported [8] an experiment which may be analyzed in
terms of this theory. They presented their subjects with a large
number of possible bets, and for each allowed him to choose whether or not to accept the bet. They selected 7 odds (7 values of
ψ), and for each they offered several different prizes, with stake
constant throughout. Each opportunity to bet was offered several
times. This is the Method of Single Stimuli mentioned above, and
permits only location of the subject's E = 0 indifference surface,
i.e., the boundary-of-play surface. (Since stake is constant, they
determined only an E = 0 indifference curve, in the stake plane
for U(S$_{5 \phi}$).) The general situation is shown in Figure 20. Since
for each value of ψ several prizes were offered, each several
times, they could compute for each ψ a cumulative "frequency
of acceptance of bet" curve, and they took the prize for which
the bet would be accepted 50% of the time as defining the E = 0
indifference curve. (See Figure 21.) If there were no error, the
cumulative frequency curve should have the shape shown in
Figure 22. They assume that psychological probability, ψ, is

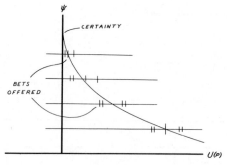

Fig. 20.

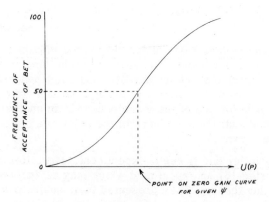

Fig. 21.

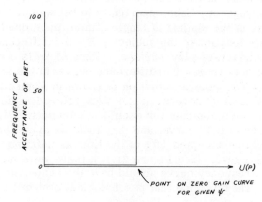

Fig. 22.

linear with objective (and experimentally explicit) probability. They obtained numbers by assuming that utility, $U(P_0) = 0$, and that utility of stake, $U(S_{5¢}) = 1$.

Then by assuming the $E = 0$ indifference curve to be a truncated rectangular hyperbola ($\psi U(P) = E = $ a constant), they were able to compute the relation of monetary value and $U(P)$. The relation between these two they plotted as the utility of money. Further portions of the experiment dealt with preferences between two alternative bets and the percentage of times compound bets would be accepted. They predicted (on the basis of the first portion of the experiment) the percentage of times one offer or the other would be chosen, or a compound bet accepted, by using the explicit objective probability, the experimentally determined $U(P)$, and computing an "expected utility."

There is some evidence [5], [6] that ψ is not a linear function of the objective probability. In this case the procedure used by Mosteller and Nogee no longer yields a unique solution for the relation of monetary value and $U(P)$.

D. <u>Experiments on the Relation Between ψ and Objective Probability.</u> Preston and Baratta [9] have attempted to determine the relation between objective probability and ψ. They had their subjects bid for prize-probability combinations which were then played. This is a variant of the pay-to-play situation in which the price to play is determined by competitive bidding. Since this situation involves assumptions about the comparability of ψ and $U(P)$ scales for different individuals, no attempt is made to analyze their results here. They did find that the function relating objective probability and ψ (computed from group data) was relatively invariant over changes of prize. A similar function was obtained by Griffith [7] in an analysis of horse-race betting. He also observed that for a large number of individuals, offers, and times, the boundary-of-play surface approximates the objective zero expected value.

Edwards [5] in a study of choice between offers varying in ψ, $U(P)$, and $U(S)$ found a function relating group data on ψ and objective probability which, like Preston and Baratta's, was invariant under changes in U. The nature of this function is very different in the two cases, however. Unpublished analyses of the data for individual subjects of Edwards suggests that grouping the data in studies of this type masks large individual differences in ψ and $U(P)$ scales.

VI. SUMMARY

This chapter has presented a general system designed to organize the field of decision-making under uncertainty and to
suggest experiments in that domain. It attempts to clarify the
differences between certain situations, and suggests explana-
tions for differing behaviors. A number of experiments in the
field of decision-making under uncertainty have been analyzed
in terms of this theory.

BIBLIOGRAPHY

1. Bohnert, H. G., The Logical Structure of Utility Theory, Chap.
XV, supra.

2. Coombs, C. H., Mathematical models in psychological scaling,
Journal of the American Statistical Association, 46 (1951), 480-
489.

3. Coombs, C. H., A method for the study of interstimulus similarity, Psychometrika, in press.

4. Coombs, C. H. and Milholland, J. E., Testing the "rationality"
of an individual's decision-making under uncertainty, unpublished manuscript, University of Michigan, 1953.

5. Edwards, W., Probability preferences in gambling behavior,
American Journal of Psychology, 66 (1953), 349-364.

6. Fliege, S. E., The relation of empirical to psychological
probability in a motor learning task, unpublished manuscript,
University of Michigan, 1954.

7. Griffith, R. M., Odds adjustment by American horse-race
bettors, American Journal of Psychology, 62 (1949), 290-294.

8. Mosteller, F. and Nogee, P., An experimental measurement
of utility, Journal of Political Economy, 59 (1951), 371-404.

9. Preston, M. G. and Baratta, P., An experimental study of the
auction-value of an uncertain outcome, American Journal of
Psychology, 61 (1948), 183-193.

10. Samuelson, P. A., Probability, utility, and the independence
axiom, Econometrica, 20 (1952), 670-678.

11. von Neumann, J. and Morgenstern, O., Theory of Games and
Economic Behavior, Princeton, 1947.

12. Wold, H., Ordinal preferences on cardinal utility? (With additional notes by G. L. S. Schackle, L. J. Savage, and H. Wold.), Econometrica, 20 (1952), 661-664.

CHAPTER XVIII

ENVIRONMENTAL NON-STATIONARITY IN A SEQUENTIAL DECISION-MAKING EXPERIMENT

by

Merrill M. Flood*

COLUMBIA UNIVERSITY

1. PROBLEM

The pilot experiment reported here was stimulated in part by some results discussed by W. K. Estes.[1] One such result is the following: In certain two-choice situations, where the reward probabilities are π_1 and π_2, some organisms will tend eventually to choose the ith alternative with probability p_i, given by

$$(1) \qquad p_i = \frac{1 - \pi_j}{2 - \pi_1 - \pi_2} \quad \text{where } i \neq j$$

For example, Estes (DP) referred to a case in which the reward probabilities were $\pi_1 = 0.5$ and $\pi_2 = 0$, and the average p_i of several human subjects was observed experimentally to be 0.67. Estes stated that formula (1) fitted all his data well, when averaged over enough subjects and trials, and remarked that it was derived from a system of mathematical axioms forming a basis for learning theory.

After Estes had presented his paper, various game-theorists in the audience argued (incorrectly) that this observed behavior was surprisingly "irrational," since the organism's proper strategy is clearly pure, rather than mixed, and so the organism

*This work was started while the author was with The RAND Corporation, under Project RAND of the Department of the Air Force. It was completed at Columbia University, under the Behavioral Models Project of the Office of Naval Research. I am indebted to Mrs. Marian Centers, of RAND, and to Mr. N. R. Stanley of Columbia for assistance in the preparation of this report.

should learn eventually to choose only the alternative providing the more frequent reward. The present writer countered this game-theoretical argument with the following two objections:

(a) The proper definition of payoff utilities would be unclear in attempts to apply game-theoretic arguments to a real case, and there is a reasonable payoff matrix that would rationalize the reported behavior. Thus, if the organism's object were to maximize its score rather than its expectation, then it should sometimes not tend to use a pure strategy. For example, one intelligent subject in a punchboard experiment conducted by the author (1952) remarked that her only hope to get a "perfect" score in a (90,10) experiment would be based on playing 90 in the 90-case and 10 in the 10-case and being lucky on each play. Hence, if absolute perfection were assigned sufficiently high utility, her optimal behavior, even in the game-theoretic sense, would not be to always choose the same case. Of course, this same argument might suggest that she should use a single-choice strategy in a (50,0) experiment, but only if she is thoroughly convinced that the other response will always be non-rewarded. At any rate, a defense of the mixed-choice behavior can be made along these general lines.

(b) The von Neumann-Morgenstern game theory is inapplicable in this situation unless the organism can assume safely that the experimental stimulus is generated by a stationary stochastic process. For example, if the organism believes that there may be some pattern (non-stationarity) over time, in the stimulus, then it can often do better by using a mixed strategy rather than a pure one, for the latter would give it no way to discover any pattern effect. At present, mathematical game theory and statistical decision theory provide no generally accepted prescription of optimal behavior in the non-stationary case; indeed, it is quite conceivable that organic behavior will be found to represent such a solution if and when it is understood. In response to our query on this point, Estes paraphrased the instructions given to his subjects. It seemed significant that he had not tried to suggest to them that they were, in fact, being confronted with a stationary process. In the author's experiments, on the other hand, we had emphasized very strongly the exact nature of the stationary process (see Appendix A) confronting the subjects,[2] and it had seemed to us that this fact had helped the subjects go to pure strategies. We conjectured, therefore, that the pure type of behavior would be found in subjects who were convinced of stationarity and that the mixed type of behavior would be found sometimes in subjects who believed that there might be non-stationarity.

These issues were much discussed during the Santa Monica Conference, and there seemed to be agreement that the matter was worthy of further experimental investigation.

R. R. Bush (DP) offered a theoretical explanation of the pure and mixed cases by showing how the Estes formula (1) is obtained by assigning certain very special values to the parameters in the Bush-Mosteller [1] mathematical learning model. Bush also derived an asymptotic mixture formula for the r-choice case, and, with G. L. Thompson (DP), has remarked on some of the pertinent experimental questions. The Bush r-choice formula is

$$(2) \qquad p_i = \frac{\dfrac{1}{1-\pi_i}}{\displaystyle\sum_{j=1}^{r} \dfrac{1}{1-\pi_j}} \qquad \text{for } (i = 1, 2, \cdots, r)$$

where p_i is the eventual probability of the organism choosing the ith alternative, and π_j is the probability that the jth alternative will be rewarded. Formula (2) was derived from the Bush-Mosteller model in [1] on the assumption that if the ith alternative is always rewarded (non-rewarded) then $p_i = 1$ (0).

The punchboard experiments to be discussed here include instances in which $r = 2$ and $r = 9$, so they provide some data that are relevant to the question concerning the applicability of the pure and mixed models discussed by Bush and Thompson (DP). In particular, we present the results of a pilot experiment carried out in an effort to devise a test of the hypothesis that behavior of human subjects is mixed or pure according as they are or are not convinced of non-stationarity in a situation that is actually stationary.

2. EXPERIMENT

The equipment and procedures used were explained in written instructions given to the subjects before the trials began. The set of instructions used in the initial 9-choice experiment, where stationarity was stressed, are summarized in Appendix A. The set used in the 2-choice experiment, where stationarity was not mentioned, is indicated in Appendix B. The reader is referred to these two Appendices for information about the equipment and procedure used, and familiarity with this material is now assumed.

In the 9-choice case, the reward probabilities were each chosen at random on the interval (0,1). In the 2-choice case, the ten pairs of reward probabilities were chosen arbitrarily so as to provide information on pairs scattered rather evenly among all possibilities. The equipment was identical in the two cases, and even the same codes were used, except that the subject was limited in the 2-choice case to choices between a pair of columns specified at the top of each code. The actual values for these pairs are indicated in the following table:

Code No. =	1	2	3	4	5	6	7	8	9	10
$100 \ \pi_1$ =	51	76	55	40	80	56	98	79	92	96
$100 \ \pi_2$ =	24	09	09	0	30	44	49	59	69	17

In the 9-choice case there were 10 subjects and each did the same 10 punchboards with 100 choices on each. In the 2-choice case there were two subjects, one of whom had previously done one punchboard following the instructions of Appendix A. All subjects were unfamiliar with game-theoretic notions.

3. HYPOTHESIS

Data are rather meaningless, of course, except as they are interpreted with respect to some well-defined hypothesis. In this instance, the hypothesis is: Behavior is asymptotically pure or mixed according as subjects are or are not convinced of non-stationarity. As one way to begin testing this general notion, a comparison is made of the frequencies of later choices, in each response class, with the asymptotic frequencies that are predicted theoretically by the Estes-Bush formula (2) for p_i in the mixed model.

There is a real difficulty in knowing what "later choices" should mean in this context. For example, if $\pi_2 = 1$, then the mixed model predicts that $p_2 = 1$ whenever $\pi_1 < 1$, even though a subject would probably show very different behavior over a large sample of early trials according as π_1 is close to zero or close to unity. Furthermore, it is quite possible that subjects may behave according to the mixed model for a certain period at the beginning and switch to the pure model after their early experience convinces them that the process is truly stationary.

We shall be interested in comparing three quantities, computed from the observations, with the theoretical value $P = p_z$ corresponding to the column z for which $\pi_z = \max_i \pi_i$. First, we let F_x^y denote the relative frequency of choice of column z during trials x through y. Next, we let c denote the number of the last trial in which column z was not chosen. Finally, we consider F_1^{100}, F_1^c, and F_{51}^{100} as estimates of P.

The use of F_1^c as an estimate is justified on the ground that the subject can not have gone to a pure strategy before trial c+1, and so F_x^c for $x < c$ represents the relative frequency of choosing column z just prior to the change to a pure strategy if this change did in fact occur after trial c. Of course, F_x^c has a downward bias due to the possibility that the change to a pure strategy may in fact have occurred several trials after trial c. Since P is supposed to refer to asymptotic behavior, we should prefer to choose x large in calculating F_x^c but this has not been done here simply because the condition $x < c$ is often incompatible with the requirement that $c - x$ be large enough to provide a suitable sample size for the calculation of F_x^c.

It might be possible to make observations more directly concerning the subject's state of belief with regard to stationarity, perhaps even by asking him after each trial. There is the obvious danger that such queries might alter the experimental stimulus and thus affect the responses. Some of this danger could be avoided, conceivably, by asking all questions at the close of the work by each subject, and this has sometimes been done. We hope to approach this question more directly in future experiments.

4. RESULTS

The data for the two-choice case are summarized in Table 1. The choices of subject FD do not seem clearly explicable in terms of the mixed model. For example, all of his choices on his last board (Code 6) were made on a column that gave wins on only 56% of the trials. One possible explanation of this behavior is that he set a standard of 50% wins as satisfactory and then did not search for a better column as long as he felt that this standard was met, as was the case on this last board after the sixth trial. A fact consistent with this explanation is that of his continued effort (42 attempts through trial 86) on his first board (Code 4) to win on a column that never paid off while the

Table 1

Stationarity Unspecified (2-Choice Case)

Code No. =	1	2	3	4	5	6	7	8	9	10
100 P =	61	79	66	63	78	56	96	66	80	95
Subject MS										
100 F_1^{100} =	54	57	77	33	70	63	100	66	93	97
100 F_1^c =	39	48	76	33	68	61	--	66	82	92
c =	79	83	94	100	95	95	--	100	38	36
Subject FD										
100 F_1^{100} =	40	96	75	58	72	100	100	97	100	89
100 F_1^c =	40	0	0	51	18	--	--	94	--	0
c =	100	4	25	86	34	--	--	52	--	11

better column was paying off less than half of the time. These possibilities are typical of the experimental complications that arise because of the particular psychological set of the subject at the start.

Subject MS, on the other hand, seems to have performed in a manner quite consistent with the mixed model, as judged by the close agreement between P and F_1^{100}. His seventh board (Code 4) is a notable exception, however, and it is a surprising fact, in this connection, that he devoted his last 28 trials to a choice that always failed and that had always failed on his previous 39 trials with it. It is significant that he kept trying both columns well through all but two of his boards, and that he remarked during and after the experiment that he was convinced that there was some sort of pattern and that he might find it if he kept on hunting for such regularities. If it is supposed that this hunting ended soon after trial c, then one would expect that F_1^c might be in even better agreement with P than is F_1^{100}. This seems to be true for subject MS, except for his ninth board (Code 1) and is further evidence of consistency between his behavior and the hypothesis that the mixed model applies until the subject believes that the process is stationary.

Table 2

Stationarity Specified (9-Choice Case)

Code	100 P	100 F_1^{100} for Subject:									
		1	2	3	4	5	6	7	8	9	10
1	57	90	81	26	14	77	74	96	100	12	75
2	55	81	86	22	0	0	0	96	0	16	0
3	41	68	83	30	0	0	68	12	85	0	61
4	100	97	78	54	100	57	100	100	0	6	88
5	35	50	0	14	7	88	0	0	25	5	67
6	29	4	40	28	23	15	80	50	85	12	64
7	56	97	0	14	1	0	92	0	48	36	3
8	55	100	100	14	0	100	0	11	0	30	0
9	57	46	100	92	0	100	0	100	0	3	95
10	58	97	0	90	0	83	90	98	100	15	24

Code	100 P	100 F_{51}^{100} for Subject:									
		1	2	3	4	5	6	7	8	9	10
1	57	86	100	52	14	100	98	96	100	12	74
2	55	98	82	44	0	0	0	94	0	12	0
3	41	84	98	60	0	0	100	6	100	0	100
4	100	100	100	100	100	100	100	100	0	6	100
5	35	64	0	8	14	100	0	0	30	10	68
6	29	0	50	46	0	16	100	96	100	12	100
7	56	100	0	8	2	0	100	0	48	0	6
8	55	100	100	14	0	100	0	14	0	52	0
9	57	68	100	86	0	100	0	100	0	6	94
10	58	100	0	100	0	100	100	100	100	24	44

The data on subjects 1 - 10 in Table 2 are rather difficult to interpret in the light of this central hypothesis. Certainly, there is no very striking agreement between P and F_1^{100}. It does seem to be the usual case that the subject is still choosing columns other than the best one through most of the 100 trials in each game, and the subjects usually fail to settle down on the very best choice within their hundred trials. Of course, it may be argued reasonably that the early trials in each game should not be taken too seriously in an investigation of asymptotic behavior. For this reason, the F_{51}^{100} data are included, but here too the interpretation is difficult.

One source of trouble in the analysis of the 9-choice case is the similarity between the π_i, in some instances, that makes it difficult for the subject to discriminate between such similar columns. For example, in Code 7, the three largest values of 100 π_i are 98, 95, and 90, so that it would not be at all surprising if a subject were to spend some of his choices on the 95% column that the mixed model would allocate to the 98% and 90% columns. Consequently, in an effort to mitigate this confusing effect, the data were regrouped for analysis by combining columns having comparable π_i values. The (arbitrary) rule for this regrouping consisted of combining all data for those columns whose π_i values differed by 7% or less from the max π_i into a new column 1, then similarly forming a new column 2 including all those columns whose π_i values differed by 7% or less from the max π_i not already included in the new column 1, and continuing until all the columns were regrouped. If r^j denotes the number of new columns formed for Code j, and π_k^j denotes the mean of the set of π_i values represented in the new column k of Code j, for k = 1, 2, $\cdots$, r^j, then, in accordance with the mixed model, the asymptotic frequencies of play p_k^j (on new column k for Code j) is given by the following expression:

$$(3) \quad p_k^j = \frac{\dfrac{1}{1-\pi_k^j}}{\displaystyle\sum_{\alpha=1}^{r^j} \dfrac{1}{1-\pi_\alpha^j}} \quad \text{for } (j = 1, 2, \cdots, 10; \ k = 1, 2, \cdots, r^j).$$

Table 3 presents a comparison of the theoretical values of p_1^j, as obtained from (3), with the relative frequency of choice of new column 1, in all 100 trials and in the last 50 trials, respectively. The average relative frequencies were computed for all but Subject 9, whose data have been omitted because his selections differed very greatly from those of the other subjects.

Table 3

Stationarity Specified (Grouped 9-Choice Case)

Code	$100\,P_1^1$	Mean $100\,F_1^{100}$	$100\,F_1^{100}$ for Subject:								
			1	2	3	4	5	6	7	8	10
1	74	70.4	90	81	26	14	77	74	96	100	75
2	67	31.7	81	86	22	0	0	0	96	0	0
3	52	45.3	68	83	30	0	0	68	12	85	61
4	100	74.9	97	78	54	100	57	100	100	0	88
5	47	64.0	86	94	25	7	88	91	81	27	77
6	39	43.2	4	40	28	23	15	80	50	85	64
7	63	63.4	99	98	33	1	97	92	99	48	4
8	68	84.7	100	100	41	100	100	100	25	100	96
9	69	96.0	75	100	96	98	100	100	100	100	95
10	85	87.9	97	99	92	99	83	90	98	100	33

Code	$100\,P_1^1$	Mean $100\,F_{51}^{100}$	$100\,F_{51}^{100}$ for Subject:								
			1	2	3	4	5	6	7	8	10
1	74	80.2	86	100	52	14	100	100	96	100	74
2	67	35.4	98	82	44	0	0	0	94	0	0
3	52	60.9	84	98	60	0	0	100	6	100	100
4	100	88.9	100	100	100	100	100	100	100	0	100
5	47	71.3	100	94	30	14	100	100	84	30	90
6	39	56.4	0	50	46	0	16	100	96	100	100
7	63	66.9	100	100	46	2	100	100	100	48	6
8	68	85.8	100	100	50	100	100	100	30	100	92
9	69	98.4	100	100	94	98	100	100	100	100	94
10	85	94.4	100	100	100	100	100	100	100	100	50

It would be difficult to argue that the data in Table 3 confirm the hypothesis of behavior in accordance with the mixed model, but even more difficult to argue that they contradict it. The author's view is that a much more extensive experiment is necessary before any real conclusions can be drawn. The most promising approach seems to involve beginning with a 3-choice case, in which the π_i are rather evenly spaced and not too close to 0 or 1, in order to check on the closeness of agreement with the Estes-Bush formula (2) for p_i.

The author would not want to undertake the problem of determining the precise nature of the experimental stimulus necessary for producing this kind of difference in behavior until experimental techniques were good enough to give repeatable and constant results, for the 3-choice case, in agreement with either the pure or mixed models—and only if this stimulus problem were understood reasonably well would he again want to work with the r-choice case for $r > 3$. It is hoped that experience in the crude pilot experiments reported on here may be of some use to others who are interested in this problem of whether to accept the pure model or the mixed model of learning behavior.

APPENDIX A

Instructions for Static-Nine Experiment

A. Static-Nine

1. The equipment for static-nine consists of a "punchboard," a "punch," a "code," and a "register." The code and register are printed forms fastened to the back and the front, respectively, of the punchboard. The punch is used on each move to make a hole in the register signifying the choice of an integer from 1 through 9. Samples of code and register are attached to these instructions.[3]

2. The register has 25 lines, and in each line the integers 1 through 9 appear in four "fields" across the page; this provides for 100 moves.

3. The code has either a 1 or a 0 in each position. A 1 denotes a win and a 0 denotes a loss. The code is arranged so that the mark 1 appears a preassigned number of times in each column. The order of the marks 1 and 0 in each column is random.

4. The first move is made by punching out one of the nine digits in row 1 of field 1. If a 1 is seen through the hole this position is circled in pencil by the player to denote a win,

otherwise it is left uncircled to denote a loss. The second move is made similarly by punching in row 2 of field 1, and circling to denote a 1 if observed. After the 25 moves in field 1 are completed, start at the top of field 2, and continue in this way until all 100 rows have been punched. The score on these 100 moves is the total number of circled positions.

5. After you have made 100 trials, you will give the umpire instructions for your plays in the next hundred trials. You do this by assigning to each choice, 1 through 9, a number indicating how often you wish that choice played in the next 100 trials. The nine numbers must add to 100. For example, you might assign 20, 32, 13, 10, 25 to digits 1, 3, 7, 8, 9 respectively, and zeros to the others, indicating that you want digit 1 played 20 times, digit 2 played no times, digit 3 played 32 times, etc. In particular, if you wish to have some one number (say 5) played all the time, then you would assign 100 to that one and zero to each of the others. These numbers should be written in the row provided on the data form for this purpose.

6. Your object is to get as many wins as you can in the 200 rows.

B. General Information

1. This is an experiment designed to obtain a quantitative comparison of the ability of people with that of rats in learning to play a certain simple intellectual game. Bush and Mosteller, at Harvard, have examined experimental data obtained by psychologists in their studies of rat learning. They have developed a mathematical model that seems to fit the rat data quite well. I am using this model, which they have called the "stat-rat," to compute the probable performance of rats in playing von Neumann-Morgenstern games. The scientific purpose is to test the validity of various mathematical theories of learning and decision.

2. The punchboard represents a mechanical umpire who determines wins and losses in the following manner. The umpire first chooses nine numbers between 0 and 1 (for example, .500 or .378) from a random number table; these are thought of as probabilities $G_1, G_2, \cdots, G_9$ that your choices of 1 through 9 will win. Each time you play a number (say 3) the umpire determines whether or not you have won by applying the corresponding probability (G_3 in this case) to make the decision; he again uses a random number table for each of those decisions. Thus, if the probability G_3 that your choice 3 would win was .700, you might

expect to win 7 times out of 10 when you choose the number 3.

3. For the second hundred trials the umpire simply multiplies the nine numbers written on your data form by the corresponding probabilities G_1, G_2, $\cdots$, G_9, and adds these products together to get your total of wins on the second hundred trials. Of course, this computational procedure produces the same result as the one that you would expect to get if the umpire actually went through the second hundred plays for you one by one.

4. We should like to have you play static-nine several times. Your average score for all your games will be compared with that of the stat-rat, and those of the other subjects in this experiment. You will be told the stat-rat's score after each game. At the conclusion of the experiment, I will send each subject a recapitulation of the names and scores of all players, including the stat-rat.

5. Thank you for participating, and good luck.

APPENDIX B

Instructions

A. Static-two

1. As in Appendix A, paragraph A1.

2. The register has 25 lines, and in each line the integers 1 through 9 appear in four "fields" across the page; this provides for 100 moves. At the top of each register you will find two digits written in red; you are to punch only one or the other of these two on each trial.

3. The code has either a 1 or a 0 in each position. A 1 denotes a win and a 0 denotes a loss.

4. The first move is made by punching out one of two digits in row 1 of field 1. If a 1 is seen through the hole this position is circled in pencil by the player to denote a win; otherwise it is left uncircled to denote a loss. The second move is made similarly by punching one of the two digits in row 2 of field 1, and circling to denote a 1 if observed. After the 25 moves in field 1 are completed, start at the top of field 2, and continue in this way until all 100 rows have been punched. The score on these 100 moves is the total number of circled positions.

5. Your object is to get as many wins as you can in the 100 moves.

B. General Information

1. As in Appendix A, paragraph B1.

2. We should like to have you play static-nine several times. Your average score for all your games will be compared with that of the stat-rat, and those of the other subjects in this experiment. At the conclusion of the experiment, I will be glad to give you a recapitulation of the names and scores of other players, including the stat-rat, if you wish.

3. Thank you for participating, and good luck.

FOOTNOTES

1. The present volume, hereinafter referred to as (DP), includes a paper by Estes reporting on these results.

2. Even though we stressed this point greatly, it was not really accepted by two colleagues who, as subjects in one experiment, made inferences from the illustrative example in the written instructions (and from apparent patterns of successes and failures in early trials) that cannot be justified on logical grounds if the assumption of stationarity were really accepted by them!

3. Samples were shown to each subject but are not included here.

BIBLIOGRAPHY

1. Bush, R. R., and Mosteller, C. F., A mathematical model for simple learning, Psychological Review, 58 (1951), 313-323.

2. Flood, M. M., An Experimental Multiple-Choice Situation, Paper No. 313, The RAND Corporation, November 1952.

3. von Neumann, John, and Morgenstern, Oskar., Theory of Games and Economic Behavior, Princeton: Princeton University Press, 1944.

CHAPTER XIX

SOME EXPERIMENTAL n-PERSON GAMES

by

G. K. Kalisch, J. W. Milnor, J. F. Nash, E. D. Nering

UNIVERSITY OF MINNESOTA, PRINCETON UNIVERSITY,
MASSACHUSETTS INSTITUTE OF TECHNOLOGY,
UNIVERSITY OF MINNESOTA.

INTRODUCTION

This paper reports on a series of experiments designed to shed light on some of the concepts important in the theory of n-person games. Interest was mainly in games of cooperation, and, in particular, the steps which lead to an agreement to cooperate. Thus the mechanics of bargaining, negotiation, and coalition formation were important features of these games. Most of the experimental games were formally of the type considered by von Neumann and Morgenstern [4]. They and others, (see Sections I.6 and II and items [1], [2] in the bibliography) have defined various theoretical concepts for such games. Our principal aim was to compare these concepts with the results of actual plays.

In addition, the bargaining process itself proved to be interesting. Discussion of various details of this process as it occurred in our experiments is included not only to provide the context in which the results should be evaluated, but to enable future designers of such experiments to profit from our experience. In particular, it was interesting to observe that personality differences played a very important role in determining a subject's measure of success in playing these games. The subjects were four men and four women, including five college students, two housewives, and one teacher. They were a remarkably intelligent and cooperative group. Certainly all understood the rules and could analyse their positions as well as could be expected of persons not specifically trained in such negotiations. The subjects were given chips to use in making the payments involved in playing the games, and at the end of each of the two days on which we ran experiments, we redeemed the chips for money. The players who ranked third and fifth on the first day moved up to first and third places, respectively, and otherwise the relative ranking was unchanged. That this was due almost entirely to personality differences was apparent to the observers. This conclusion may also be inferred from the discussion in section I.3.

Some of the games had features which distinguished them from games of the von Neumann and Morgenstern type [4]. One experiment concerned a game in which side-payments were not permissible. In others, the negotiation procedures were formalized (e.g., the identities of a player's opponents were concealed from him and he was allowed to bid, accept, decline, or counter-bid in a very limited number of ways through the intermediation of a referee). The construction of a theory to deal with an unlimited or very large number of negotiation possibilities is as yet so difficult that it seems desirable to restrict and severely formalize the negotiation procedure to the point where a meaningful theory can be constructed. These experiments were essentially pilot experiments and served to test the workability of formal negotiation models.

In general, the authors think that these experiments were fruitful and indicate that further experiments along these lines are feasible and should prove valuable for the further development of game theory. The field of n-person games has had very little empirical investigation; for this reason, and because of the relatively undeveloped status of the theory, the authors feel that the use of the experimental approach is strongly indicated.

I. COOPERATIVE GAMES WITH SIDE PAYMENTS

1. Description of Games. Six constant-sum games, of the type studied by von Neumann and Morgenstern, [4] (that is, co-operative games with side payments allowed), were played by our experimental subjects. Four of these were four-person games which were played eight times each. A five-person game was played three times and a seven-person game was played twice. These games were presented simply by giving their characteristic functions. The players were rotated after each play, to discourage permanent coalitions. Perhaps the best way to describe these games is to give a digest of the material which was given to the subjects. This is done in the following. Note that games 1 and 4 are strategically equivalent and that games 2 and 3 are strategically equivalent. Game 3 is just the symmetric four-person game. The five- and seven-person games are taken from examples in [4].

Instructions to the Subjects.

a) <u>General Instructions</u>. Approximately one typewritten page of general instructions was issued before the subjects started the experiments proper.

First, the subjects were acquainted with the general aim of the experiments ("to further the experimenters' understanding of the Theory of Games"); the system of rotation alluded to above was explained. Next, the possibility of forming coalitions was explained. A coalition was stated to have been formed whenever a set of players had decided to act in concert and had decided how to distribute among its members its common gain or loss. Finally, this part of the instructions sought to emphasize the aspects of aggressiveness and selfishness the players were to exhibit during the experiment; they were exhorted to act only on the merits of the game situation as such (their ultimate objective being the maximization of their gain) - without reference to personal preferences or outcomes of previous runs. They were told that modest monetary rewards were to be distributed at the end of the experiment in proportion to the totals of points (represented by chips which was the universal mode of exchange during the experiment) earned during their ludal activities.

b) <u>Specific Instructions</u>. The "characteristic function" was explained to the players as the rule determining the total payment to each coalition in existence at the end of the game. Furthermore, the characteristic function was given to them diagrammatically (see Figure 1, game # 1, for sample). The players were told that their objective was to form "final coalition agreements" which would determine both a set of players, and the distribution of any gain or loss accruing to the coalition. These final coalition agreements were then to be communicated to an umpire who recorded them, read them back, and ascertained that they reflected the will of the group. The latter provision was necessary, particularly in the case of the seven-person game. This type of formal agreement was binding on the players (enforced by the umpire) but was to be preceded by informal and tentative bargaining which was not binding. In addition to the formal "final coalition agreement" there also were possibilities of various well defined kinds of formal and binding intermediate agreements which again could be preceded by informal bargaining, and which were communicated to the umpire who recorded them and enforced their terms.

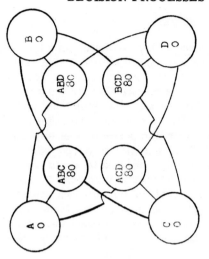

Single and Triples

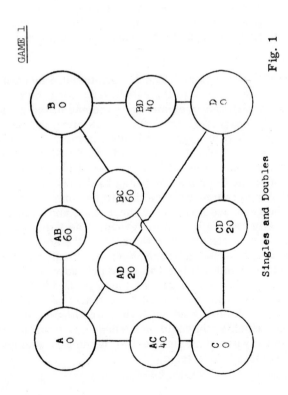

Singles and Doubles

Fig. 1

Coalition	Game #1	2	3	4
A	0	-40	-20	-20
B	0	10	-20	-40
C	0	0	-20	-40
D	0	-50	-20	-20
AB	60	10	0	30
AC	40	0	0	0
AD	20	-50	0	-10
BC	60	50	0	10
BD	40	0	0	0
CD	20	-10	0	-30
ABC	80	50	20	20
ABD	80	0	20	40
ACD	80	-10	20	40
BCD	80	40	20	20

Game #5

Coalition			Coalition		
A	-60		ABC	40	
B	-30		ABD	10	
C	-20		ABE	20	
D	-50		ACD	20	
E	-40		ACE	30	
AB	10		ADE	0	
AC	20		BCD	0	
AD	-10		BCE	10	
AE	0		BDE	-20	
BC	0		CDE	-10	
BD	-30		ABCD	40	
BE	-20		ABCE	50	
CD	-20		ABDE	20	
CE	-10		ACDE	30	
DE	-40		BCDE	60	

Game 6

Number of Players in a Coalition	Payoff to the Coalition
1	-40
2	0
3	-20
4	20
5	0
6	40

Table I - Coalitions are indicated by the letters of the players
they contain. The entries indicate the value of the
characteristic function of the coalition on the right in
the game on the top. Games #1 - 4 are four-person
games; game #5 is a five-person game; game #6 is a
symmetric seven-person game.

A run was over at the end of 10 minutes or whenever there
was no further possibility or desire to form further coalitions,
if that occurred before 10 minutes had elapsed. The players
were permitted to include in their coalition agreements the al-
lotment of payments to outsiders. (This was never done, however.)

2. <u>General Discussion.</u> There was a tendency for members
of a coalition to split evenly, particularly among the first members of a coalition. Once a nucleus of a coalition had formed, it
felt some security and tried to exact a larger share from subsequent members of a coalition. The tendency for an even split
among the first members of a coalition appeared to be due, in
part, to a feeling that it was more urgent to get a coalition
formed than to argue much about the exact terms.

Another feature of the bargaining was a tendency to look upon
the coalitions with large positive values as the only ones worth
considering, often overlooking the fact that some players could
gain in a coalition with a negative value to their mutual benefit
(this was especially noticeable in Game 2, where B and C were
always together).

Coalitions of more than two persons seldom formed except by
being built up from smaller coalitions. Further coalition forming was usually also a matter of bargaining between two groups
rather than more.

A result of these tendencies was that the coalition most likely to form was the two-person coalition with the largest value, even though this coalition did not always represent the greatest net advantage for the participants; and this coalition usually split evenly. Thus it frequently happened that the player with apparently the second highest initial advantage got the most of the bargaining. The player with the apparently highest initial advantage was most likely to get into a coalition, but he usually did not get the larger share of the proceeds of the coalition.

Initially the players were more inclined to bargain and wait or invite competing offers. This remained true to some extent in those games where the situation did not appear to be symmetric. However, later and in those games which were obviously symmetric, the basic motive seemed to be a desire to avoid being left out of a coalition. Hence there was little bargaining, and the tendency was to try to speak as quickly as possible after the umpire said "go," and to conclude some sort of deal immediately. Even in a game which was strategically equivalent to a symmetric game, the players did not feel so rushed. A possible reason might be that some players felt they were better off than the others whether or not they got into coalitions, while others felt that they were worse off whether or not they got into coalitions. They seemed to pay little attention to the fact that the net gain of the coalition was the same to all.

It is worth pointing out that in an interview after the runs, one of the subjects stated that she did appreciate the fact that the favored player did not strike the best deal. When she was in the position of the favored player she felt that to demand her due would seem so unreasonable to the others that she wouldn't get into a coalition, and when she was not the favored player, it was not to her advantage to say anything about it.

Personality differences between the players were everywhere in evidence. The tendency of a player to get into coalitions seemed to have a high correlation with talkativeness. Frequently, when a coalition formed, its most aggressive member took charge of future bargaining for the coalition. In many cases, aggressiveness played a role even in the first formation of a coalition; and who yelled first and loudest after the umpire said "go" made a difference in the outcome.

In the four-person games, it seemed that the geometrical arrangement of the players around the table had no effect on the result; but in the five-person game, and especially in the seven-person game, it became quite important. Thus in the five-person game, two players facing each other across the table were quite

likely to form a coalition; and in the seven-person game, all coalitions were between adjacent players or groups of players. In
general as the number of players increased, the atmosphere became more confused, more hectic, more competitive and less
pleasant to the subjects. The plays of the seven-person game
were simply explosions of coalition formation.

Despite the exhortation contained in the general instructions
to instill a completely selfish and competitive attitude in the
players, they frequently took a fairly cooperative attitude. Of
course, this was quite functional in that it heightened their
chances of getting into coalitions. Informal agreements were always honored. Thus it was frequently understood that two players would stick together even though no explicit commitment
was made. The two-person commitments which were made were
nearly always agreements to form a coalition with a specified
split of the profits, unless a third player could be attracted, in
which case the payoff was not specified. This left open the possibility of argument after a third party was attracted, but such
argument never developed. In fact, the split-the-difference principle was always applied in such cases.

In the seven-person game the characteristic function made
coalitions with an even number of players much more desirable
than those with an odd number of players. With the bargaining
procedures being used, this made it inevitable that one player
should lose heavily. There was a feeling among some of the
players that no individual should lose twice in a row, so perhaps
a rotation system would have developed if there had been more
plays. (This was also indicated in subsequent interviews).
There was, however, no tendency for the winning coalition to
pay any compensation to the loser.

The subsequent discussion will be based on the assumption
that the utility of an outcome to a player, in the sense of von
Neumann and Morgenstern [4] is directly proportional to the
number of chips won. Of course, this is far from true. For example, it is hard to prevent the subjects from making a distinction between plays in which they gain and plays in which they
lose. Thus the graph of utility against chips won might look like
the graph in Fig. 2.

It is very difficult to judge whether phenomena such as this
were significant. It was noticeable, however, that some players
had a convex utility function which expressed itself in a desire
to randomize, while others did not like to randomize. It the last
play of Game 3, for example, all four players randomized to see

which three-person coalition would form. One player objected
strenuously to this procedure on the grounds that it would be un-
fair to the player who was left out. She was forced to comply,
however, by the threat of a three-person coalition against her.

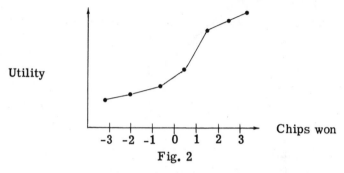

Fig. 2

3. <u>Compatibility with the Shapley Value</u> [2]. The Shapley
values for different positions are compared with the average observed outcomes in Fig. 3. More detailed numerical data will
be found in charts 2-7. There seems to be a reasonably good
fit between the observed data and the Shapley value, considering
the small number of plays which are being averaged. There is,
however, a tendency for the actual outcome to be more extreme
than the Shapley value. This is especially noticeable in Game 1.
Apparently this is due to the fact that coalitions with large payoffs were much more likely to form. Thus the players with relatively high Shapley values were rewarded not only by high payoffs
when they got into coalitions but also by a strong tendency to be
in coalitions. In Game 2 and in the five-person game, where
there were two players whose Shapley values were noticeably
high, the second highest player did just as well as the first. (See
the discussion in Section 2.)

4. <u>Compatibility with Strategic Equivalence</u> [4]. If graphs
analogous to Fig. 3 are constructed showing the average outcomes for these games after transforming them into some normalized form by strategic equivalence, we might expect that
strategically equivalent games (1 and 4; 2 and 3) should show
fairly close agreement; also the symmetries existing in the
games (A and C are symmetric in Game 1; all players are symmetric in Game 3; B, C, D, E are symmetric in Game 5) might
be expected to be reflected in such graphs. The actual results
don't agree very well with these hypotheses. The discussion in

COMPATIBILITY OF SHAPLEY VALUE WITH OBSERVED OUTCOMES

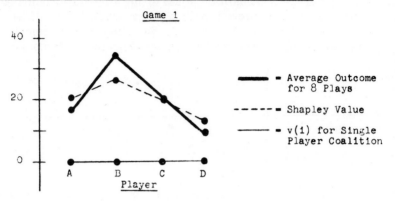

Game 1

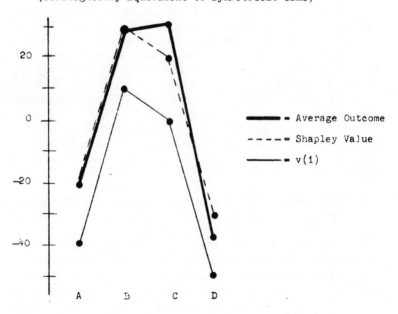

Game 2

(Strategically Equivalent to Symmetrical Game)

Fig. 3

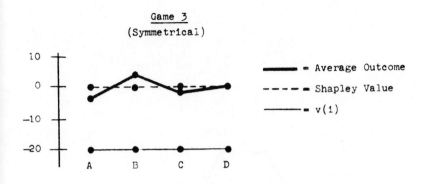

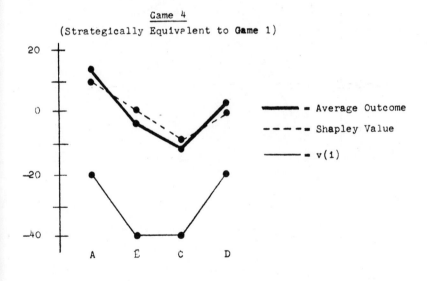

Fig. 3 (cont.)

Five-person Game

(Strategically Equivalent to Game
which is Symmetrical among Players
B, C, D, and E)

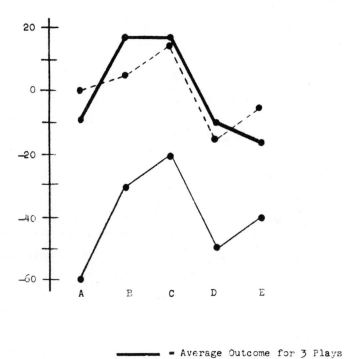

Fig. 3 (concluded)

Section 2 hints at some possible reasons for this discrepancy. Thus, the fact that coalitions with high characteristic function are most likely to form, the tendency of members of a coalition to split evenly, and the non-linearity of the utility function all tend to disrupt the concept of strategic equivalence.

5. Compatibility with von Neumann-Morgenstern Solutions [4]. It is extremely difficult to tell whether or not the observed results corroborate the von Neumann-Morgenstern theory [4]. This is partly so because it is not quite clear what the theory asserts. According to one interpretation a "solution" represents a stable social structure of the players. In order to test this theory adequately, it would probably be necessary to keep repeating a game, with a fixed set of players, until there seemed to be some stability in the set of outcomes which occurred. One could then see to what extent the outcomes of this final set dominate each other and to what extent other possible imputations are not dominated by them.

This suggests that we find out to what extent the observed outcomes for each game dominate each other. This is not too fair a test of the theory, but not much more can be done with the available data. The following are all the significant dominations (denoted by $>$) which occur between the eight observed outcomes for each of the four-person games. Dominations which occur because of a difference of one chip or so are ignored.

Game 1. 2, 6, 7 $>$ 3;

3, 4, 7 $>$ 1;

5 $>$ 1, 2, 3, 4, 6, 7, 8.

Game 2. 1 $>$ 2, 4; 3 $>$ 1, 7, 8;

4 $>$ 3, 5; 5 $>$ 1, 7;

6 $>$ 1, 7; 7 $>$ 1, 2, 4;

8 $>$ 1, 2, 6.

Game 3. 3 $>$ 1, 5, 7, 8; 4 $>$ 3.

Game 4. 2, 3, 8 $>$ 6;

6 $>$ 1; 3 $>$ 2.

Thus for Game 2, so many dominations occur that the set of

outcomes cannot be related to any solution. For Game 1 there is some hope, since outcomes 2, 4, 6, 7 and 8 do not dominate each other.

For Game 3, the situation is quite satisfactory. Outcomes 1, 2, 4, 5, 6, 7, and 8 do not dominate each other, and furthermore they are clearly related to a familiar solution to this game: namely, the solution consisting of (10, 10, 0, -20) and its permutations together with (0, 0, 0, 0). The other point, 3, also belongs to a familiar solution: that consisting of (6 2/3, 6 2/3, 6 2/3, -20), (6 2/3, 6 2/3, -6 2/3, -6 2/3) and their permutations. These results are more or less explained by the symmetry of the game, so it is not clear that they are significant.

For Game 4, the outcomes 1, 3, 4, 5, 7 and 8 do not dominate each other. It would be necessary to try extending this set to a solution in order to test the significance of this result.

In another interpretation of the theory, a solution represents a collection of outcomes under consideration by the players at some state of the bargaining procedure. Thus, a solution refers to a single play of a game rather than a number of plays. It is very difficult to tell just what outcomes were under consideration by the players at any particular time. What was actually observed was a number of offers, made sequentially. Frequently each offer dominated the immediately preceding offer. A more thorough study of the data would be necessary, however, actually to refute this interpretation.

An example of a case where such an interpretation did seem reasonable is given by the following. In one play of a four-person game, a coalition of two was formed, but the agreement was made in such a way that the coalition could not be expanded. This left the other two players with a pure bargaining situation. Actually they chose to split evenly, rather than go through the ordeal of bargaining. If they had bargained, however, the set of possible outcomes would have formed part of a Shapley quota-type solution [3].

6. Compatibility with "Reasonable Outcomes". The following definitions, due to J. W. Milnor, establish several bounds for the amounts which a player i or a set of players S should get in any play of an n-person game. In particular, upper bounds b(i) and b(S) are defined by the following:

$$b(i) = \text{Max } (v(S) - v(S - i)),$$
$$i \in S$$

$$b(S) = Max \ (v(S') - v(S' - S)).$$
$$S' \supset S$$

A theoretical plausibility consideration for these definitions is given by the fact that one would not expect a player i to exact more from a coalition S of which he is part than his presence contributes to it, i.e., $v(S) - v(S - i)$ should be as much as he could reasonably expect as his share. The set B of imputations $\alpha = \{\alpha_i\}(\alpha_i \leqslant b(i))$ is a rather large set - for example, in the normalized zero-sum essential three-person game (see [4]), B equals the set of all imputations. It can be proved that B always contains the Shapley value (see [2]), and also every solution in the sense of von Neumann and Morgenstern (see [4]). Section 7 contains comparisons between b(i), and the actual outcomes. It appears that b(i) is usually compatible with the outcomes, in particular in the case of the four-person games (a deviation in one of the cases was subsequently related to the statement made by one of the subjects after the experiment was over that he had made a mistake in reasoning). The agreement is less favorable in the case of the five-person game - some players getting more than their "maximum share" b(i) - a circumstance which may be related to the fact that the players rushed into coalitions, splitting the payoff evenly, without really studying the strategic possibilities.

A lower bound, $\ell(S)$, was also defined for the payoff to each coalition. Its definition is the following:

$$\ell(S) = \underset{S_1 \subset S}{Min}(v(S_1) + v(S - S_1)); \ L = \text{all imputations} \ \alpha = \{\alpha_i\}\left(\underset{i \in S}{\Sigma}\alpha_i \geqslant \ell(S)\right)$$

It is not hard to see that $\ell(S) = v(I) - b(I - S)$ in the constant sum case - which makes $\ell(S)$ a plausible candidate for a lower bound. It is possible to show that under rather strong assumptions (viz., bargaining will always result in the formation of just two opposing coalitions; in order for a coalition T to form it must distribute its payoff $v(T)$ among its members in a way which is "stable" in the sense that every subset T_1 of T is given at least $v(T_1)$) the outcome of a play must lie in L; a v. Neumann-Morgenstern solution [4] may fail to be contained in L, nor need L contain the Shapley value [2] of the game. The sixth game (a seven-person game) was an example of a game for which there exists a v. Neumann-Morgenstern solution giving to a set S less than

$\mathfrak{k}(S)$ - the quota solutions of this game contain outcomes such as (-40,40,0,0,0,0,0) giving some five-person sets -40 whereas $\mathfrak{k}(S)$ = -20 for all five-person sets. It turned out that the actual minimum outcomes for five-person sets S were in 11 instances substantially higher and in one instance equal to $\mathfrak{k}(S)$. An outcome (payoff) falling within the limits defined above is called a "reasonable outcome".

7. Numerical Data. The actual outcomes from these games are given in the following tables. Expected outcomes are given in the few cases where the players randomized. Game 1 is a constant-sum game with v(I) = 80. The others are all zero-sum (the characteristic functions are given in Section 1).

The commitments listed in the last column include only formal agreements processed through the umpire. Many information agreements were made and kept. The numbers b(S) and the Shapley value are to be construed in the light of Sections 3 and 6 above.

II. EXPERIMENTAL WORK WITH NEGOTIATION MODELS

A negotiation model is a non-cooperative game [1] which is based on a strictly formalized negotiation procedure applied to a cooperative game. In principle such a model can be studied and analyzed in terms of equilibrium point theory [3] as a non-cooperative game, and the kind of solution thus obtained may then be considered as a possible solution of the underlying cooperative game. One of the aims of the experiments related in this paper is to gain information on the workability of the model.

Actually, we use the phrase "negotiation model" somewhat more broadly than is implied above. The model, as a non-cooperative game, may not have anything like a really satisfactory non-cooperative solution. It may only be an intermediate model which would have to be further modified (perhaps by putting in preceding commitment moves) before anything very satisfactory for a theoretical solution would be obtained. Some such modification may show up if the game is actually played by the subjects. Another possible aim of experimentation may be to observe the effects of repeated playing of the same game by the same set of players. This may make the (negotiation) game more cooperative because information can then be transmitted and inferred by the history of the previous plays; precedents can

DATA FOR GAME 1

(Strategically Equivalent to Game 4)

Set of Players S	A	B	C	D	AB	AC	AD	BC	BD	CD	Coalitions or Commitments Made
Payoff in run number 1	0	32	24	24	32	24	24	56	56	48	CD, BCD
2	0	34	34	12	34	34	12	68	46	46	BC, BCD
3	10	30	30	10	40	40	20	60	40	40	BC, AD
4	10	35	35	0	45	45	10	70	35	35	BC, ABC
5	20	40	10	10	60	30	30	50	50	20	AB, CD
6	34	34	0	12	68	34	46	34	46	12	ABD
7	15	35	30	0	50	45	15	65	35	30	BC, ABC
8	35.5	35.5	0	9	71	35.5	44.5	35.5	44.5	9	AB, ABD
Average Payoff	15.6	34.4	20.3	9.6	50.0	35.9	25.2	54.8	44.1	30.0	
b (i)	60	60	60	40							
Shapley Value	20	26.7	20	13.3	46.7	40	33.3	46.7	40	33.3	
No. of times S was part of coalition	6	8	6	6	5	2	3	5	4	3	

Chart 2

DATA FOR GAME 2

(Strategically Equivalent to Symmetrical Game)

Set of Players S	A	B	C	D	AB	AC	AD	BC	BD	CD	Coalitions or Commitments Made
Payoff in run number											
1	-4	20	30	-46	16	26	-50	50	-26	-16	AD, BC
2	-2	26	26	-50	24	24	-52	52	-24	-24	BC, ABC
3	-25	25	25	-25	0	0	-50	50	0	0	AD, BC
4	-20	35	35	-50	15	15	-80	70	-15	-15	ABC
5	-23	25	25	-27	2	2	-50	50	-2	-2	BC, AD
6	-18	25	25	-32	7	7	-50	50	-7	-7	BC, AD
7	-40	42	41	-43	2	1	-83	83	-1	-2	BCD
8	-40	34	34	-28	-6	-6	-68	68	6	6	BC, BCD
Average Payoff	-21.5	29.0	30.1	-37.6	7.5	8.6	-59.1	59.1	-8.6	-7.5	
b (i)	0	50	40	-10	10		-50	50	0	-10	
Shapley Value	-20	30	20	-30		0	-50	50	0		
No. of times S was part of coalition	6	8	8	6	2	2	4	8	2	2	

Chart 3

DATA FOR GAME 3

(Symmetrical)

Set of Players S	A	B	C	D	AB	AC	AD	BC	BD	CD	Coalitions or Commitments Made
Payoff in run number											
1	0	0	0	0	0	0	0	0	0	0	AB, CD
2	-20	1	9	10	-19	-11	-10	10	11	19	CD, BCD
3	7	6	7	-20	13	14	-13	13	-14	-13	ABC
4	10	9	-20	1	19	-10	11	-11	10	-19	AB, ABD
5	0	0	0	0	0	0	0	0	0	0	AC, BD
6	-20	9	2	9	-11	-18	-11	11	18	11	BD, BCD
7	0	0	0	0	0	0	0	0	0	0	CD, AB
8	0	0	0	0	0	0	0	0	0	0	ABCD
Average Payoff	-2.9	3.1	-0.2	0	0.2	-3.1	-2.9	2.9	3.1	-0.2	
b (i)	20	20	20	20							
Shapley Value	0	0	0	0	0	0	0	0	0	0	
No. of times S was part of coalition	6	8	7	7	5	3	2	4	5	5	

Chart 4

DATA FOR GAME 4
(Strategically Equivalent to Game 1)

Set of Players S	A	B	C	D	AB	AC	AD	BC	BD	CD	Coalitions or Commitments Made
Payoff in run number 1	25	-40	-10	25	-15	15	50	-50	-15	15	ACD
2	-20	10	10	0	-10	-10	-20	20	10	10	BC, BCD
3	15	-40	15	10	-25	30	25	-25	-30	25	AC, ACD
4	25	25	-40	-10	50	-15	15	-15	15	-50	AB, ABD
5	24	24	-40	-8	48	-16	16	-16	16	-48	AB, ABD
6	-5	5	5	-5	0	0	-10	10	0	0	BC, AD
7	25	25	-40	-10	50	-15	15	-15	15	-50	AB, ABD
8	15	-40	10	15	-25	25	30	-30	-25	25	ACD
Average Payoff	13.0	-3.9	-11.2	2.1	9.1	1.7	15.1	-15.1	-1.7	-9.1	
b (i)	70	50	50	40							
Shapley Value	10	0	-10	0	10	0	10	-10	0	-10	
No. of times S was part of coalition	7	5	5	8	3	3	7	2	4	4	

Chart 5

DATA FOR FIVE-PERSON GAME

(Strategically equivalent to game symmetric between B, C, D, E)

Player i	A	B	C	D	E	Coalitions or Commitments Made
Payoff in run number 1	10	10	10	10	-40	BC, AD, ABCD
2	23	23	23	-50	-19	ABC, ABCE
3	-60	20	20	10	10	BC, BCD, BCDE
Average Payoff	-9.0	17.7	17.7	-10	-16.3	
b (i)	40	20	30	0	10	
Shapley Value	0	5	15	-15	-5	
No. of times i was member of coalition	2	3	3	2	2	

Chart 6

DATA FOR SEVEN-PERSON GAME

(Symmetric)

Player i	A	B	C	D	E	F	G	Coalitions or Commitments Made
Payoff in run number 1	-40	6	6	7	7	7	7	BC, DE, FG; DEFG; BCDEFG
2	-26	5	5	5	5	3	33	CE, DB, FG; BCDE; AFG

Chart 7

be established; players may convince others that they will continue to behave in certain ways in future games (for instance, by a persistent use of a certain strategy).

We performed experiments on a three-person model and on a four-person model. In both cases the players' communication with each other was strictly formalized and was effected through the umpire.

In the three-person game the players were blindfolded and indicated their moves to the umpire by means of hand signals. In the four-person games each player sat where he was unable to see any of the other players (of whose identities he was unaware) and made his moves by writing them on paper.

The rules of the three-person game were as follows:

First move: Player A may either (1) wait or (2) make an offer to form a coalition with either player B or C; this offer is to specify the share d_A of the proceeds of the proposed coalition which A intends to obtain for himself (d_A, etc., must be integers). Players B and C make similar first moves--and all three make their moves simultaneously and independently.

If two players, say A and B, have made offers to each other, and if $d_A + d_B \leq 15$, the game is over and the payoffs are the following: A gets d_A, B gets d_B, C gets $-(d_A+d_B)$. If $d_A + d_B > 15$, all three get zero.

If a coalition was formed, the play is over, and all three players get zero.

If, say, A has "waited" at his first move and was offered a coalition by another player, he has a second move where he may either choose to accept or to reject. In either case, the play is over. The payoffs in the first case are (if A accepts B's offer): A gets $15 - d_B$, B gets d_B, C gets -15. In the second case all three players get zero.

This game has been treated theoretically. Let us change the normalization, so that a coalition gets +1, the outsider 0. A demand can be any real number between 0 and 1, and the payoff is 1/3, 1/3, 1/3 when no coalition forms. If the above-described game were changed by disallowing demands greater than 1/2, the new game would have a symmetric equilibrium point where each player offers with probability .544, with probability .456, and distributes his demands between .415 and .500, the average demand being .455.

The observed behavior of the players corresponds fairly closely to this strategy; 85 per cent of the demands were within the theoretical range. Waiting was somewhat neglected, occurring only 33 per cent instead of the theoretical 41 per cent. The theoretical strategies are not quite at equilibrium in the game with unrestricted demands, for the demand of $2/3 - \epsilon$ would be a strategy with an expected payoff of about .34, a little more than $1/3$, which is the expectation for demands in the lower range. Of course, such high demands would not be advantageous against the actual play pattern in the experiment; waiting was not frequent enough.

The true non-pathological equilibrium point for this game seems to be the same as for the game in which only coalitions formed by one player offering and the other player waiting and accepting are allowed. Here the offering probability is only 42 per cent, and demands start at .53 and run up to $2/3$, with most of the weight of the distribution at the low end. This distribution is completely non-overlapping with the distribution described before.

The four-person games were derived by formalizing the negotiation from two of the cooperative games which were investigated in the part of our experiment devoted to free bargaining (namely games 3 and 4). Again all players moved simultaneously and independently at each stage, all players being informed, after each move, of the choices made by the others. There were two kinds of moves: one in which offers may be made, and one in which offers made in the move immediately preceding may be accepted by a player who had passed--"waited" during that preceding move. A more detailed description can perhaps best be gleaned from the presentation of a sample play of the game.

Example

(This is based on Game 4)

Player	A	B	C	D
Proposal	ABC	AB	AC	DC
	6	6	0	0

This is the first move. Here each player has made a proposal. The number under the letter of a player indicates his demand, the set of letters the proposed coalition. No potential coalition has the property that all its members have either named it or waited. If all had named it and had made mutually compatible demands it would have been formed at this first move. Once formed, coalitions are permanent unless enlarged.

Player	A	B	C	D
Proposal	Wait	ABD 6	ABC 6	DC 0

This is the second move. Since no coalition can arise from the first move, the second move proceeds again afresh, except for the information from Move 1. Still no coalition can form.

Player	A	B	C	D
Proposal	Wait	ABD 6	Wait	Wait

This third move makes it possible for ABD to form and an acceptance move is inserted in the game. In the acceptance move each of the players involved, A and D in this case, can reject or accept the proposed coalition. Acceptance must be associated with a demand for a certain payoff, and is conditional on obtaining the amount demanded.

Acceptance Move:

Players	A	B	C	D
Proposal	ABD 6	No Move	No Move	ABD 7

Now A and D have made their acceptance proposals. The coalition ABD is successfully formed because 20 points are available to ABD and only 6+6+7=19 have been spoken for. The play is over now because the coalition formation is complete. (Since we were working with zero-sum games we excluded the coalition of all four players.) A, B, and D are paid their demands, 6, 6, and 7 respectively. C receives -19 to make the game zero-sum.

There are not many data from this part of the experiment, but it showed that the model was workable. The number of moves per game decreased as the players learned better strategies than they began with. Afterwards, the subjects reported that they enjoyed this part of the experiment more than any other because it didn't involve the exhausting face-to-face haggling.

Thus further experiment with negotiation models may well be profitable.

III. A STOOGE GAME

The "stooge game" was a zero-sum three-person game with (integral valued) side payments. Each play proceeded as follows At the end of four minutes, or when the players reported agreement to the observer (whichever was the earlier), the following payoffs were made: if no coalition was formed each player got 0; if a coalition was formed (the formation of a coalition implied an agreement on how to split its proceeds), it received 10 chips from the odd player. A coalition was permitted to make a payment to the odd player (this, however, was never done). There were three runs of five plays each. The stooge had instructions to offer a 7 - 3 split to one or the other of the two subjects in the majority of cases, three to himself and seven to the other player.

During the first run, the stooge had difficulties establishing himself, since the game proceeded very rapidly and was over in a matter of minutes or even less. During the second run, the stooge did manage every time to get a 7 - 3 split and during the third run, the subjects "caught on" and the 7 - 3 split offered by the stooge occurred only twice (once it occurred between the two subjects).

In spite of occasional statements made by the subjects that they wanted to play the game non-competitively, the stooge's behavior caused a very competitive atmosphere and there was sharp and intense bargaining all the time. Two tendencies that could be observed were that first coalitions often persisted, and that tentative coalitions formed almost at once. In general, the plays proceeded very rapidly.

One of the purposes of this experiment was to see if a competitive atmosphere could be induced by a stooge--and, as expected, this was possible. Another purpose was to see if von Neumann-Morgenstern's discriminatory solution of a three-person game (see [4]) could be established. This definitely was not achieved in this experiment.

IV. A THREE-PERSON COOPERATIVE GAME WITH NO SIDE PAYMENTS

In an effort to get some ideas about the proper theory for games without side payments, the following three-person game was played. Each player was given two playing cards, each representing one of his opponents. A player moved by placing one of his cards face down on the table, thus "voting" for one of his opponents. If some player got two votes, then he was awarded 40 chips and each of the other two was penalized 20 chips. If each player got only one vote, then there was no transfer of chips. The actual play was preceded by a bargaining period during which the players could make any deals or commitments they wished subject only to the following two restrictions: (1) there must be no side payments involved, and (2) the deal or commitment must refer only to the individual play of the game under consideration. There were three runs of four, each run involving a new set of players.

The results of this experiment were rather negative. The players were simply unwilling to play competitively. In two of the three runs the players equalized the expectations either by playing randomly or by rotating the winning player over three plays, violating prescription (2). In the other run some of the plays were still random although there was a tentative deal of the form "if you vote for me I will vote for you," and a threat of the form "unless you vote for me I will vote for him." It is of course extremely difficult to bargain effectively in this game, but it had been hoped that some more positive result would be attained.

The following suggestions may be made in case experiments of this type are carried on in the future. It would be better to play an unsymmetrical game so that there would be no obviously fair method of arbitrating the game and avoiding competition. The same set of players should not be together repeatedly since there is too much of a tendency to regard a run of plays as a single play of a more complicated game. A competitive attitude should be fostered by proper and more thorough indoctrination or otherwise; possibly the proper use of stooges may induce a more competitive mode of behavior (see "Stooge Game").

BIBLIOGRAPHY

1. Nash, J. F., Non-cooperative Games, Annals of Mathematics, (2), 54, 1951, 286 - 295.
2. Shapley, L. S., A Value for n-Person Games, Contributions to the Theory of Games, II, Princeton, 1953, 307 - 318.
3. Shapley, L. S., Quota Solutions of n-Person Games, ibid., 343 - 360.
4. von Neumann, John, and Morgenstern, Oscar, Theory of Game Games and Economic Behavior, Princeton, 1944.

APPENDIX A

University of Michigan Summer Seminar at Santa Monica, California
Summer 1952

Participants

Name	Institution	Sponsor
David C. Beardslee	University of Michigan*	ONR and Ford Foundation
W. C. Biel	RAND Corporation	RAND Corporation
Herbert G. Bohnert	RAND Corporation	RAND Corporation
Robert R. Bush	Harvard University	Ford Foundation
Robert L. Chapman	RAND Corporation	RAND Corporation
Clyde H. Coombs	University of Michigan	ONR and Ford Foundation
James T. Culbertson	University of Southern California	RAND Corporation
Norman C. Dalkey	RAND Corporation	RAND Corporation
Robert L. Davis	University of Michigan	ONR and Ford Foundation
William K. Estes	Indiana University	Ford Foundation
Leon Festinger	University of Minnesota	Ford Foundation
Merrill M. Flood	RAND Corporation**	RAND Corporation
D. R. Fulkerson	RAND Corporation	RAND Corporation
Leo Goodman	University of Chicago	Ford Foundation
Olaf Helmer	RAND Corporation	RAND Corporation
Clifford Hildreth	University of Chicago	Cowles Commission and Ford Foundation
Gerhard K. Kalisch	University of Minnesota	ONR
Abraham Kaplan	U.C.L.A.	RAND Corporation
Sam Karlin	California Institute of Technology	RAND Corporation
John L. Kennedy	RAND Corporation	RAND Corporation
Paul Kecskemeti	RAND Corporation	RAND Corporation
T. C. Koopmans	University of Chicago	Cowles Commission
Douglas Lawrence	Stanford University	Ford Foundation
Jacob Marschak	University of Chicago	RAND Corporation
Oskar Morgenstern	Princeton University	RAND Corporation
Frederick Mosteller	Harvard University	RAND Corporation
Evar Nering	University of Minnesota	ONR
A. Newell	RAND Corporation	RAND Corporation
Roy Radner	University of Chicago	Cowles Commission and Ford Foundation
Lloyd Shapley	Princeton University***	RAND Corporation
Herbert Simon	Carnegie Institute of Technology	RAND Corporation
Gerald Thompson	Princeton University****	Ford Foundation and ONR
Robert M. Thrall	University of Michigan	RAND Corporation and ONR
Stefan Vail	University of Michigan	Ford Foundation
Ruth Wagner	RAND Corporation	RAND Corporation
John D. Williams	RAND Corporation	RAND Corporation
Robert Wolfson	University of Michigan*****	Ford Foundation

*Now at Wesleyan University   ****Now at Dartmouth College
**Now at Columbia University   *****Now at University of Chicago
***Now at RAND Corporation

APPENDIX B

Michigan Project - Summer Seminar

List of Papers Presented

Norman Dalkey - Cooperative Aggregation

C. H. Coombs, H. Raiffa, and R. M. Thrall - Some Views on Mathematical Models and Measurement Theory

Clyde H. Coombs - The Measurement of Social Utility

Douglas Lawrence - The Determination of Alternatives in a Choice Situation

Leon Festinger - Some Remarks on the Relationship between Mathematics and Social Psychology

Clifford Hildreth - Alternative Conditions for Social Orderings

Allen Newell - Experimental Study of Organizations

Robert J. Wolfson - Notes on Methodology

John Kennedy - Experiments in Social Sciences

Robert R. Bush - The Acquisition of Preferences

G. L. Thompson - A Simplified Bridge Game

Roy Radner - An Example of Individual Decision Making Under Uncertainty

Merrill M. Flood - Report on Some Experimental Games

Abraham Kaplan - Philosophical Theory of Value

John Milnor - Games Against Nature

Evar Nering - Solutions of n-Person Games

John Nash - N-Person Games and the Need for a Better Theoretical Basis

W. K. Estes - Theory and Experiments Concerning Individual Behavior in Uncertain Situations

Paul Kecskemeti - Science and Policy

L. S. Shapley - Stable Sets in the Theory of Games

Herbert A. Simon - A Model for Group Interaction

Oskar Morgenstern - Experiment and Computation in Economics

Jacob Marschak - Some Remarks on Teams and Organizations

James T. Culbertson - Neuroeconomy in Hypothetical Robots

Robert Chapman - Experimental Study of Organizations

Gerhard Kalisch - Remarks on n-Person Games

John von Neumann - Remarks on Chess-playing Automata

Robert R. Bush and G. L. Thompson - General Stochastic Model

Leo Goodman - Methods of Amalgamation

Roy Radner and Abraham Kaplan - Questionnaire Approach to Ψ Probability

W. K. Estes, R. J. Wolfson, and Roy Radner - Group and Individual Prediction

G. L. Thompson - Trapping Theorems

R. R. Bush - Estimation of Model Parameters

Festinger, Lawrence, Kalisch, and Nering - An Experiment on Coalitions

Kalisch, Marschak, Wagner, Fulkerson, and Estes - Experiments on Bargaining and Game Theory

Sam Karlin - Mathematical Aspects of the Learning Model